Project-Based Inquiry Science™

ENERGY

Janet L. Kolodner

Joseph S. Krajcik

Daniel C. Edelson

Brian J. Reiser

Mary L. Starr

HERFF JONES EDUCATION DIVISION

IT's ABOUT TIME®
HERFF JONES EDUCATION DIVISION

84 Business Park Drive, Armonk, NY 10504
Phone (914) 273-2233 Fax (914) 273-2227
www.its-about-time.com

Program Components

Student Edition	Durable Equipment Kit
Teacher's Planning Guide	Consumable Equipment Kit
Teacher's Resources Guide	Multimedia
	— Physical Science Content DVD

Project-Based Inquiry Science™ (PBIS) Copyright © 2010: Georgia Tech Research Corporation. Licensed exclusively to It's About Time, Herff Jones Education Division.

All student activities in this textbook have been designed to be as safe as possible, and have been reviewed by professionals specifically for that purpose. As well, appropriate warnings concerning potential safety hazards are included where applicable to particular activities. However, responsibility for safety remains with the student, the classroom teacher, the school principal, and the school board.

Printed and bound in the United States of America.

The 1st printing of *Energy* was completed by Courier Kendallville, Inc. in Kendallville, IN in August 2009.

ISBN 978-1-58591-626-9

2 3 4 5 13 12 11

This project was supported, in part, by the **National Science Foundation** under grant nos. 0137807, 0527341, and 0639978. Opinions expressed are those of the authors and not necessarily those of the National Science Foundation.

Principal Investigators

Janet L. Kolodner is a Regents' Professor in the School of Interactive Computing in the Georgia Institute of Technology's College of Computing. Since 1978, her research has focused on learning from experience, both in computers and in people. She pioneered the Artificial Intelligence method called *case-based reasoning*, providing a way for computers to solve new problems based on their past experiences. Her book, *Case-Based Reasoning*, synthesizes work across the case-based reasoning research community from its inception to 1993.

Since 1994, Dr. Kolodner has focused on the applications and implications of case-based reasoning for education. In her approach to science education, called Learning by Design™ (LBD), students learn science while pursuing design challenges. Dr. Kolodner has investigated how to create a culture of collaboration and rigorous science talk in classrooms, how to use a project challenge to promote focus on science content, and how students learn and develop when classrooms function as learning communities. Currently, Dr. Kolodner is investigating how to help young people come to think of themselves as scientific reasoners. Dr. Kolodner's research results have been widely published, including in *Cognitive Science, Design Studies,* and the *Journal of the Learning Sciences.*

Dr. Kolodner was founding Director of Georgia Tech's EduTech Institute, served as coordinator of Georgia Tech's Cognitive Science program for many years, and is founding Editor in Chief of the *Journal of the Learning Sciences.* She is a founder of the International Society for the Learning Sciences, and she served as its first Executive Officer. She is a fellow of the American Association of Artificial Intelligence.

Joseph S. Krajcik is a Professor of Science Education and Associate Dean for Research in the School of Education at the University of Michigan. He works with teachers in science classrooms to bring about sustained change by creating classroom environments in which students find solutions to important intellectual questions that subsume essential curriculum standards and use learning technologies as productivity tools. He seeks to discover what students learn in such environments, as well as to explore and find solutions to challenges that teachers face in enacting such complex instruction. Dr. Krajcik has authored and co-authored over 100 manuscripts and makes frequent presentations at international, national, and regional conferences that focus on his research, as well as presentations that translate research findings into classroom practice. He is a fellow of the American Association for the Advancement of Science and served as president of the National Association for Research in Science Teaching. Dr. Krajcik co-directs the Center for Highly Interactive Classrooms, Curriculum and Computing in Education at the University of Michigan and is a co-principal investigator in the Center for Curriculum Materials in Science and The National Center for Learning and Teaching Nanoscale Science and Engineering. In 2002, Dr. Krajcik was honored to receive a Guest Professorship from Beijing Normal University in Beijing, China. In winter 2005, he was the Weston Visiting Professor of Science Education at the Weizmann Institute of Science in Rehovot, Israel.

Daniel C. Edelson has been engaged in research and development in geosciences and geography education since 1992. From 1994-2007, he was a faculty member in the School of Education and Social Policy at Northwestern University, where he founded and led the Geographic Data in Education (GEODE) Initiative. In addition to his work on *Planetary Forecaster* and *Ever-Changing Earth* for PBIS, Dr. Edelson is the author of a high-school environmental science text, *Investigations in Environmental Science: A Case-Based Approach to the Study of Environmental Systems,* and of *My World GIS™*, a geographic information system for inquiry-based learning. His research on science education and educational technology has been widely published, including articles in the *Journal of the Learning Sciences, the Journal of Research on Science Teaching, Science Educator,* and *The Science Teacher.*

Brian J. Reiser is a Professor of Learning Sciences in the School of Education and Social Policy at Northwestern University. Professor Reiser served as chair of Northwestern's Learning Sciences Ph.D. program from 1993, shortly after its inception, until 2001. His research focuses on the design and enactment of learning environments that support students' inquiry in science, including both science curriculum materials and scaffolded software tools. His research investigates the design of learning environments that scaffold scientific practices, including investigation, argumentation, and explanation; design principles for technology-infused curricula that engage students in inquiry projects; and the teaching practices that support student inquiry. Professor Reiser also directed BGuILE (Biology Guided Inquiry Learning Environments) to develop software tools for supporting middle school and high school students in analyzing data and constructing explanations with biological data. Reiser is a co-principal investigator in the NSF Center for Curriculum Materials in Science. He served as a member of the NRC panel authoring the report Taking Science to School.

Mary L. Starr is a Research Specialist in Science Education in the School of Education at the University of Michigan. She collaborates with teachers and students in elementary and middle school science classrooms around the United States who are implementing *Project-Based Inquiry Science*. Before joining the PBIS team, Dr. Starr created professional learning experiences in science, math, and technology, designed to assist teachers in successfully changing their classroom practices to promote student learning from coherent inquiry experiences. She has developed instructional materials in several STEM areas, including nanoscale science education, has presented at national and regional teacher education and educational research meetings, and has served in a leadership role in the Michigan Science Education Leadership Association. Dr. Starr has authored articles and book chapters, and has worked to improve elementary science teacher preparation through teaching science courses for pre-service teachers and acting as a consultant in elementary science teacher preparation. As part of the PBIS team, Dr. Starr has played a lead role in making units cohere as a curriculum, in developing the framework for PBIS Teacher's Planning Guides, and in developing teacher professional development experiences and materials.

Acknowledgements

Three research teams contributed to the development of *Project-Based Inquiry Science (PBIS)*: a team at the Georgia Institute of Technology headed by Janet L. Kolodner, a team at Northwestern University headed by Daniel Edelson and Brian Reiser, and a team at the University of Michigan headed by Joseph Krajcik and Ron Marx. Each of the PBIS units was originally developed by one of these teams and then later revised and edited to be a part of the full three-year middle-school curriculum that became PBIS.

PBIS has its roots in two educational approaches, Project-Based Science and Learning by Design™. Project-Based Science suggests that students should learn science through engaging in the same kinds of inquiry practices scientists use, in the context of scientific problems relevant to their lives and using tools authentic to science. Project-Based Science was originally conceived in the hi-ce Center at the University of Michigan, with funding from the National Science Foundation. Learning by Design™ derives from Problem-Based Learning and suggests sequencing, social practices, and reflective activities for promoting learning. It engages students in design practices, including the use of iteration and deliberate reflection. LBD was conceived at the Georgia Institute of Technology, with funding from the National Science Foundation, DARPA, and the McDonnell Foundation.

The development of the integrated *PBIS* curriculum was supported by the National Science Foundation under grant nos. 0137807, 0527341, and 0639978. Any opinions, findings and conclusions, or recommendations expressed in this material are those of the authors and do not necessarily reflect the views of the National Science Foundation.

PBIS Team

Principal Investigator
Janet L. Kolodner

Co-Principal Investigators
Daniel C. Edelson
Joseph S. Krajcik
Brian J. Reiser

NSF Program Officer
Gerhard Salinger

Curriculum Developers
Michael T. Ryan
Mary L. Starr

Teacher's Planning Guide Developers
Rebecca M. Schneider
Mary L. Starr

Literacy Specialist
LeeAnn M. Sutherland

NSF Program Reviewer
Arthur Eisenkraft

Project Coordinator
Juliana Lancaster

External Evaluators
The Learning Partnership
Steven M. McGee
Jennifer Witers

The Georgia Institute of Technology Team

Project Director:
Janet L. Kolodner

Development of PBIS units at the Georgia Institute of Technology was conducted in conjunction with the Learning by Design™ Research group (LBD), Janet L. Kolodner, PI.

Lead Developers, Physical Science:
David Crismond
Michael T. Ryan

Lead Developer, Earth Science:
Paul J. Camp

Assessment and Evaluation:
Barbara Fasse
Jackie Gray
Daniel Hickey
Jennifer Holbrook
Laura Vandewiele

Project Pioneers:
JoAnne Collins
David Crismond
Joanna Fox
Alice Gertzman
Mark Guzdial
Cindy Hmelo-Silver
Douglas Holton
Roland Hubscher
N. Hari Narayanan
Wendy Newstetter
Valery Petrushin
Kathy Politis
Sadhana Puntambekar
David Rector
Janice Young

The Northwestern University Team

Project Directors:
Daniel Edelson
Brian Reiser

Lead Developer, Biology:
David Kanter

Lead Developers, Earth Science:
Jennifer Mundt Leimberer
Darlene Slusher

Development of PBIS units at Northwestern was conducted in conjunction with:

The Center for Learning Technologies in Urban Schools (LeTUS) at Northwestern, and the Chicago Public Schools
Clifton Burgess, PI
for Chicago Public Schools;
Louis Gomez, PI.

The BioQ Collaborative
David Kanter, PI.

The Biology Guided Inquiry Learning Environments (BGuILE) Project
Brian Reiser, PI.

The Geographic Data in Education (GEODE) Initiative
Daniel Edelson, Director

The Center for Curriculum Materials in Science at Northwestern
Daniel Edelson,
Brian Reiser,
Bruce Sherin, PIs.

The University of Michigan Team

Project Directors:
Joseph Krajcik
Ron Marx

Literacy Specialist:
LeeAnn M. Sutherland

Project Coordinator:
Mary L. Starr

Development of PBIS units at the University of Michigan was conducted in conjunction with:

The Center for Learning Technologies in Urban Schools (LeTUS)
Phyllis Blumenfeld,
Barry Fishman,
Joseph Krajcik,
Ron Marx,
Elliot Soloway, PIs.

The Detroit Public Schools
Juanita Clay-Chambers
Deborah Peek-Brown

The Center for Highly Interactive Computing in Education (hi-ce)
Phyllis Blumenfeld,
Barry Fishman,
Joseph Krajcik,
Ron Marx,
Elizabeth Moje,
Elliot Soloway,
LeeAnn Sutherland, PIs.

Field-Test Teachers

National Field Test
Tamica Andrew
Leslie Baker
Jeanne Bayer
Gretchen Bryant
Boris Consuegra
Daun D'Aversa
Candi DiMauro
Kristie L. Divinski
Donna M. Dowd
Jason Fiorito
Lara Fish
Christine Gleason
Christine Hallerman
Terri L. Hart-Parker
Jennifer Hunn
Rhonda K. Hunter
Jessica Jones
Dawn Kuppersmith
Anthony F. Lawrence
Ann Novak
Rise Orsini
Tracy E. Parham
Cheryl Sgro-Ellis
Debra Tenenbaum
Sarah B. Topper
Becky Watts
Debra A. Williams
Ingrid M. Woolfolk
Ping-Jade Yang

New York City Field Test
Several sequences of PBIS units have been field- tested in New York City under the leadership of Whitney Lukens, Staff Developer for Region 9, and Greg Borman, Science Instructional Specialist, New York City Department of Education

6th Grade
Norman Agard
Tazinmudin Ali
Heather
  Guthartz Aniba
Asher Arzonane
Asli Aydin
Shareese Blakely
John J. Blaylock
Joshua Blum
Tsedey Bogale

Filomena Borrero
Zachary Brachio
Thelma Brown
Alicia Browne-Jones
Scott Bullis
Maximo Cabral
Lionel Callender
Matthew Carpenter
Ana Maria Castro
Diane Castro
Anne Chan
Ligia Chiorean
Boris Consuegra
Careen Halton Cooper
Cinnamon Czarnecki
Kristin Decker
Nancy Dejean
Gina DiCicco
Donna Dowd
Lizanne Espina
Joan Ferrato
Matt Finnerty
Jacqueline Flicker
Helen Fludd
Leigh Summers Frey
Helene Friedman-Hager
Diana Gering
Matthew Giles
Lucy Gill
Steven Gladden
Greg Grambo
Carrie Grodin-Vehling
Stephan Joanides
Kathryn Kadei
Paraskevi Karangunis
Cynthia Kerns
Martine Lalanne
Erin Lalor
Jennifer Lerman
Sara Lugert
Whitney Lukens
Dana Martorella
Christine Mazurek
Janine McGeown
Chevelle McKeever
Kevin Meyer
Jennifer Miller
Nicholas Miller
Diana Neligan
Caitlin Van Ness
Marlyn Orque
Eloisa Gelo Ortiz
Gina Papadopoulos
Tim Perez
Albertha Petrochilos
Christopher Poli

Kristina Rodriguez
Nadiesta Sanchez
Annette Schavez
Hilary Sedgwitch
Elissa Seto
Laura Shectman
Audrey Shmuel
Katherine Silva
Ragini Singhal
C. Nicole Smith
Gitangali Sohit
Justin Stein
Thomas Tapia
Eilish Walsh-Lennon
Lisa Wong
Brian Yanek
Cesar Yarleque
David Zaretsky
Colleen Zarinsky

7th Grade
Mayra Amaro
Emmanuel Anastasiou
Cheryl Barnhill
Bryce Cahn
Ligia Chiorean
Ben Colella
Boris Consuegra
Careen Halton Cooper
Elizabeth Derse
Urmilla Dhanraj
Gina DiCicco
Lydia Doubleday
Lizanne Espina
Matt Finnerty
Steven Gladden
Stephanie Goldberg
Nicholas Graham
Robert Hunter
Charlene Joseph
Ketlynne Joseph
Kimberly Kavazanjian
Christine Kennedy
Bakwah Kotung
Lisa Kraker
Anthony Lett
Herb Lippe
Jennifer Lopez
Jill Mastromarino
Kerry McKie
Christie Morgado
Patrick O'Connor
Agnes Ochiagha
Tim Perez
Nadia Piltser
Chris Poli

Carmelo Ruiz
Kim Sanders
Leslie Schiavone
Ileana Solla
Jacqueline Taylor
Purvi Vora
Ester Wiltz
Carla Yuille
Marcy Sexauer Zacchea
Lidan Zhou

8th Grade
Emmanuel Anastasio
Jennifer Applebaum
Marsha Armstrong
Jenine Barunas
Vito Cipolla
Kathy Critharis
Patrecia Davis
Alison Earle
Lizanne Espina
Matt Finnerty
Ursula Fokine
Kirsis Genao
Steven Gladden
Stephanie Goldberg
Peter Gooding
Matthew Herschfeld
Mike Horowitz
Charlene Jenkins
Ruben Jimenez
Ketlynne Joseph
Kimberly Kavazanjian
Lisa Kraker
Dora Kravitz
Anthony Lett
Emilie Lubis
George McCarthy
David Mckinney
Michael McMahon
Paul Melhado
Jen Miller
Christie Morgado
Maria Jenny Pineda
Anastasia Plaunova
Carmelo Ruiz
Riza Sanchez
Kim Sanders
Maureen Stefanides
Dave Thompson
Matthew Ulmann
Maria Verosa
Tony Yaskulski

Energy

Energy is based on *How Can You Use Trash to Power Your Stereo?*, a unit developed by the University of Michigan Center for Highly Interactive Classrooms, Curricula & Computing in Education (hi ce) and The Center for Learning Technologies in Urban Schools.

Energy
Lead Developers
Mary L. Starr
Francesca Casella

Contributing Field-test Teachers
Kathy Critharis
Vito Cipolla
Patrecia Davis
Christie Francisci-Morgado
Steven Gladden
Mike Horowitz
Kimberly Kavazanjian

Lisa Kraker
Dora Kravitz
Anthony Lett
Emilie Lubis
David McKinney
Michael McMahon
Anastasia Plaunova
Kim Sanders
Dave Thompson

How Can You Use Trash to Power Your Stereo
Lead Developer
David Fortus

Developers
Joe Krajcik
Jeff Nordine
Julia Plummer
Aaron Rogat
Anna Switzer

Contributing Teachers
Chris Gleason
Ann Novak

Curriculum Contributors
Amanda Benedict

The development of *Energy* was supported by the National Science Foundation under grant nos. 0137807, 0527341, and 0639978. The development of *How Can You Use Trash to Power Your Stereo* was been supported by the National Science Foundation under grants no. 9553583, 9818828, and 0208059. Any opinions, findings, and conclusions or recommendations expressed in this material are those of the authors and do not necessarily reflect the views of the National Science Foundation.

Table of Contents

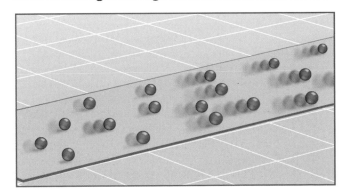

Learning Set 4

Science Concepts: *Sound energy, light energy, sound intensity, human ear—form and function, waves and energy, mechanical waves, longitudinal waves and transverse waves, characteristics of waves (wavelength, frequency, amplitude), speed of waves in different media, seismic waves, light intensity, solar energy, weather and solar energy, the Sun as a source of energy, renewable and nonrenewable resources, thermal energy and climate, electromagnetic waves, scattering, reflection and refraction, electromagnetic spectrum, visible light, wave-particle duality, human eye—form and function, comparing through observation, sharing inferences, making careful observations, using evidence to support claims, developing explanations, using science knowledge, making measurements, organizing and analyzing data, comparing and contrasting data, understanding models.*

Learning Set 5

Science Concepts: *Electrical energy, magnetic energy, batteries, electricity, electric current, circuits, forces and work, electric and magnetic fields, electromagnetism, electromagnets, series and parallel circuits, generators, energy transformations, electrochemical cells, alternating and direct current, conductors and insulators, voltage and resistance, distribution of electric power, making careful observations, collaboration, sharing data, building on the work of others, communicating plans, using scientific tools, using science knowledge, designing an experiment, making measurements, developing explanations.*

Learning Set 6

Science Concepts: *Energy transformations, the Sun as a source of energy, energy efficiency, potential and kinetic energy, types of energy, mechanical energy, conservation of energy, energy resources, alternative energy (wind, hydroelectric, solar, biomass, wave, geothermal), consequences of energy use, nuclear energy, fusion and fission, energy pathways, making careful observations, sharing, collecting, and analyzing data, making graphs, comparing and contrasting data, making recommendations, using science knowledge.*

Address the Big Challenge

Your machine may use energy
world, people are designing an
ways to do serious work. One
designed a dance floor that use
and disco lights. They use the t
conversion of fun into energy s
of children at a playground to
energy to turn a merry-go-roun
the village to use. In both exam
fun is put to good use.

There are many types of energy
energy into a different form nee
water pump you read about tra
be used to pump water. In a fla
the energy released by a light b
transformed into energy that m

To succeed with this Unit's chall

- how to identify and descr

- what affects how much e

- how to store energy,

- how energy moves from

- how to transform one typ

- how to control energy so

Get Started

Meet Rube Goldberg. Rube Gold
amusingly complex machines. E
steps that combined together to
simple task is to turn off a light
drawings and did not really carr
and they amused millions of peo
are often called "Rube Goldberg

---

4) Scientists…coll

Scientists never do all their
(collaborate) and share their
scientist by giving you lots o
ideas, and discoveries with
together in small groups to
things. Sometimes you will
You will also have lots of op
the rest of your classmates
learning.

Investigation Expo

In an *Investigation Expo*,
investigation they've done.
make a poster detailing wh
investigation, what you did
data. The text gives you hir
for in other groups' presen
followed by discussions abc
science well. You may also
investigation.

Plan Briefing/Solu

Briefings are presentations
chance to get advice from
forward. During a *Plan Br*
It might be a plan for an e
or achieving a challenge. I
your solution in progress a
solution better. During an
get the best advice from y
in support of your plan, so
a poster to help you make
always followed by discuss
move forward.

Solution Showcas

Solution Showcases usua
a *Solution Showcase*, yo
product—either your answ
challenge. You also tell th
or solution, what evidenc
solution, and what you tri
answer or solution. Some
a competition. It is almos
and contrasting the differ
up with. You may be aske
Solution Showcase.

Introducing PBIS

What Do Scientists Do?

1) Scientists…address big challenges and big questions.

You will find many different kinds of *Big Challenges* and *Questions* in *PBIS* Units. Some ask you to think about why something is a certain way. Some ask you to think about what causes something to change. Some challenge you to design a solution to a problem. Most of them are about things that can and do happen in the real world.

Understand the Big Challenge or Question

As you get started with each Unit, you will do activities that help you understand the *Big Question* or *Challenge* for that Unit. You will think about what you already know that might help you, and you will identify some of the new things you will need to learn.

Project Board

The *Project Board* helps you keep track of your learning. For each challenge or question, you will use a *Project Board* to keep track of what you know, what you need to learn, and what you are learning. As you learn and gather evidence, you will record that on the *Project Board*. After you have answered each small question or challenge, you will return to the *Project Board* to record how what you've learned helps you answer the *Big Question* or *Challenge*.

Learning Sets

Each Unit is composed of a group of *Learning Sets*, one for each of the smaller questions that need to be answered to address the *Big Question* or *Challenge*. In each *Learning Set*, you will investigate and read to find answers to the *Learning Set's* question. You will also have a chance to share the results of your investigations with your classmates and work together to make sense of what you are learning. As you come to understand answers to the questions on the *Project Board*, you will record those answers and the evidence you've collected. At the end of each *Learning Set*, you will apply your knowledge to the *Big Question* or *Challenge*.

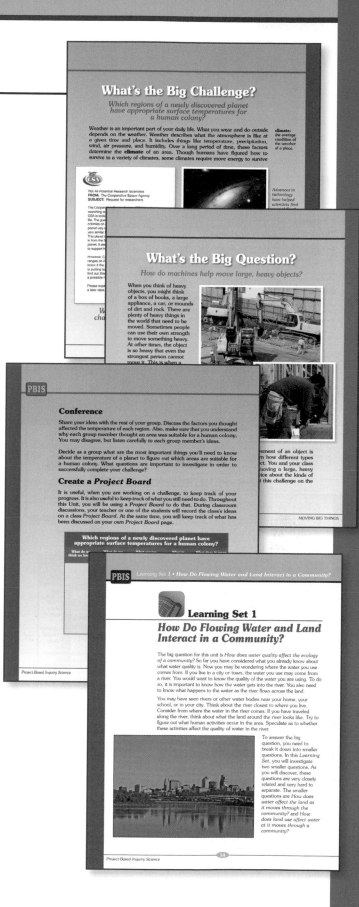

Your teacher w...
different ways, ...

Sketch the diffe...
water flow thr...
attention to th...
the river chang...

- how the s...
- where al...
- where the...

Stop an...

Look at your ...
about the river...
you notice ab...

Reflect

Think about the book support you designed and built so far. Try to think about the science concepts you have read about and discussed as a class. Answer the following questions. Be prepared to discuss your answers with the class.

1. Was your structure strong? If not, did it collapse because of folding, compression, or both?
2. How could you make the structure stronger to resist folding or...

Analyze Your Data

Calculate the temperature range for each...
one shown.

Temperature Ra...

Location	High Temperature	Month
Greenland (81°N 36°W) polar		
Helsinki, Finland (60°N 24°E) mid latitude north		

Mess Abo...

Messing About: an exploratory activity that gives you a chance to become familiar with the materials you will be using or the function of the product you will be designing.

structure: the way the parts of an...

To help you think...
messing about ...
appears on the b...

You will get a tem...
below. The whistl...
call them by thos...
know what you are...

Cut out the templ...
two paper clips to...

What's the Point?

Through *messing about*, you became familiar with th...
work. You developed a feel for the materials you will ...
also able to identify some of the variables that might ...
parachute will fall. This allowed you to do two things...

- Identify the criteria and constraints of the chall... to accomplish and the limitations).
- Identify questions you need to investigate to be... best parachute.

In your class discussions around the *Project Board* yo...
that would be appropriate to investigate. Different gr...
different ideas of what affects a parachute's fall. It w...
(working together as a class) that you were able to ne...
questions about how the parachute might work.

Think Abou...
Design a Rube...

Usually, when you ...
use muscles to pus...
of pushing down a ...
and work mean. Fo...
change and work a...
understanding ener...
you will be able to g...

You will be learning...
Challenge. The *Big*...
machine that does ...
will allow you to use ...
your machine will a...
loud. However, the ...
use several types of ...
one kind of energy ...

*Children playing on this merry-go-round...
provide the energy to power a water pum...*

The Can Picker

3. You may
involved
anything
and any

Commu

Share You

Share with
sketch does
your machi
operation o
identify abo
happen. Dis
your machi

The Orange Squeezer

Your Challenge

Your challenge is to design a machine to turn off a light. Your machine will include at least five steps and use at least three types of energy. You will design your machine and describe how and why each part of it operates properly. You will also describe the ways energy is transformed from one form to another.

You will not build your design. You will only draw it on paper. However, you must be able to convince your classmates that it would operate properly if built. That means each step must be believable, and the sequence of steps must be logical. Remember the cartoons and videos you have seen so far. Some of the steps in those machines seemed outrageous. But the steps combined in a way that completed a task.

Your machine should use materials commonly found in a home, a supermarket, or a hardware store. Even though you are not going to be building the machine, it should be designed to be safe enough to operate with a parent or teacher around to help. For example, it can use fire, but it should not use explosives.

Identify Criteria and Constraints

criteria (singular: criterion): conditions that must be satisfied to successfully achieve a challenge.

constraints: factors that limit how you can solve a problem.

Before you start, make sure you understand the **criteria** and **constraints** of your challenge. Criteria are conditions that must be satisfied to achieve the challenge. One criterion is that your machine must have at least five steps. Another criterion is that, in at least three of its steps, energy must be transformed from one form to another.

Constraints are factors that limit how to solve a problem. You will not build the machine, only design it and sketch it. However, one constraint is that each step must be logical and believable. Your classmates need to believe that it would operate properly if built. Another constraint is that the design must use easy-to-find materials. Another constraint is safety. Your design must be safe enough to operate with adult supervision.

Record the criteria and constraints in a table like the one shown below, so you can refer to them as you move through the Unit.

Design a Rube Goldberg machine to turn off a light	
Criteria	**Constraints**

Create a *Project Board*

It is useful to keep track of your progress when you are designing something. It is also useful to keep track of what you already know and what you still need to learn as you move through a challenge. Throughout this Unit, you will be using a *Project Board* to do this. During classroom discussions, the ideas from the class will be recorded on a class *Project Board*. At the same time, you will keep a record of what has been discussed on your own *Project Board* page.

Remember that a *Project Board* has space for answering five guiding questions:

- What do we think we know?

- What do we need to investigate?

- What are we learning?

- What is our evidence?

- What does it mean for the challenge or question?

1.1 Understand the Challenge

How Can You Identify Energy?

In the *Introduction,* you observed real Rube Goldberg machines on video and then analyzed energy transformations in sketches of imaginary Rube Goldberg machines. You saw objects moving, falling, burning, and bubbling. When an object moves, falls, burns, or bubbles, it is changing. An object that gives off noise, light, or heat is also changing. All of these changes **indicate**, or show, that energy is being transformed.

indicate: to show.

indicators: observations that can tell you about the presence of some state or condition.

inference: a plausible conclusion or interpretation based on observations or evidence.

infer: to interpret from observations.

To design a machine that transforms energy, you need to be able to recognize when energy is being transformed and what type of energy is transformed into what other type. You will need to identify **indicators** that allow you to make an **inference** about the use of energy. An indicator is something you can observe and measure that tells you about the presence of something else. An inference is a plausible interpretation or conclusion based on observations or evidence. Once you know which indicators to look for, you will be able to **infer** when energy is being transformed.

You can see the change in an icicle as it melts. Melting is an indicator. From observing the icicle, you can infer that energy must be added to solid ice to transform it to liquid water.

Some indicators of energy transformations are difficult to observe. But you can experience many indicators of energy transformations with your five senses—touch, sight, hearing, taste, and smell. The simplest example is when you observe through sight that something has started to move. Energy is always being transformed when an object speeds up or slows down.

You can also see indicators of energy use when matter is changing form, such as when ice melts into water. Energy must be added to solid ice to transform it to liquid. When an object is burning, there may be several indicators to observe. You might see flames or smoke, and also smell smoke and hear the crackle and rush of the flames. All of these are indicators of energy transformations.

To practice identifying energy and indicators of
energy transformation, you will participate in a class
demonstration. You will use a simple device called a
radiometer. A radiometer uses a sealed glass bulb similar
to a light bulb. Inside the bulb is a spindle with four flags
attached at its top. Under some conditions, the flags inside
the radiometer start to turn. Because this is a change,
you know that some kind of energy is being tranformed.
You will observe the radiometer to determine the type of
energy that is transformed into the motion of the flags.

Demonstration 1

Throughout the demonstration, carefully observe the
radiometer. Focus your attention on the four flags at
the top of the spindle inside the bulb. Record your
observations on your *Radiometer Observations* page.

Observe

1. Your teacher will pass the radiometer from group to
   group. Watch the four flags at the top of the spindle
   for a few moments. What is happening to the flags?
   If the flags are still, how do you think they might
   move? Carefully turn it over and examine it. Can you
   figure out what might make the flags move or stop
   moving? Record your observations in the top chart of a
   Radiometer Observations page. If you have any ideas
   about what makes the flags move, record those in the
   Causes column. Make special note of anything that
   surprises you.

2. Observe the radiometer as it is placed on a table and a
   flashlight is held about 1 m from it. The light from the
   flashlight will shine on the radiometer for a full minute.
   Again, observe carefully and look for any changes in
   the radiometer that might be indicators of energy use.
   Record in the *Conditions* column the conditions of
   the demonstration. Record your observations of the
   radiometer in the *Observations* column.

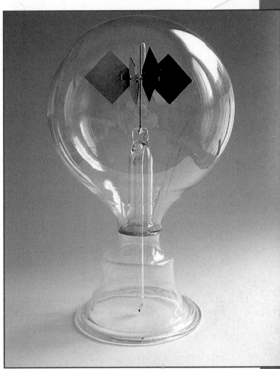

A Crookes radiometer.

3. Observe as the flashlight is turned off. Observe the radiometer carefully. Record in the *Conditions* column that the light was turned off, and record your observations in the *Observations* column.

Analyze Your Data

1. What indicators of energy transformation did you record when you were passing the radiometer around? If you observed an indicator of energy transformation, what type of energy do you think was transformed into what other type of energy?

2. What indicators of energy transformation did you record when the flashlight was held 1 m from the radiometer? If you observed an indicator of energy transformation, what type of energy do you think was transformed into what other type of energy?

3. What happened when the flashlight was turned off? Does this confirm your thoughts in *Steps 1* and *2*? Why or why not? Record your reasoning in the *Causes* column of your table.

Demonstration 2

Now that you have some ideas about indicators and sources of energy that caused the radiometer to turn, you will test your ideas. You will begin by predicting what will happen in several different situations. Then you will observe what actually happens in those situations. Record your predictions and observations in the second table of the *Radiometer Observations* page.

Predict

1. What do you think will happen if you turn on the flashlight and shine the light at the radiometer for 1 min from a distance of less than 1 m? Record your predictions in the first row of the table.

2. What do you think will happen if you turn on the flashlight and shine the light at the radiometer for 1 min from a distance of 2 m? Record your predictions in the second row of the table.

3. What do you think will happen if you shine the flashlight on the radiometer from 2 m away and then slowly move it closer to the radiometer? Record your predictions in the third row of the table.

Observe

Watch as your teacher performs the procedures described in the *Predict* section. First, observe the radiometer as the flashlight shines on it from up close for 1 min. Then observe the radiometer when the flashlight is held 2 m from the radiometer. Finally, repeat the procedure again, holding the flashlight 2 m away and slowly moving it toward the radiometer. Record your observations.

Analyze Your Data

1. What do you think is the source of energy for the motion of the flags in the radiometer?

2. Why do you think the radiometer reacts differently to a flashlight that is close to it than to a flashlight that is farther away?

3. Now think about the flashlight. What indicators do you have that energy is being transformed when the flashlight is turned on? What form of energy is being transformed to what other form of energy?

ENERGY

kinetic energy: the energy an object has because of its motion.

light energy: visible energy that is given off by some objects in the form of radiation.

radiation: energy that moves in the form of rays, waves, or particles.

Energy in the Crookes Radiometer

The Crookes radiometer is a device used to detect the presence of light energy. Flags are mounted on a spindle inside a sealed glass bulb. Most of the air is removed from inside the radiometer. When no direct light shines on the radiometer, the flags do not move, and the radiometer is at rest.

When light is shined on the radiometer, a change takes place. The flags begin to rotate on the spindle. This motion is an indicator that energy is transformed into the radiometer's motion.

Something in the design of a radiometer transforms the energy in light into the energy of motion. When the flashlight is closer to the radiometer, more light shines on it, and the flags move more quickly. When the flashlight is farther away, less light shines on the radiometer, and the flags move more slowly or not at all.

The energy of movement is called **kinetic energy.** This motion can be in a straight line, like a raindrop falling from the sky, or in a circle, like the flags in the radiometer, or along any type of path. Spinning objects, such as tops, also have kinetic energy. Any time you can detect motion in an object, you can say that the object has kinetic energy.

The energy of light, called **light energy,** is another form of energy. You know light energy is present when you see light. Light energy is given off by objects such as the Sun or a light bulb. Light energy travels through empty space and also through air, water, and many other materials. Light energy is a form of *electromagnetic* **radiation**. Radiation is energy that travels in the form of rays, *waves,* or particles. (You will be learning more about electromagnetic radiation and how it travels later in this Unit.) The root word *radio* means "ray." This same root word is used in the words *radiation* and *radiometer.*

A radiometer transforms light energy into the kinetic energy of the flags. You will be identifying other examples of energy transformations throughout this Unit.

Light energy from the Sun travels in the form of electromagnetic radiation.

Moving trains have kinetic energy.

Energy in a Flashlight

A flashlight also uses energy and transforms energy. It transforms energy stored in a battery into light energy. When a flashlight is turned on, the filament of the bulb begins to glow, and the flashlight **radiates** light. The change in the filament and the presence of light are both indicators that energy is being transformed. You can use your sense of sight to detect these indicators.

When you see a light bulb glowing, you can infer that the bulb is transforming energy. The filament of a bulb shines because *electricity* flows through the filament. Electricity is a form of **electrical energy** that flows between the negative and positive terminals of a battery. You cannot see the electrical energy, but you know that a light bulb needs electrical energy to glow.

In the case of a flashlight, the source of the electrical energy is the **chemical energy** stored within a battery. Chemical energy is energy that is stored until it is released by the reaction of chemicals in the battery. When the positive and negative terminals of a battery are connected by a wire, chemicals in the battery react to release energy to the wire.

When a flashlight is turned on, two energy transformations take place. First, chemical energy in the battery is transformed into electrical energy that travels through the filament wire. Then, the electrical energy traveling through the filament heats the filament and causes it to radiate light energy. The light energy given off by the flashlight is an indicator that chemical energy in the battery is transformed into electrical energy in the wire, which is transformed to the light given off by the flashlight.

radiate: give off energy.

electrical energy: the energy of moving electric charges.

chemical energy: energy stored in chemical bonds.

Chemical energy stored in batteries is transformed to light the light.

Stop and Think

1. What indicators of energy transformation did you see in the demonstration of the Crookes radiometer?

2. What types of energy transformation did you see in the demonstration?

3. Where did the energy for the light of the flashlight come from?

4. Do you need to see the batteries in the flashlight to know they are there? Why or why not?

5. Where did the energy that was transformed into the motion of the radiometer come from?

Reflect

This fluorescent light bulb transforms electrical energy into light energy.

1. What types of energy transformations do you observe every day?

2. How could you determine the amount of energy that is being transformed?

3. Think about the pictures you observed at the beginning of this section. How could you control the amount of energy transformed on a swing? Playing basketball? Sailing a boat?

4. What else do you need to know about energy and energy transformations to be able to design a Rube Goldberg machine to turn off a light?

Update the *Project Board*

In this section, you thought about types of energy transformations. You identified indicators of some types of energy transformations and some changes caused by the transformation of energy. Update the *Project Board* by adding ideas from your readings and the demonstrations in the *What do we think we know?* column. Be sure to add to the *Project Board* the ideas your class agreed on and areas you are not sure about. You may have questions about what energy is and the relationship between energy and motion. You may have ideas about investigations to help you find out more about energy and motion. Record your questions and ideas for investigations in the *What do we need to investigate?* column.

Design a Rube Goldberg machine to turn off a light				
What do we think we know?	What do we need to investigate?	What are we learning?	What is our evidence?	What does it mean for the challenge or question?

What's the Point?

By observing indicators, you can identify when energy is being transformed. An indicator is something you can observe and measure. You can experience many indicators with your senses—touch, sight, hearing, taste, and smell. The simplest example is seeing something start to move. You know an object has kinetic energy when it is moving, similar to the flags in the radiometer. When light energy enters a radiometer, it is transformed into the energy of motion, or kinetic energy. In a flashlight, when the flashlight is switched on, chemical energy is transformed into electrical energy, which is then transformed into light energy.

1.2 Explore

What Types of Energy Transformations Occur in Your Everyday Life?

A kitchen is a great place to find different types of energy transformations and indicators of them. Many people use a pop-up toaster to make a warm slice of golden-brown toast to eat with their breakfast. How does a pop-up toaster transform energy to complete its task? What are the indicators of a toaster transforming energy? To prepare you to examine the energy transformed in other everyday devices, you will observe a toaster demonstration and discuss the energy transformations it shows. Then you will explore other devices you are familiar with and share with the class the many kinds of energy transformations and any indicators of them that you identify.

Many different energy transformations occur in a pop-up toaster.

Demonstration

As you observe the pop-up toaster, pay attention to all of the changes that are occurring. Every change is an indicator of energy transformation. Use as many of your senses as you can as you observe the toaster. You will not be close enough to touch or taste anything, but use your other senses. Make a list of all the changes you identify.

Analyze Your Data

Share your list of changes with your group, and answer these questions.
Be prepared to share your answers with the class.

- What changes did you identify?

- What type of energy was transformed to what other type in each change you saw?

- What energy transformations can you identify in the toaster? Read *Three Other Types of Energy* to help you understand some of the types of energy you have not seen before in this Unit.

- Which of these indicators show that energy is being transformed? Describe each energy transformation.

- How would you describe energy based on what you observed in this demonstration? Use your own words.

Three Other Types of Energy

The toaster uses three types of energy that you have not explored yet in this Unit. One type is **elastic energy.** This is the type of energy stored in a rubber band or a spring. This type of energy can be transformed into kinetic energy. When a spring or rubber band is stretched and held motionless, it has elastic energy. Releasing the elastic energy transforms it into kinetic energy.

elastic energy:
the energy stored in an object when the shape of the object is changed.

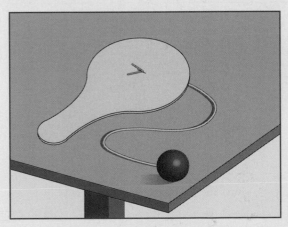

A paddleball uses elastic energy. Elastic energy is stored in the rubber band.

ENERGY

Another type of energy is **sound energy.** Sound energy, like light energy, moves in waves. Sound waves are *vibrations* that travel through matter. You detect sound waves when they strike your eardrum, causing it to vibrate. Your brain interprets the vibration of the eardrum as sound.

 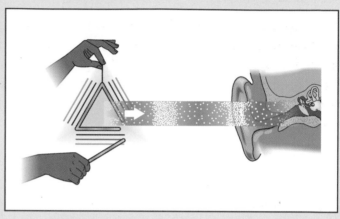

The strings in a harp and a triangle struck by a wand produce sound energy.

sound energy: vibrating air that travels as waves to your ears.

thermal energy: experienced as heat; the energy of motion of all the particles in an object.

A third type of energy is **thermal energy.** You know that thermal energy is present when you feel something warm or feel something get warmer. Thermal energy is energy associated with the motion of particles (atoms or molecules) in an object. An object that feels hot to the touch has faster-moving particles than an object that feels cold. The hotter object has more thermal energy. You will learn more about these types of energy later in this Unit.

When an electric burner is turned on, it produces thermal energy.

What Types of Energy Play a Role in Everyday Devices, and What Are Their Indicators?

You have already begun to identify indicators of many different types of energy. As you complete this Unit, you will learn more about different types of energy. In this exploration, you will look for indicators of energy in everyday objects. Each group will explore and observe a different set of objects from the list of materials. After your exploration, you will report back to the class. Organize your observations on your *Energy Observations* page.

Procedure

1. List each object you have been given on your *Energy Observations* page.

2. Operate the object as it was intended to be used.

3. Record how the object operates and the energy indicators you observe. Record your observations about the types of energy present in the object. If you see a new form of energy, describe it as best you can. After you learn about more types of energy, you will return to this page.

Analyze Your Data

1. What changes did you observe that indicated the presence of a particular type of energy? List a change for each object you investigated. Record it in the *Observations* column.

2. If you observed changes that you were not able to link to a type of energy, describe them.

3. What indicators were similar among the objects you observed? Explain why you think the indicators were similar.

Materials

- tuning fork and wooden rod
- scissors with piece of paper
- spring-powered toy
- maracas
- bouncy ball
- flashlight
- spring with mass
- suction/pop-up toy
- Newton's cradle
- yo-yo

Energy Observations   1.2.1/2.1.1

Name: _____   Date: _____

Object	Observation of how the object works	Indicator	Type(s) of energy

© It's About Time

ENERGY

4. How many types of energy were you able to identify in your objects? Describe each type of energy, including the indicator or indicators that allowed you to detect it.

5. What were the most common energy indicators you observed?

Communicate

Investigation Expo

Each group investigated a different set of objects. So that everyone in the class will experience each of the objects, you will present your objects to the class and describe how they operate. Before beginning, quickly make a small poster. It should include

- the information in your chart,

- your list of the forms of energy you identified and the indicators for each, and

- the most common indicators for your types of energy.

Do not worry if you do not know names of some of the types of energy you observed.

When it is your group's turn to present, take turns presenting different features of each object. Begin by demonstrating how your object operates. Then,

- identify the changes you observed and the indicators that allowed you to detect each type of energy,

- share your ideas with the class about the types of energy you saw in your objects, including any questions you have, and

- present the list of forms of energy and their indicators, and tell the class which indicators are most common for each form of energy.

As you are listening, note the different types of energy each group has identified and the indicators for each type. If you do not understand what a group is presenting, or if you disagree with their conclusions, ask questions. Remember to be respectful.

After all of the groups have presented their results and shared their ideas, update your *Energy Types* page with all the energy types you learned about in this *Learning Set* and in the presentations. You can revise some of the information already recorded.

Reflect

At the beginning of this section, you wrote a description of energy based on what you observed in the demonstration of the pop-up toaster. How would you describe energy now that you have observed the operation of so many different objects?

Update the Project Board

As you read about different types of energy, you probably identified indicators for some of the types of energy you know about. Record what you have learned about indicators for each type of energy in the *What are we learning?* column. Record your evidence in the *What is our evidence?* column. Use the *What do we need to investigate?* column to record any new questions you have about energy and indicators.

Energy Types	0.0.1/1.2.2/2.5.2/2.6.2/ 3.2.2/3.6.2/4.5.2/5.1.3/5.5.1

Name: _____   Date: _____

Type of energy	Indicators that this type is being transformed	Factors that affect the amount of energy

© It's About Time

Design a Rube Goldberg machine to turn off a light				
What do we think we know?	What do we need to investigate?	What are we learning?	What is our evidence?	What does it mean for the challenge or question?

What's the Point?

Changes are caused by the transformation of energy. Your senses, especially sight, are valuable in detecting indicators that show different types of energy transformations. The toaster and the objects you explored transformed electrical, kinetic, light, elastic, sound, chemical, and thermal energy. You identified indicators for each of these. Because energy is used everywhere, it is easy to observe many different energy indicators. Each type of energy is different from the others. What they all have in common is that they all are used to produce change.

A fire transforms chemical energy (contained in the fuel) into thermal energy.

Learning Set 1

Back to the Big Challenge

Design a Rube Goldberg machine to turn off a light.

Your challenge is to design a machine that will turn off a light when light is no longer needed. To succeed at this task, you will use your creativity and imagination. In this *Learning Set*, you learned about some types of energy and about the indicators you can observe to know when energy is being transformed. Now you will examine your energy-transformation cartoon and apply what you have learned. You will identify the types of energy transformations in the cartoon and the indicators of each. Then you will use what you have learned about different types of energy and their indicators to begin designing your own Rube Goldberg machine.

Energy-transformation Cartoon

0.0.3/1.BBC.1/3.BBC.1/
4.1.2/4.BBC.1/5.1.2/6.3.1

Name: _____ Date: _____

Fill in the letter of the step you are analyzing. Then fill in other information about that step.

Name of your machine:			Purpose of your machine:	
Step	Changes/Work done	Energy type in	Energy types out	Indicators of energy transformations

Record questions about anything on which your group does not agree and anything you do not understand.

© It's About Time

Observe

During the introduction to this Unit, you examined an energy-transformation cartoon, and you identified many of the energy transformations in it. You have learned more about energy since then, and you can probably identify more types of energy than you could before. With your group, identify as many types of energy in the cartoon as you can. For each, identify the indicators that tell you what type of energy is being transformed to what other type. Record your ideas on an *Energy-transformation Cartoon* page.

PBIS

✓

renewable
resource: a
resource that
is continually
resupplied; for
example, light
energy from the
Sun.

nonrenewable
resource: a
resource that
exists in a limited
supply; for
example, coal
and oil.

fossil fuel: an
energy source
that comes from
the remains of
living things; for
example, coal, oil,
and natural gas.

Why Is it Important to Save Energy Resources?

You might wonder why you should turn off the lights when you do not need them. For many reasons, it is important to turn out the lights. Like in a flashlight, the lights in your home transform electrical energy into light energy. The simple answer to the question, then, is that if you turn out the lights when you are not in a room, you will need less electrical energy than if you leave the lights on.

Some of the resources that provide electrical energy are renewable. A **renewable resource** is one that is continually re-supplied. For example, the energy that sunlight provides is a renewable resource. However, most of the natural resources people use to generate electrical energy for homes are **nonrenewable resources.** A nonrenewable resource is one that exists in a limited supply, such as coal or oil. Coal and oil formed under Earth's surface over hundreds of millions of years. When a nonrenewable resource runs out, it cannot easily be made again.

The electrical energy you use in your home and school is probably generated by power plants. Some power plants transform the kinetic energy of falling water into electrical energy. However, most power plants burn coal, oil, or natural gas to make electrical energy. Burning one of these fuels transforms the chemical energy stored in the fuel into heat, which can then be converted by a generator into electrical energy. Coal, oil, and natural gas are all nonrenewable resources.

The chemical energy in coal, oil, and natural gas comes from the remains of plants and animals that lived hundreds of millions of years ago. Plants and animals store chemical energy in molecules in their bodies. When plants and animals die, their bodies still have chemical energy in their molecules. Over time, through the actions of heat, pressure, and chemical reactions, the plant and animal remains are converted into coal, oil, and natural gas. These energy sources are called **fossil fuels** because they come from the fossil remains of long-dead plants and animals.

It takes hundreds of millions of years for fossil fuels to form, and there is a limited amount of coal, oil, and natural gas in the ground. When the fossil fuels are used up, there will be no more. If people want to have electricity in their houses for many years to come, they have to use fossil fuels more slowly or develop other ways of generating and saving electricity.

Burning fossil fuels to produce electrical energy also causes air pollution. Air pollution can cause health problems in people, harm plant and animal life, and damage buildings. People will generate less air pollution when they reduce the amount of electricity used.

A final reason to save energy resources is that preparing coal and oil for use in a power plant requires a large amount of energy. It takes a large amount of energy to dig up coal or pump oil. More energy is required to process these fuels for use in the power plants. Even more energy is used to transport the fossil fuels to power plants. Whenever people use electricity, they are consuming the energy from the fuel itself and also the energy needed to make that fuel available to the power plants.

Scientists and engineers are investigating ways to generate electricity more cleanly, and from resources that are not as limited as fossil fuels. Even when these new methods are available to everyone, people will still have to be careful about the energy resources they use

This sequence of pictures shows how plants are transformed into light energy in your home. Notice where energy is needed in these steps and which steps cause pollution.

Step 1: Fossil fuels, such as coal, come from the fossil remains of plants and animals.

Step 2: The coal is mined.

Step 3: The coal is transported to power plants.

Step 4: Power plants
burn the coal to
produce electricity.

Step 5: Power lines carry
electricity to homes.

Step 6: Electricity is
used to light your
living-room lamp.

Update the *Project Board*

As you examined the energy-transformation cartoons, you probably identified
indicators for many of the types of energy you know about. Record indicators
on your *Energy Types* page. Record any new questions you have about
energy, indicators, energy transformation, work, and generating energy in the
What do we need to investigate? column.

Design a Rube Goldberg machine to turn off a light				
What do we think we know?	What do we need to investigate?	What are we learning?	What is our evidence?	What does it mean for the challenge or question?

Learning Set 2

What Affects How Much Energy an Object Has?

When you observed the radiometer, sometimes the flags moved faster. Sometimes they moved more slowly. And sometimes they did not move at all. You know that when an object is in motion, it has kinetic energy. However, you do not yet know what affects *how much* energy an object has or how its energy determines the amount of work that can be done.

In this *Learning Set,* you will explore some of the **factors** that affect how much energy objects have. A factor is a characteristic that you can measure. The factors that determine how much energy an object has are different for each type of energy. You will explore the factors that affect *kinetic energy, gravitational potential energy,* and *elastic potential energy.* You will also explore how objects can store energy and how work is used to change the amount of energy in an object. To design your best Rube Goldberg machine for turning off a light, you will need to know how to control factors that affect the amount of energy available at each step.

factor: a characteristic that can be measured.

PBIS

2.1 Understand the Question

Think About What Affects How Much Energy an Object Has

The machine you design should have just the right amount of energy to turn off a light. If there is too much kinetic energy, the light switch might break. If there is not enough kinetic energy, the switch will not move. To design the last step, you will need to know how to control factors that affect the amount of kinetic energy available in each part of the machine. For some parts of your machine, you may want to know how to produce a lot of kinetic energy so an object will move quickly. For other parts, you may need to know how to slow or stop an object quickly and safely. In this section, you will begin to explore the factors that determine how much energy an object has.

Materials

- windup toy
- Newton's cradle
- bouncy ball

Use each toy as it was intended to be used. The ball should not be thrown hard; it should be thrown only at the floor, never at anybody or anything.

Get Started

Your group will explore three toys. Each toy has kinetic energy when it moves. Each toy gets energy from somewhere that allows it to move. Each toy performs differently depending on how much energy it has available. You will focus on three concepts as you operate each toy: the types of energy that play a role in its operation, the indicators of each type of energy, and the factors that affect how much energy it has.

In your group, examine each toy, one at a time.

Answer the following questions about each toy, and record your answers on your *Energy Observations* page.

1. How do you know the toy has kinetic energy? What indicators did you use?

2. How can you increase its kinetic energy?

3. How do you know when its kinetic energy has increased?

4. Where do you think the toy gets the energy that allows it to move?

5. What factors affect how the toy moves?

Communicate

Share Your Ideas

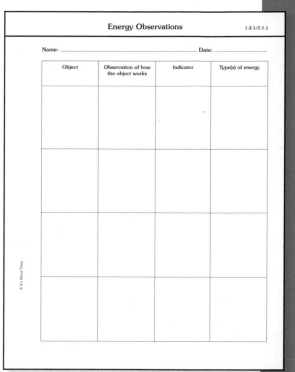

With your class, discuss the available energy of the toys you examined. Share your ideas about the types of energy in the toys and what indicators you observed. Also share your ideas about how you can control the amount of energy in each toy. It may be difficult to determine exactly where the energy came from, but think about it, and express it in your own words.

What Indicates That Kinetic Energy Is Present? What Affects How Much Kinetic Energy an Object Has?

You knew energy was present in all of the objects as you were playing with them because you could see the objects moving. Motion is an indicator of kinetic energy. You found ways to increase the motion of each of the toys. When you wound the windup toy tighter, it moved faster or for a longer time. When you pulled the steel ball higher before letting go of it, the ball on the opposite side also sprung up higher. When you dropped the ball from a higher position or threw it toward the ground with more force, it moved faster and bounced higher. When you saw more movement, you knew the objects had more energy in them.

But what allowed each object to move? And why did it have more energy sometimes than at other times? You may have figured that out for some of the objects.

ENERGY

potential energy:
energy that is
stored to be
transformed at a
later time.

**elastic potential
energy:** stored
energy released
when an object's
shape is changed
(as in a stretched
rubber band or a
coiled spring).

**gravitational
potential energy:**
stored energy of
an object based on
its position above
the ground.

When you wind up the windup toy, energy is stored in its spring. Although you cannot see it, the spring holds **potential energy**. Potential energy is energy that is stored up until it is released and transformed. A battery in a flashlight stores chemical energy that it releases as electrical energy when you turn on the flashlight. A similar thing happens in the windup toy. The spring in the toy stores up potential energy until you release it. Then the potential energy is transformed into kinetic energy, and the toy moves. The particular type of potential energy in the spring of the windup toy is **elastic potential energy**. Elastic energy is present when something "stretchy" or "springy" is taken from a relaxed position to a position where it is under stress.

Newton's cradle presents a different way to transform potential energy into kinetic energy. In this device, a steel ball is raised and then released so that it swings into the other balls. You may have figured out that lifting and then dropping one of the steel balls provides the energy to the toy. If you don't lift the ball, there is no motion and no kinetic energy. When you lift a ball, however, you tranfer energy to the toy. This energy is called **gravitational potential energy.** Gravitational potential energy is the energy an object stores because of how high above the ground it is.

The bouncy ball gets its energy both from elastic potential energy and gravitational potential energy. When you drop the ball to the floor, it bounces back up at you. Then it falls down and bounces again. Many energy transformations keep it in motion.

Reflect

Answer the following questions based on the toys you examined:

1. Describe the energy that was transformed to make each toy move.

2. What did you do to control each type of energy you observed?

3. What factors controlled the amount of energy available in each of the toys you examined? Remember, a factor is a characteristic that you can measure.

4. In each trial with a particular toy you examined, the toy could have had a different amount of kinetic energy. What indicators allowed you to compare the kinetic energy in different trials?

5. In the windup toy, the bouncy ball, and Newton's cradle, the motion eventually stopped. What did this tell you about the amount of kinetic energy in each toy?

6. What else do you need to know about kinetic and potential energy to control the motion in the machine you will design?

Update the *Project Board*

In this section, you thought about where the energy to move an object comes from. Update the *Project Board* by adding ideas to the *What do we think we know?* column. Add your ideas about how you would control the amount of energy available for motion. Also, record the factors you think determine the amount of kinetic energy. Be sure to add to the *Project Board* the ideas your group agreed on and ideas you are not sure about. You may have questions about how much a factor will control energy or how you can know how much kinetic energy or potenial energy an object has. Record your questions and ideas for investigations in the *What do we need to investigate?* column.

Design a Rube Goldberg machine to turn off a light				
What do we think we know?	What do we need to investigate?	What are we learning?	What is our evidence?	What does it mean for the challenge or question?

ENERGY

What's the Point?

Kinetic energy is the energy associated with motion. Motion can be started when an object's energy potential is released. The windup toy gets its kinetic energy from elastic potential energy in the toy's spring. The first ball in Newton's cradle gets its kinetic energy from the gravitational potential energy of the ball when it is raised. The bouncy ball has many different energy sources. You know that there is energy in motion and that stored energy can be transformed into kinetic energy to make something move. You know, too, that there are ways to control the amount of energy available for movement. You do not know, however, exactly what factors control movement and how to control those factors. In the rest of this *Learning Set,* you will be investigating how different types and amounts of potential energy affect the kinetic energy of an object.

Rides at the amusement park have kinetic energy and do work.

2.2 Explore

What Factors Determine the Amount of Kinetic Energy of an Object?

Imagine that a neighbor just bought a new car. Near where he parked it, four of your friends are playing catch with a ball. Two are using a baseball, and the other two are using a hollow plastic ball of the same size. The owner of the car hears a loud "THUNK!" when one of the balls hits the car. You know that the baseball has caused the noise. Since the noise was loud, you know that the dent made by the ball is probably pretty big. But you may not know that the baseball had more kinetic energy than the plastic ball. In this section, you will identify some of the factors that affect how much kinetic energy an object has.

The ball had kinetic energy before it struck the car.

Conference

With your group, make a first attempt at identifying factors that determine how much kinetic energy an object has. Use the following scenarios and questions to help you.

1. Think about the situation above. What factors do you think would determine the size of the dent in the car?

2. Imagine being hit by a ball. How would it feel to be hit by a plastic ball thrown by a child? What about a baseball thrown by a child? What about a plastic ball thrown by a baseball player? What about a baseball thrown by a baseball player? What do you think would happen to the ball, in each case, after it hit you? What factors determine how much the ball would hurt?

3. You know that when a faster-moving ball hits something, the result is different than when a slower-moving ball hits something. Using what you know about what happens when a ball hits something, what factors do you think you could measure to compare the kinetic energy in two different moving objects?

Communicate

Share Your Ideas

Discuss the answers to the *Conference* questions as a class. Make a class list of factors you think determine the amount of kinetic energy of a ball. Then discuss what you could measure to determine how much kinetic energy a moving object has.

Observe

What Affects a Cart's Kinetic Energy?

You will get a chance now to test your ideas about how different factors determine the amount of kinetic energy in an object. You are going to observe a set of videos showing a small cart running downhill into a ball of clay. Before each video, you will predict what will happen to the ball of clay.

Procedure

1. Begin by looking at the cart in its start position in the first video. This cart has a mass of 250 g (8.8 oz) and will be going 4 kph (2.4 mph) at the moment it hits the clay. Predict what will happen to the clay, and record your prediction in the *Predicted Smoosh* column on your *Cart-Clay Data* page.

2. Then watch the video, and observe what happens to the clay. Record the data from your observations in the *Actual Smoosh* column.

3. Now take a break from the videos. With your group, answer these three questions on your *Cart-Clay Data* page:

   a) What does the dent produced in the ball of clay mean?

   b) How do you think the dent in a ball of clay can be used to measure the kinetic energy of the cart?

   c) How do you think you might be able to change the kinetic energy of the cart?

4. Before going on, discuss your answers with the class.

5. Repeat *Steps 1* and *2* for the second and third videos. The mass and speed of the cart in each video is recorded in the *Cart-Clay Data* page.

Cart–Clay Data Table 2.2.1

Name: _____ Date: _____

Run #	Mass of cart and weight	Speed of cart	Predicted smoosh	Actual smoosh
1	250 g	4 km/hr		

Question 1 What does the dent produced in the ball of clay mean?

Question 2 How do you think the dent in a ball of clay can be used to measure the kinetic energy of the cart?

Question 3 How do you think you might be able to change the kinetic energy of the cart?

2	750 g	4 km/hr		
3	250 g	12 km/hr		

© It's About Time

Analyze Your Data

With your group, answer these questions:

1. Which cart had the most kinetic energy at the moment it hit the clay? Which cart had the least kinetic energy? How do you know?

2. Place the cart runs in order of least kinetic energy to most kinetic energy. What is your evidence for this order of the cart runs?

3. What factors do you think determined the cart's kinetic energy at the moment it hit the clay?

Communicate

Share Your Ideas

Share your ideas about which cart had the most kinetic energy and which cart had the least kinetic energy at the moment of impact. Discuss what evidence you used to make the determination. Then make a class list of the factors that determined the kinetic energy of the carts in the videos.

Reflect

1. Choose a sport, such as football, softball, or track, and list three ways increased kinetic energy helps one team score or win over another team.

2. Which do you think is more important in determining the amount of kinetic energy: speed or mass? Or do you think they have about the same effect? Why do you think so?

3. How might knowing the speed and mass of objects in motion help you with your design challenge?

4. What ideas do you have about how to increase the speed or mass of an object?

5. You will be learning about many different forms of energy in this Unit. Now is a good time to use a new *Energy Types* page to summarize what you know about each type of energy, or you may edit the *Energy Types* page you began earlier. Record what you now know about kinetic energy—the indicators that tell you it is present, the factors that affect how much kinetic energy an object has, and examples you have seen of objects with kinetic energy.

	Energy Types	0.0.1/1.2.2/2.5.2/2.6.2/ 3.2.2/3.6.2/4.5.2/5.1.3/5.5.1

Name: _____ Date: _____

Type of energy	Indicators that this type is being transformed	Factors that affect the amount of energy

© It's About Time

2.3 Explore

How Does Work Decrease Kineti

When you saw the toys moving, yo
is an indicator of kinetic energy. Y
each of the toys. When you threw
more force, it moved faster and bo
movement, you knew the ball had

One way to think about the kinetic
about how much **work** you would
work when you apply a **force** thro
an object. A force can be a push or

Imagine that you and several friend
food cart. Suddenly, the person los
The cart is moving at 2 m/s. You a
bringing the cart to a stop. It takes

Now imagine that later that day
you are playing in a baseball
game. You are the catcher on
the team. The pitcher throws
you a ball at 30 m/s, and you
catch it. The ball stings your
hand, but you have no trouble
stopping it with your glove. It
did not take much work to stop
the ball. Which do you think
had more kinetic energy, the
fastball or the food cart? Why?
You may not be able to answer
these questions now. The
activity you will do will help you
better answer these questions.

The PlayPump® Story

Everybody needs water to live—to drink, to cook, and
to wash. However, about one person in seven on Earth
does not have a readily available source of clean water.
Rural African villages that do not have electricity are
especially at risk.

Since there is no life without water, and there are no
electric pumps to bring the water into the villages,
women and children spend
much of their time hauling
water. This is a chore that
must be done every day.
The water is heavy to carry,
and the women and children
require a lot of time and
energy to lift the water and
move the heavy buckets of
water to their homes. In some
of these villages, the children
spend so much time on chores
they have no chance to go
to school.

But help is on the way. An
engineer in South Africa
designed a simple system
that connects a water pump
to a merry-go-round. As
children play on the merry-go-
round, their kinetic energy is
transformed into energy to pump water from wells
and move it to where it is needed. The pumps can
pull water up from a depth of 100 m (328 ft)
underground and bring it closer to people's homes
than is possible without the pumps. People do not have to use so much
energy and time to bring the water to their homes.

More than 1000 pumps are in use in Africa today under the name
PlayPump®. These machines transform some of the children's kinetic
energy into energy that is used to pump water. The children's kinetic

Children have fun spinning on the PlayPump® merry-go-round. (1) Clean water is pumped (2) from a well (3) into a tank (4). A tap (5) makes it easy for adults and children to draw water. Excess water goes from the storage tank back down into the well (6).

energy
Becaus
to play
money

When you transfer kinetic energy to your bicycle, you cause it to move.

What's

Kinetic ene
determine t
baseballs of
speed has n
the same sp
has a great

Materials

• **1 small marble**
• **1 large marble**
• **2 paper cups**
• **tape**
• **marker**

Observing Kinetic Energy and Work

To help you understand the relationship between work and kinetic energy, you will observe the difference in kinetic energy between two objects and the difference in the amount of work that is done. If your classroom is large, you will be able to do this activity with your group. If there is not room for that, your teacher will set it up as a demonstration. Make sure you can see the cups move.

Procedure

1. On the floor, place two strips of tape. The strips should be about 1 m apart. Label one strip *finish line* and the other strip *starting line.*

2. Place the two paper cups on their sides along the finish line as shown in the diagram. Both cups should face toward the starting line. Add a third strip of tape about half a meter behind the starting line.

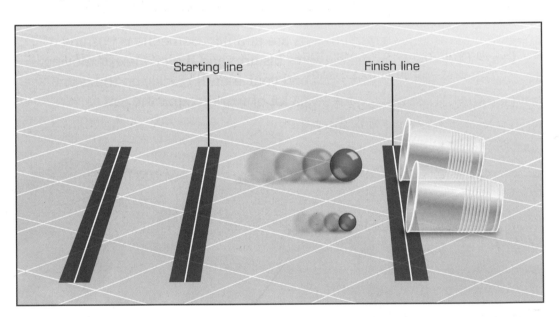

Starting line   Finish line

3. One student should take the two marbles and sit or kneel behind the starting line. With one marble in each hand, place the marbles on the third strip of tape. Slide the marbles along the floor and release them at the starting line so they each roll into a paper cup. The marbles should be released right at the starting line at the same time and reach the finish line (and the cups) at the same time. It may take several trials to get the aim and timing correct. You may find it easier to have each marble rolled by a different student. Measure and record how far each cup moves.

4. Repeat *Step 3* until you have at least three trials where both marbles reach the cups at the same time.

5. Look across your trials. Compare the movement of the paper cup hit by the small marble to the movement of the cup hit by the large marble.

Reflect

Discuss with your group the answers to these questions. Be prepared to share your answers with the class.

1. When the marbles enter the paper cups, are the marbles traveling at the same speed? How do you know?

2. When the marbles enter the paper cups, do you think the marbles have the same amount of kinetic energy or different amounts of kinetic energy? Why?

3. Do you think one of the marbles does more work on the paper cup? How do you know?

4. Do you think one hand (or student) does more work on a marble to bring it from rest to the starting line? How do you know?

5. The marbles do work on the paper cups by pushing them away from the finish line. Do you think the paper cups also do work on the marbles? How do you know?

6. Which do you think takes more work to stop, a fast-moving baseball or a slow-moving car? Why?

7. Return to the energy-transformation cartoon you analyzed earlier in the Unit. Choose a step that involves kinetic energy. Describe how this step uses kinetic energy to do work. Then describe how work was done to input kinetic energy into the step.

Communicate

As a class, discuss the answers to the first six questions above. Then take turns sharing your analyses of the relationship between work and kinetic energy for a step in the energy-transformation cartoons.

Elastic and rubber bands also store elastic potential energy. When you stretch a rubber band and then release it, its elastic potential energy is transformed to kinetic energy. The rubber band will fly across the room. The more you stretch the rubber band, the more elastic potential energy it has, and the faster it will fly.

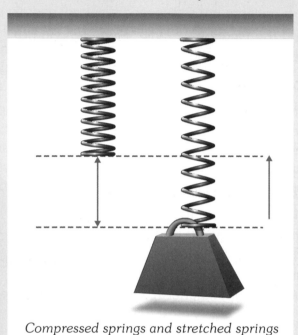

Compressed springs and stretched springs both store elastic potential energy.

The bouncy ball stores elastic potential energy in a similar way. When the ball hits the floor, it is compressed, giving it elastic potential energy. When that elastic potential energy is released, it is transformed into kinetic energy, and the ball moves.

In general, if you see that an object can stretch or compress, you know that it can store elastic potential energy.

A windup music box or airplane stores elastic potential energy in its spring.

How Is Potential Energy Stored Using Gravity?

Newton's cradle shows how **gravity** is used to store and transform potential energy. You have lived with gravity your whole life, yet for most people it remains a mysterious force. Part of the mystery is that gravity acts at a distance. When Earth pulls a steel ball toward the ground, there is nothing visible that connects the ball and the ground. Yet the indicators of gravity are familiar. Any time you see an object falling or see the effort it takes to lift a weight, you are seeing indicators of gravity.

By now you know that work is done when a force acts through a distance to change an object's motion or position. Sometimes you do work to overcome gravity. Just think back to the last time you climbed three flights of stairs. You did a lot of work to lift your body higher. As you did this work, you applied an upward force using the muscles in your legs.

When you lift the steel ball in Newton's cradle, you do work. This work is stored as potential energy in the ball. This type of potential energy is called gravitational potential energy—the energy an object stores because of its position above the ground. When you release the ball, its gravitational potential energy is transformed into kinetic energy, which is then transferred to the other balls.

gravity: the force of attraction between any two masses. Near Earth's surface, gravity is the force that attracts objects toward the center of Earth.

You were able to control the amount of kinetic energy in the balls in the Newton's cradle by moving the steel ball higher or lower. If you lifted the ball higher, you did more work, so the ball stored more gravitational potential energy. This resulted in more kinetic energy when the released ball hit the other balls. When the greater amount of kinetic energy was transmitted through the other balls, the ball at the end of the line moved faster and higher.

You can control the amount of kinetic energy in the Newton's cradle by moving the steel ball higher or lower.

ENERGY

Conservation of Mechanical Energy

Think back to your experience with the bouncy ball. The ball can have kinetic energy from elastic potential energy and gravitational potential energy. When you lift the ball, you are doing work to increase its gravitational potential energy. When you then release the ball, gravitational energy is transformed into kinetic energy as the ball falls. When the ball hits the floor, the ball's shape changes as it flattens against the floor. The ball stops moving for an instant, so it no longer has kinetic energy. All of the ball's kinetic energy has been transformed into elastic potential energy. The ball then bounces upward, releasing its elastic potential energy, which is transformed back into kinetic energy, and so on. Many energy transformations keep the ball in motion.

Scientists often think about energy in terms of the total energy of a **system,** a collection of objects that interact. A system can have one object or many objects. If there are no forces that oppose motion, like friction or air resistance, and no energy is added to or removed from the system, then the **mechanical energy** of a system remains constant. Mechanical energy is the sum of the kinetic energy, gravitational potential energy, and elastic potential energy of a system. This concept is called the **conservation of mechanical energy.** Each time energy is transformed, all of the energy can be accounted for—none of the energy is lost.

system: a collection of objects that interact.

mechanical energy: the sum of the kinetic energy, gravitational potential energy, and elastic potential energy in a system.

conservation of mechanical energy: if there is no friction or air resistance, the mechanical energy of a system changes only if the system does work on something else or energy is added from outside the system.

When you release the ball, gravitational potential energy is transformed into kinetic energy as the ball falls.

It may help to think about what happens to the bouncy ball *after* it bounces upward and all of its energy is kinetic energy (KE). As the ball travels upward, it gains gravitational potential energy (PE) as it goes higher, but it also loses kinetic energy as it slows down. However, at each point, the sum of the gravitational potential energy and the kinetic energy is the same. When the ball reaches its peak, all of its energy is gravitational potential energy. Then as the ball falls, gravitational potential energy decreases (because height decreases) while kinetic energy increases (because speed increases). At each point in its path, the mechanical energy of the ball remains constant.

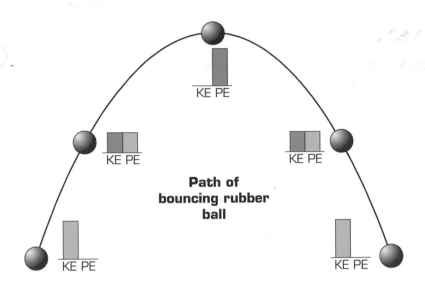

Path of bouncing rubber ball

As the ball travels upward, it gains gravitational potential energy. What happens when the balls travels downward?

Reflect

Work with your group to answer these questions. Be prepared to share your answers with the class.

1. Think back to the step of the energy-transformation cartoon that you analyzed at the end of the last section. Was any potential energy stored or released during the step? Rewrite your description of the step from the last section if necessary, using what you have learned about gravitational and elastic potential energy.

2. How are potential energy and kinetic energy related?

3. What is the connection between work and energy?

Update the *Project Board*

You know a lot now about the relationships between potential energy and kinetic energy. Add what you know about the relationship between potential energy and kinetic energy to the *What are we learning?* column of the *Project Board*. Don't forget to add evidence to the *What is our evidence?* column. If you have new questions about potential energy, kinetic energy, or work, add them to the *What do we need to investigate?* column.

ENERGY

What's the Point?

Elastic potential energy is energy that is stored when an object, such as a spring, is stretched or compressed. When you release the spring, the potential energy is transformed into kinetic energy. Gravitational potential energy is energy that is stored by moving an object to a greater height above the ground. This energy is transformed into kinetic energy when the object is allowed to fall.

You can use work to add kinetic energy to a system or to increase potential energy in the system. Potential energy stored in any system can be released as kinetic energy. Kinetic energy can be transformed to do work or to increase potential energy. Sometimes energy is transferred without being transformed. This occurs when the balls in Newton's cradle transfer kinetic energy. Mechanical energy is the sum of the kinetic energy and potential energy in a system. The mechanical energy of a system remains constant if there is no friction or air resistance and no energy is added to or taken away from the system.

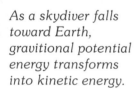

As a skydiver falls toward Earth, gravitional potential energy transforms into kinetic energy.

2.5 Investigate

How Are Gravity and Kinetic Energy Related?

You know that if you drop a pencil, it will fall to the ground. You do not need to throw it toward the ground. You have already learned that when an object falls, gravitational potential energy is transformed into kinetic energy. In this section, you will investigate factors that determine how much gravitational potential energy an object has.

Demonstration

You will soon design an experiment to measure how different factors affect the amount of gravitational potential energy an object has. First, you will watch a marble roll down a track.

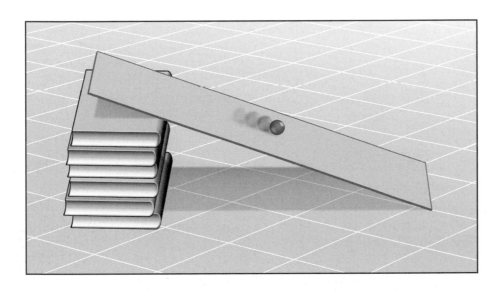

Watch as the marble rolls down the track.

One end of the track has been placed on a stack of books so that one end is higher than the other. To catch the marble, there is a paper cup at the bottom of the track. You cannot see the paper cup in the picture.

Observe carefully as the marble is released at the top of the track. Pay attention to the motion of the paper cup as the marble strikes it. What you observe in this demonstration will help you design your experiment.

Stop and Think

Answer these questions with your group. Be prepared to discuss the answers with the class.

1. What type of energy does the marble have when it is placed at the top of the track? What indicators can you directly observe for this type of energy?

2. What types of energy does the marble have as it is rolling down the track? How do you know?

3. What do you think made the cup at the bottom of the track move?

4. How do you think you could change the amount of potential energy the marble has at the top of the track?

5. What do you think you can measure to know how a change affects the marble's potential energy?

Design an Experiment

Your class may now have some ideas about factors that can increase the potential energy of the marble at the top of the track. Each group will investigate the effects of one of these factors.

In your group, you will discuss and then design an experiment to investigate the effects of your factor on a marble's potential energy. You will begin by developing a question that your experiment will answer.

Then develop a procedure on which your group agrees. Record each step in the procedure in enough detail so that someone else could run your experiment. After you decide on your procedure, think about how trustworthy your data will be. If you think you can improve your data, revise your procedure.

When you are all in agreement that your procedure is the best you can develop, everyone in the group should record it on their *Gravitational Potential Energy Experiment Plan* page. Make sure you are prepared to share your experiment with others. Everyone in your class will need to know what makes your procedure a good one. The advice on the next page will help you design your experiment.

Materials

- marbles of several different sizes
- ball bearings of several different sizes
- ruler with a track in the middle
- pieces of wood to make tracks of different lengths
- tape
- stack of books
- triple-beam balance
- paper cup

Question

What question are you investigating and answering with this experiment? Your question will probably be in this form:

What is the effect of *[your factor]* on the potential energy of a marble at the top of a track?

Prediction

What do you think the answer is, and why do you think that?

Variable Identification

- What variable will you manipulate (change) in your experiment to test the effects on the potential energy of the marble? This is your **independent (manipulated) variable**.

- What conditions and procedures will you keep the same (hold constant or control) in your experiment? These are your **control variables.**

- How will you identify the effects of your variable? What will you measure? These are your **dependent (resulting) variables**.

- How many trials will you run for each value of the variable you manipulate?

Procedure and Data

Write detailed instructions for how to conduct the experiment. Include the following information:

- how you will set up the marble track

- how you will control other variables while changing only one variable at a time

- how you will measure your dependent (resulting) variable, the factor affected by changes in the independent (manipulated) variable

- how you will record the data, including the data table you will use

- how many trials you will complete for each value of your independent (manipulated) variable

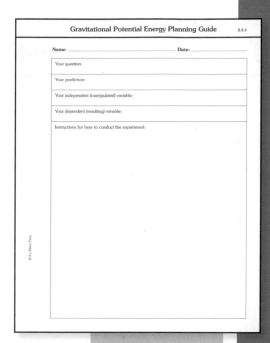

control variables: conditions or procedures that are held constant.

independent (manipulated) variable: a factor that is changed to affect changes in the dependent (resulting) variable.

dependent (resulting) variable: a factor that is affected by changes in the independent (manipulated) variable.

Communicate

Plan Briefing

To help you check your experimental design, you will share it with another group. When it is your turn to present, first state the question you are answering. Then present the variable you will manipulate and what you will measure. Finally, share your procedure.

When you are listening to the other group's presentation, consider the following questions:

- How will their procedure help them answer their question?

- Is the other group controlling all of their variables except for the independent variable?

- Do they have a good way to measure the dependent variable?

- Do you think they are going to run enough trials?

- Do they have places on their data table to record the results of each trial? Do they have places to record the average of all the trials?

- Will they be recording their data in a way that will allow them to easily see how the value of their independent variable affects the value of their dependent variable?

Share your ideas about how you would revise the other group's plan.

Revise Your Plan

With your group, decide if you want to revise your experimental plan based upon your discussion with the other group. Before you start your investigation, check to make sure each member of your group understands the procedure.

Run Your Experiment

Run the experiment, carefully following your recorded procedure. As you carry out your experiment, remember to record your results and any additional notes that will help you understand your results. When you are done running the experiment, you will graph and analyze your data and then report your results to the class.

Be sure to have your teacher check your plan before you conduct any experiment. You should conduct the experiment only as described in your procedure.

Analyze Your Data

Finding Trends and Making Claims

You have collected data that may tell you how the gravitational potential energy of a marble affects its kinetic energy. You most likely measured the marble's kinetic energy by measuring the movement of the paper cup. It is now time to **interpret** those results. To interpret means to figure out what something means. Interpreting the results of an experiment means identifying what happens as a result of changing the independent (manipulated) variable.

For example, you may have used marbles of different masses. If so, you should look at how far the paper cup moved when you changed the mass of the marble. Ask yourself if the distance the cup moved increased or decreased as the mass of the marble increased.

You will do three things to interpret your results. First, you will graph your data. Second, you will try to identify a **trend** in the graph of your data. A trend is a pattern that you can see over several trials. For example, if the mass of the marbles was your independent variable, you might find that, as the mass increased, the distance the paper cup moved increased. Your trend would be, "As the mass of the marble increased, the distance the cup moved increased." Finally, you will decide what your trend shows about how potential energy affects kinetic energy.

Follow the steps below to graph your data, find a trend in your data, and interpret what the trends mean about how your variable affects gravitational potential energy.

interpret: to find the meaning of something.

trend: a pattern or a tendency you can see over a broad range of data.

1. Begin your data analysis by graphing the results. Make your own individual line graph. Be careful how you set up your graph, and make sure you label the *x*-axis and *y*-axis correctly. The *x*-axis should represent the variable you changed—your independent variable. The *y*-axis will represent the dependent variable, the variable you measured.

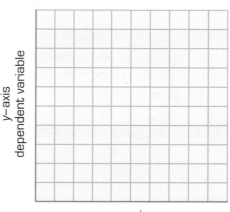

ENERGY

2. What trends do you see in the data? Try to state your trend this way:

   When the value of [*the independent variable*] is [*increased/decreased*], the value of the [*dependent variable*] [*increases/decreases/stays the same*].

claim: a statement that draws a conclusion about a set of facts or data.

3. Based on the trend you identified, arrange the trials in order, from the one with the most gravitational potential energy to the least. Describe why you ordered them that way.

4. Make a **claim** about the way the factor you investigated affects gravitational potential energy. Try to state your claim this way:

   When [*your factor*] [*increases/decreases*], gravitational potential energy [*increases/decreases/stays the same*].

5. Describe the evidence from your experiment that supports your claim.

Communicate Your Results

Investigation Expo

Different groups in the class investigated different factors that might affect gravitational potential energy. You will share your results in an *Investigation Expo.* You will need everyone else's results to successfully design your machine to turn off a light. In preparation for the *Investigation Expo,* create a poster that clearly shows what you learned from your investigation. It should include the following:

- the question you were answering in your investigation

- your independent variable

- your procedure, including the dependent variable you chose, and how you measured your dependent variable

- your data chart

- your graph, with a title and labeled axes

- a description of your trend

- your claim, why you think it is correct, and how confident you are that it is correct

You will begin this *Investigation Expo* by looking at all of the posters. Notice similarities and differences in the results and claims of groups that investigated the same factor. You will want to remember if you see different results or claims from groups that investigated the same question so that you can ask about that later. Make sure you understand why each group made their claim. Remember any claims with which you disagree, so you can ask later. You may want to record notes as you view the posters.

After you look at all the posters, one group assigned each factor will present. If your group presents, use your poster to help you organize your presentation. Remember that your classmates will want the following information:

- the question you were trying to answer in your investigation

- the procedure you used to answer the question, and your reasons for designing your procedure the way you did

- your results

- your graphs and the trends you identified

- your claim and how confident you are

As you listen to other groups present, decide if their results are trustworthy and whether you agree with their claims. Make sure you understand the claims. If there were groups with different results or claims, ask why.

As a class, make a list of the factors that affect how much gravitational potential energy an object has. You may also wish to make a list of factors that do not affect the amount of gravitational potential energy.

What Factors Affect Gravitational Potential Energy?

You know that an object falls because gravity pulls it toward Earth. According to legend, the great Italian physicist and mathematician, Galileo Galilei (1564–1642) dropped two balls of different masses from the top of the Leaning Tower of Pisa. Whether or not this really happened, Galileo was able to show that the two balls would strike the ground at the same time.

acceleration: the rate at which speed changes.

The Leaning Tower of Pisa

Think back to the videos you watched of the three carts running into clay at the end of a track. Imagine going to Pisa, Italy, to try Galileo's experiment, but add a new twist by putting a layer of clay in the area where the two balls will land. You drop the balls, and they travel together as they fall. The balls hit the ground at the same time, so you know they are moving at the same speed. But the balls have different masses, so the ball with more mass has greater kinetic energy. Because the kinetic energy is greater, the heavier ball makes a bigger dent in the clay. If you did this, it would prove that at the top of the tower, the ball with more mass had more gravitational potential energy.

Mass is one factor that determines the amount of gravitational potential energy an object has. Height is another factor. Galileo knew that if you ignore air resistance, all objects fall with the same **acceleration**. The longer an object falls, the faster it moves. If an object is speeding up, what do you think happens to its kinetic energy? You know the answer to this. If it is travelling faster, it has more kinetic energy.

Because objects speed up, or accelerate, as they fall, they gain kinetic energy as they fall toward Earth. The mass of an object and its height above Earth's surface are the two most important factors controlling the amount of gravitational potential energy an object possesses.

In your experiments, you measured the kinetic energy of a marble at the bottom of the track by seeing how much work the marble did as it moved a cup. All of the ball's energy at the bottom of the track is kinetic energy. All of its energy at the top of the track is gravitational potential energy. According to conservation of mechanical energy, the kinetic energy at the bottom of the track must equal the gravitational potential energy the marble had at the top of the track. That is why you can use kinetic energy to indirectly measure gravitational potential energy.

Reflect

1. Return to the energy-transformation cartoon machine you analyzed earlier in the Unit. Find three objects that could have their potential energy changed. How would you increase it? How would you decrease it?

2. Why might it be important when designing your machine to turn off a light to know how much gravitational potential energy an object has?

3. Update your *Energy Types* page with what you now know about gravitational potential energy—its indicators and factors that affect the amount of energy.

Energy Types	0.0.1/1.2.2/2.5.2/2.6.2/ 3.2.2/3.6.2/4.5.2/5.1.3/5.5.1

Name: _____ Date: _____

Type of energy	Indicators that this type is being transformed	Factors that affect the amount of energy

© It's About Time

ENERGY

2.6 Explore

How Does Elastic Potential Energy Affect Kinetic Energy?

Materials

- compression spring
- extension spring
- rubber band
- pop-up toy
- 50-g mass and spring
- 100-g mass and spring
- windup toy
- bouncy ball
- marble
- maraca
- flashlight
- Newton's cradle
- scissors
- tuning fork
- hand-crank generator

As you have learned, potential energy is stored energy and cannot be seen. When you put a marble at the top of a track, the marble has gravitational potential energy. This potential energy is a result of the marble's position. Elastic potential energy is also energy that results from an object's position. Think back to the pop-up toaster example. When you push down the toaster's lever, you compress a spring inside the toaster. It takes work to change the position of the lever and compress the spring. When the spring releases, the elastic potential energy is transformed into kinetic energy.

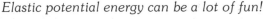

Elastic potential energy can be a lot of fun!

The spring on a screen door can store elastic potential energy.

Many everyday things, including toys, containers, and clothing, transform elastic potential energy. Your group will explore a variety of objects that transform elastic potential energy. As you make your observations, think about the factors that determine how much elastic potential energy an object has.

Explore Elastic Potential Energy

Your group will explore several objects from the list of materials. Some of these objects transform elastic potential energy and some do not. You will begin your exploration by classifying the objects into two sets. Set 1 will include all of the objects that transform elastic potential energy in some way. Set 2 will include all of the objects that do not transform elastic potential energy. First, you will identify the indicators that determine in which set each item belongs. Then, you will further examine the items that transform elastic potential energy and identify the factors that affect how much elastic potential energy they have.

When the pole-vaulter's pole bends, it stores elastic potential energy. As the pole straightens, it transforms the elastic potential energy into kinetic energy, which does the work of sending the pole-vaulter over the bar.

Procedure

1. Explore the objects you have available, using them the way they are intended to be used. Identify which items transform elastic potential energy and which do not. Record your choices on your *Elastic Energy Explorations* page.

2. For each object, identify the indicators you used to decide whether or not it transforms elastic potential energy. Record the indicators in the *Indicators* column.

3. Continue to explore the items that you think transform elastic potential energy, and answer these questions:

   a) What do all of the objects in Set 1 have in common?

   b) How does this common property allow each object to store elastic potential energy?

   c) What factors affect how much elastic potential energy is stored? How do you know? How can you increase or decrease the amount of stored energy in each object? Record these factors on your *Elastic Energy Explorations* page.

Elastic Energy Explorations   2.6.1

Name: _____   Date: _____

Set 1 Items transforming elastic energy	Indicator	Factors	Set 2 Items not transforming elastic energy	Indicator
1.			1.	
2.			2.	
3.			3.	
4.			4.	
5.			5.	
6.			6.	

ENERGY

4. Select one of the objects that transforms elastic potential energy. Prepare a description of how it operates. Make sure your list of indicators used to classify the object as having elastic potential energy is complete. Also, develop a good description of the factors that determine how much elastic potential energy it stores and how those factors can be changed. Be prepared to show the class your example and describe the factors.

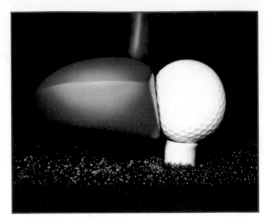

The elastic potential energy in a golf ball transforms into kinetic energy when the golf club hits the ball.

Communicate

Share Your Ideas

When it is your group's turn to share your object, describe the object and what it does. Also, share the indicators you used to decide it transforms elastic potential energy and the factors that determine how much elastic potential energy is stored in it.

Listen carefully as each group presents. If the object presented is one you have investigated, compare their ideas to what you recorded on your *Elastic Potential Energy Explorations* page. If the object is different, add it to your page. Describe it well. Make sure you include the indicators and factors.

If you disagree with, or do not understand, a group's presentation, ask questions. Make sure you ask respectfully.

Reflect

1. Return to the energy-transformation cartoon machine you analyzed earlier in the Unit. Identify steps where elastic potential energy is used.

2. For each step, what indicators did you use to decide whether or not it transforms elastic potential energy?

3. For each step, how do you think you could increase the elastic potential energy? How do you think you could decrease it?

4. What would happen if you changed the elastic potential energy available in each step? What would still be successful? What would no longer be successful? What would operate differently?

5. Why might it be important to know how much elastic potential energy an object has when designing your machine to turn off a light?

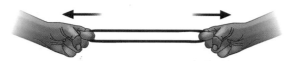

Some materials, like rubber, readily return to their original shape after being deformed.

deformed: changed in shape because of an applied force.

elasticity: ability of a material to return to its original shape after it is deformed.

What Factors Affect Elastic Potential Energy?

Elastic potential energy is the energy stored in a springy material when the material is stretched, compressed, or otherwise **deformed**. When the material returns to its original shape, the potential energy is released, usually as kinetic energy. Many different materials, including rubber bands, trampolines, springs, and an archer's bow, can be deformed to store potential energy. The factors that determine the amount of elastic potential energy being stored include the type of material and the amount it is deformed. The more an object is deformed, the more stored energy it has.

Many sports use elastic materials in balls to provide the needed transformation of kinetic energy to potential energy and back to kinetic energy. These include golf balls, tennis balls, baseballs, basketballs, and footballs, as well as many others. In each case, the materials are selected for their **elasticity**.

Many of the objects you looked at use springs made of metal. You may never have thought you could stretch or compress metal. Because of its hardness and strength, metal is usually used to provide protection or structure. However, under certain conditions, a metal's elasticity can store elastic potential energy, as in a spring.

Pulling the bowstring compresses the bow. The more the archer compresses the bow, the farther the arrow will go.

ENERGY

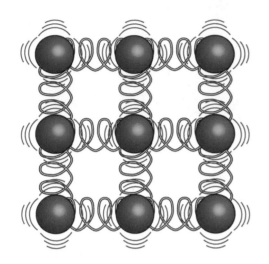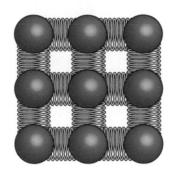

This model of the atoms of a metal connected by imaginary springs shows what happens when the metal is deformed.

This coiled metal spring toy was invented in 1945 by a naval engineer while designing a part for battleships. Each toy is made from over 24 m (80 ft) of wire.

elastic limit: limit beyond which a deformed material does not return to its original shape.

To understand metal's elasticity, it is necessary to think about the atoms of metals. In metals, the atoms are usually evenly spaced, and they are held in place by forces of attraction. When you bend the metal, the atoms on one side stretch apart, while on the other side, the atoms are compressed together. When you release the metal, the forces tend to snap the atoms back in place. In fact, one way to model the atoms of a metal is to show them held together as if by springs.

When a metal spring is stretched, the distance between the atoms increases. When the spring is released, the atoms return to their original positions, and the spring returns to its original shape. When a spring is compressed, the distance between the atoms decreases. When the compressed spring is released, the atoms are pushed away from each other and return the spring to its original shape. It is possible to exceed a spring's **elastic limit** by stretching it too far. When this happens, the spring does not return to its original shape.

Springs are used to store elastic potential energy in many familiar objects, including screen doors, mattresses, and some light switches. The compression spring, extension spring, and masses with springs are some of the objects you examined that store elastic potential energy.

A basketball stores elastic potential energy.

Stop and Think

1. Describe how a coiled toy spring stretches and compresses when used as intended.

2. What do you think happens to the distance between atoms in a spring that exceeds its elastic limit?

3. Describe how a rubber ball is deformed when it bounces. Describe how a basketball is deformed when it bounces. What about a tennis ball? What about a baseball? Which kinds of balls do you think can store more elastic potential energy? Why?

4. Describe how a bow is deformed when it is used to shoot an arrow. Which part of the bow, the string or the wood, do you think stores more elastic potential energy? Why?

5. Suppose a car has a dent in it. Do you think there is elastic potential energy stored in that dent? Why or why not?

Reflect

Update your *Energy Types* page with what you now know about elastic potential energy. Revise your list of indicators. Add factors that affect how much elastic potential energy an object has.

Energy Types		0.0.1/1.2.2/2.5.2/2.6.2/ 3.2.2/3.6.2/4.5.2/5.1.3/5.5.1
Name:		Date:
Type of energy	Indicators that this type is being transformed	Factors that affect the amount of energy

ENERGY

Update the *Project Board*

Now is a good time to summarize what you have learned so far about the energy in objects and add it to the *Project Board*. Add what you have learned about kinetic and potential energy to the *What are we learning?* column. Add your evidence to the *What is our evidence?* column. If you have new questions, add them to the *What do we need to investigate?* column.

What's the Point?

Indicators of elastic potential energy may sometimes be difficult to observe, but often you can feel them when you do work to compress or stretch an object. Several factors determine how much elastic potential energy an object has stored. One factor is the material the object is made of. Some materials, like rubber, readily return to their original shape after being deformed. A second factor that affects elastic potential energy is the amount of deformation. When the deformation is greater, more force is needed to deform the material, and the elastic potential energy stored is greater.

Learning Set 2

Back to the Big Challenge

Design a Rube Goldberg machine to turn off a light.

The *Big Challenge* for this Unit is *Design a Rube Goldberg machine to turn off a light.* At the end of *Learning Set 1,* you began to think about what kind of light you want to turn off and what the last step of your design needs to do. Your last step almost certainly has some object that needs to move. You now know enough about the energy of objects to figure out how to give that object kinetic energy and how to control the amount of kinetic energy it will have. You will now continue to design backward to address the challenge. You will use what you know to make your last step more specific. You will identify what has to happen before the last step for the last step to operate successfully. But first, you will describe energy one more time.

Conference

You wrote a description of energy at the beginning of *Learning Set 1,* before you knew a lot about different kinds of energy. You described energy again after you thought about the different ways your energy-transformation cartoon transformed energy. Before moving on, you will once again describe energy. This time, you will use what you have learned about the energy of objects. You now know about several types of energy—kinetic energy, gravitational potential energy, and elastic potential energy. You know how to identify when each is present, and you know the factors that determine how much of each is present.

Revise your description of energy so it takes into account all the different things you now know about energy. Keep track of the changes you make in your description, and record why you are making the changes.

What are the indicators that this car is storing potential energy? What happens to that energy after the car goes over the top of the hill?

Communicate

Share Your Ideas

Take turns sharing your descriptions of energy. Tell the class how you changed your description and why you changed it.

Listen to the descriptions of others, and compare their descriptions to yours. As you listen, you may find that you have left something important out of your description, or that there is a part of it that is not correct. Record anything you hear that you might want to add to your description. If there are parts of the descriptions you do not agree with, raise your hand and tell the class why you think that part is not correct. If a group has something in their description you do not understand, ask questions that will help you understand.

You will be learning much more about energy as you continue through this Unit, and you will have opportunities to revise your description. Even though you do not yet have a full understanding of energy, enjoy the fact that you know much more now than you did earlier in the Unit.

Revise Your Design

You developed three possible last steps for your design. Each of them probably has a moving part. Every movement involves kinetic energy. You know a lot now about how objects can get kinetic energy and how the amount of kinetic energy they have can be controlled. Now analyze each of your possible last steps. Use what you know about the factors that affect the amount of kinetic energy and potential energy, and how potential energy is transformed into kinetic energy. Your analysis should include three parts:

1. Identify how much kinetic energy your machine will need in its last step—a little, a lot, or a huge amount.

2. Identify how the moving part in your last step could get kinetic energy.

3. Identify how you might control the amount of kinetic energy of the moving part in your last step.

You may get some ideas about how to supply energy to your last step from the energy-transformation cartoons the class examined.

Sketch your ideas about how to supply energy to the last step of your design. Make sure to show the moving part that will turn off the light. Identify what type of energy you might transform to supply energy to your last step. Be prepared to present your ideas to the class, including any ideas about which you are still unsure. Update your *My Rube Goldberg Machine* page with all of your design revisions and ideas.

My Rube Goldberg Machine	1.BBC.2/2.BBC.1/4.BBC.3/ 5.BBC.2/6.BBC.2/ABC.1

Name: _____   Date: _____

Sketch of machine. Label each step with a number.

Step	Description of step	Energy Type(s) In	Energy Type(s) Out	Work done
1				
2				
3				
4				
5				

Use this space to record ideas.

© It's About Time

ENERGY

Communicate

Plan Briefing

Very briefly, show the class the ideas you have about the energy your machine needs in its last step and how you might supply that energy to it. Report to the class anything about which you are still unsure. As you listen, if you have an idea for some other group or can answer the questions a group is wondering about, offer your ideas. Try to be brief. There will be plenty of time later to continue designing your machine.

Update the *Project Board*

You now know a lot about kinetic energy and potential energy and have thought about how these energy types might be involved in the last step of your Rube Goldberg machine. Update the *Project Board* with questions you still have about energy and about designing your machine. Record your questions in the *What do we need to investigate?* column.

As you climb a mountain, you gain potential energy. What kind of potential energy?

Learning Set 3

What Are Thermal Energy and Chemical Energy?

Imagine biting into a warm stack of pancakes. The warmth of the pancakes easily melts a golden pat of butter. Before you even take a bite, the aroma tells you that this breakfast is going to be delicious. But, just minutes ago, these pancakes were a cool, runny blob of pale pancake batter. The unappealing batter was transformed into an appetizing treat for the eyes, nose, and mouth by thermal and chemical energy. Then thermal energy from the warm pancakes warmed the butter, causing it to melt.

Thermal energy and chemical energy are transformed in cooking to produce delicious results from raw ingredients.

The energy-transformation cartoons you examined all have examples of thermal energy and chemical energy. You might want to use thermal or chemical energy in the machine you are designing. In this *Learning Set*, you will explore these two types of energy and learn the indicators of each, the factors that affect how much energy is available, and how each type of energy is transformed to do work. As you are investigating them, notice how often the two types of energy are related to each other.

ENERGY

3.1 Understand the Question

Think About Thermal Energy and Chemical Energy

You are already familiar with several types of energy. Some energy tranformations are easy to spot. For example, a child at the top of a playground slide has gravitational potential energy. The child has fun transforming this energy into kinetic energy. However, some types of energy are harder to see. The indicators are less visible. The factors may also be difficult to measure. As you explore thermal and chemical energy, pay attention to how their indicators and factors differ from those of other types of energy you have explored.

Get Started

Earlier in this Unit, you observed a pop-up toaster as it made a slice of toast. At that time, you made a list of all the kinds of energy you saw. Your list probably included transformations involving thermal energy and chemical energy, even if you did not yet have the names for them. You will return to that list now and review your observations of the operation of a toaster.

Thermal clothing helps keep thermal energy in so a person stays warm.

Look at your notes from the toaster demonstration and answer the following questions. Some will be easy to answer, and some might be difficult. If you do not know the answer to any of these questions now, you will by the end of this *Learning Set*.

- Thermal energy is experienced as *heat.* What happens in the toaster as a result of thermal energy? How do you know the toaster transforms thermal energy? What do you think might be an indicator of thermal energy?

- How can you tell how much thermal energy is present? What factors do you think would control how much thermal energy an object has?

- Chemical energy is energy that is related to *chemical changes.* What role do you think chemical energy plays in the toaster?

- Do you think thermal energy is a type of potential energy or a type of kinetic energy?

- Do you think chemical energy is a type of potential energy or a type of kinetic energy?

Communicate

Share Your Ideas

Share your answers to the questions with the class. Discuss what roles thermal energy and chemical energy play in the toaster. Discuss whether each is kinetic or potential energy. Note any disagreements you have. Later, you will have a chance to put questions on the *Project Board* that you need to answer to settle your disagreements.

Explore

Skiers often use hand warmers when they are outside in cold weather. Hand warmers are small plastic pouches with a liquid in them. When you activate a hand warmer by snapping it, it gets warm without the use of batteries. You will be making some observations of a hand warmer. Observe the changes that happen, and look for indicators of thermal energy and chemical energy.

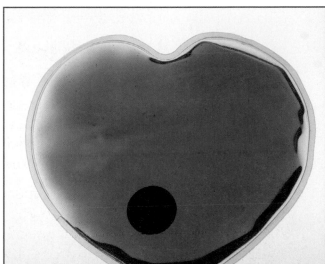

Procedure

1. You will receive a hand warmer. Pass the hand warmer around your group. Handle it carefully so it is not activated before everybody in your group gets to examine it.

2. Make a drawing of the hand warmer, and record what you see and feel.

3. After everyone has examined it, activate the hand warmer by snapping it. Pay attention to the hand warmer from the time it is snapped. Record any changes you see, feel, or hear occurring inside the hand warmer.

4. Pass the hand warmer around again, and record other observations using your senses of sight and touch.

Materials

• **hand warmer**

ENERGY

Analyze Your Results

After you have recorded all of your observations, discuss the following questions with members of your group.

1. What changes did you observe in the hand warmer after it was activated?

2. What do you think caused the change in temperature? Think about the events that occurred immediately after it was activated to help you justify your answer.

3. What types of energy can you identify in the hand warmer? What are the indicators of each type? Can you think of any factors that might affect the amount of energy?

4. Compare and contrast the operation of a hand warmer to the operation of a pop-up toaster. How are they alike? How are they different?

5. Can you think of other ways to generate these types of energy?

Communicate Your Results

Share Your Ideas

As a class, share your observations and ideas about the changes you observed in the hand warmer. Discuss the types of energy present in the hand warmer. Also, discuss their indicators, the factors that might affect how much energy is available, and other ways to generate thermal and chemical energy. Note any disagreements you have. Later, you will have a chance to put questions on the *Project Board* that will help you settle those disagreements.

heat: thermal energy that is transferred from one place to another.

exothermic: giving off heat because of a chemical change.

How Do Hand Warmers Work?

In the type of hand warmer you explored, a pouch contains water, a chemical called sodium acetate, and a small piece of metal. When the metal is bent, tiny pieces of the metal chip off. The metal chips are a perfect place for sodium acetate crystals to form. Before you know it, all of the sodium acetate has formed crystals. During this process, **heat** is given off. The heat is thermal energy that is transferred from inside the pouch to your hand. This is why you felt the *temperature* of the hand warmer rise. A process that gives off heat is called an **exothermic** process. The pouch also becomes harder as the liquid transforms into solid crystals.

In the exploration, you noticed the indicator for thermal energy, which is an increase in temperature. Hand warmers like the one you observed can be used again and again. To reuse the pouch after it cools off, you place it in boiling water for a few minutes. Heat from the hot water is transferred to the water in the pouch. In a short while, the crystals come apart. A process such as this, which requires an input of heat, is called an **endothermic** process. After the pouch cools off, it is ready to be used again.

You may think that the crystals of sodium acetate melted, but, in fact, they dissolved. When a crystal dissolves, tiny particles break off the crystal and mix completely with water. Eventually, all of the solid dissolves, and you see only a liquid inside the pouch. You may have seen this process if you have stirred sugar into tea. At first, you can see the crystals swirl around as you mix the tea, but after a while, they disappear because they have dissolved. The process of the sodium acetate crystals in the hand warmer coming out of the water and going back in when heated is a physical change.

There is another type of hand warmer that is not reusable. This type uses iron powder with water, salt, and air. The salt speeds up the exothermic reaction of the iron with oxygen in air so that a lot of heat is given off. This is a **chemical change** and produces a new, reddish-orange chemical, iron oxide. Iron oxide, or rust, cannot be easily transformed back into iron. Some of the indicators of a chemical change can be seen in this reaction, such as a change in color and heat being given off. Another indicator of a chemical change is the formation of a new substance in the form of a gas or a solid.

When a chemical change occurs, at least one new substance is made, and an energy transformation generally occurs. If the change is exothermic, chemical energy is transformed into thermal energy. If the change is endothermic, thermal energy is transformed into chemical energy.

endothermic: requires heat for a chemical change.

chemical change: a change that produces one or more new substances.

A burning candle gives off heat. Do you think this is an endothermic process or an exothermic process?

ENERGY

Reflect

1. Look again at the energy-transformation cartoon you analyzed previously to find examples of thermal energy and chemical energy. For each example, what happens as a result of transformations involving thermal or chemical energy?

2. What other examples can you think of in which thermal energy or chemical energy is transformed to power something or make something happen?

3. What do you think are indicators that thermal energy or chemical energy is involved in energy transformation?

4. How do you think heat and chemical energy are related? How do you think heat and thermal energy are related?

5. What might be factors that determine how much thermal energy or chemical energy an object has?

Update the *Project Board*

The question for this *Learning Set* is, *What are thermal energy and chemical energy?* You are just beginning to build your understanding of thermal energy and chemical energy. Add what you think you know about thermal and chemical energy to the *What do we think we know?* column of the *Project Board.* Your class probably has some disagreements about these energy types. You may have identified some things you do not yet understand about thermal and chemical energy. For example, you might not agree about whether each is kinetic energy or potential energy. In the *What do we need to investigate?* column, record questions that, when answered, will help you resolve these disagreements and address the *Big Challenge.*

What's the Point?

When the hand warmer is activated, the liquid sodium acetate inside it turns solid. As it crystallizes, heat is given off, and the hand warmer becomes warmer and harder. Change in temperature is an indicator of thermal energy. Thermal energy is transferred from the hand warmer to the hands of the person holding it. In another type of hand warmer you read about, a chemical change takes place. Iron powder is changed into rust. Changes in temperature and color are indicators of chemical change. So is the formation of a new substance.

3.2 Investigate

What Factors Affect How Much Thermal Energy an Object or Substance Has?

When you made observations of the hand warmer, you noticed that the temperature of the hand warmer changed. When you watched toast in the toaster, you observed that the heating elements warmed the toast. Each of these examples included a change in temperature. A change in temperature is an indication that heat has been transferred from one place to another.

All objects have some amount of thermal energy. Hotter objects have more thermal energy than cooler ones. When you increase the temperature of an object, it has more thermal energy. If the object is warmer than its surroundings, it will transfer some of its thermal energy into the surroundings as heat. One example of this is the hand warmer after it has been activated.

Why is thermal energy transferred? How is thermal energy related to heat and temperature? Is thermal energy a kind of kinetic energy, or is it potential energy? These are all good questions, and after you understand their answers, you will know how to put steps that use heat, fire, or even ice, into your Rube Goldberg machine.

You will start answering these questions by investigating the thermal energy of a single substance—water. You will run an experiment to compare the amount of thermal energy in three beakers of water. When you analyze your results, you will be able to identify two factors that affect the water's thermal energy.

Each group in the class will do either *Experiment 1* or *Experiment 2*. The groups doing *Experiment 1* will investigate the effects of temperature on water's thermal energy. The groups doing *Experiment 2* will investigate the effects of the mass of the water on its thermal energy.

Materials
- 2 beakers, 1000 mL
- warm water (35°C–45°C)
- 400 mL of cold water (15°C–25°C)
- 3 identical, sealable plastic bags, each containing 100 g of frozen water (ice)
- triple-beam balance
- 2 straws
- 2 thermometers
- 1 graduated cylinder, 100 mL
- 2 different-colored pencils or markers

PBIS

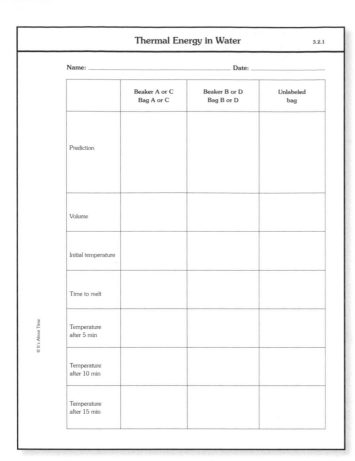

Set Up Experiment 1

Procedure

1. Label the two large beakers as A and B.

2. Pour 400 mL of cold water into Beaker A. Pour 400 mL of warm water into Beaker B.

3. Feel the sides of each beaker. Record your observations on your *Thermal Energy in Water* page.

4. Predict what would happen if you put the same mass of ice into each beaker. Which beaker do you think would melt the ice faster? Why? Record your predictions on your *Thermal Energy in Water* page. Then discuss your answers with your group and take notes of any differing opinions.

Set Up Experiment 2

Procedure

1. Label the two large beakers as C and D.

2. Pour 400 mL of warm water into Beaker C. Pour 200 mL of warm water into Beaker D.

3. Feel the sides of each beaker. Record your observations on your *Thermal Energy in Water* page.

4. Predict what would happen if you put the same mass of ice into each beaker. What will happen to the temperature of the water in each beaker? Why? Record your prediction on your *Thermal Energy in Water* page. Then discuss your answers with your group, and take notes of any differing opinions.

Run Experiment 1 and Experiment 2

Procedure

5. You will work with three bags of ice. Label two of the bags A and B or C and D. Use the balance to find the mass of each bag and record the data on your *Thermal Energy in Water* page.

6. Measure the initial temperature of the water in both beakers.

7. If the warm water is below 35°C, pour it out and get new warm water. Your warm water should be between 35°C and 45°C. Record the temperature and volume of the water in each beaker on your *Thermal Energy in Water* page (Time=0 min). Leave a thermometer in each beaker.

8. Leave the unlabeled bag of ice on the table as a control. At the same time, place Bag A (or C) into Beaker A (or C) and Bag B (or D) into Beaker B (or D). Use the straws to hold the ice beneath the surface of the water in both beakers. Record the time that the bags went into the beakers.

9. Measure and record the temperature of the water in each beaker after 5 min and 10 min. Measure to the nearest 0.5°C. Gently swirl the water for 15 s to mix it before measuring the temperature each time.

10. After 15 min, remove the bags of ice from the beakers. Working quickly, measure and record the final temperature of the water in each beaker.

11. Working quickly, open Bag A (or C), pour the melted water into the graduated cylinder, and measure its volume. Be careful not to spill the water or let pieces of ice get into the graduated cylinder. Record the volume of water. Empty the graduated cylinder and repeat the process for Bag B (or D) and for the unlabeled bag.

Analyze Your Data

1. Begin your analysis by making a line graph of the temperatures you measured in the two beakers.

- Label your graph clearly as "Experiment 1" or "Experiment 2."

- Label the horizontal axis "Time" and divide it into minutes. For each beaker, you should have four data points—0, 5, 10, and 15 min.

- Label the vertical axis "Temperature" and use 10°C increments from 0°C to 50°C.

- Use one colored pencil or marker for graphing the data from Beaker A (or C) and another color for the data from Beaker B (or D).

- For each beaker, plot the four data points and draw a line to connect the points. Include a key so people reading the graph will know which color represents which beaker.

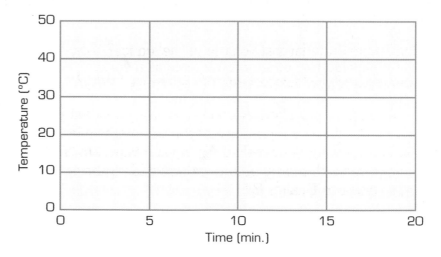

2. Set up a bar graph showing the volume of the water recovered from the three bags of ice.

- Use the same colors you used in your line graph for bags A, B, C, and D.

- Use a regular pencil or pen for the data from the unlabeled bag.

- Include a key that identifies the color used for each bag. Make the scale of your bar graph such that differences in your data are apparent.

- Label the graph clearly as "Experiment 1" or "Experiment 2."

3. Examine your data table and your graphs and answer these questions:

- Which beaker had the larger temperature change?

- Which ice bag had the largest volume of melted ice? Which had the least?

- What trend, if any, do you see in your line graphs?

Reflect

With your group, answer the questions. Be prepared to share the answers with the class.

1. What do you think caused the temperature of the water in each beaker to change? Why do you think the temperatures did not all change by the same amount?

2. Which ice bag had the largest volume of melted ice? Why?

3. Which ice bag had the least volume of melted ice? Why?

4. a) In *Experiment 1,* Beakers A and B had the same volume of water. However, the initial temperature of the water was different. How did this affect the volume of melted ice in each bag? Which do you think had more thermal energy before ice was added: the water in Beaker A or the water in Beaker B?

b) In *Experiment 2,* the water in Beakers C and D had the same initial temperature, but Beaker C contained more water than Beaker D. How did this affect the volume of melted ice in each bag? Which do you think had more thermal energy before ice was added: the water in Beaker C or the water in Beaker D?

5. In both experiments, one bag was placed in 400 mL of warm water, and another was not in any water at all. Which bag had more melted ice in it? What does this tell you about the thermal energy of the warm water?

6. *Experiment 1* only: Did the cold water in Beaker A have thermal energy? Why or why not?

7. At the end of your experiment, which beaker had water with more thermal energy? What evidence supports your answer?

8. There was less thermal energy in the water in each beaker at the end of the experiment than at the start of the experiment. Where did the thermal energy go? Use your data to support your answer.

9. In your experiment, what factor affected the decrease in thermal energy in the water in each beaker? How does this factor help determine the amount of thermal energy?

Communicate Your Results

Investigation Expo

Each group in your class completed one trial of *Experiment 1* or *Experiment 2.* When you share your data with one another, you will be able to see if the trends in your data match the trends in the data of the other groups in your class. If the trends match, you can be more certain that you have identified the way temperature and mass affect thermal energy.

Prepare a small poster of your results to share with the class. Label the poster clearly as "Experiment 1" or "Experiment 2." This poster should include the following:

- your line graph showing how the temperature of the water in the beakers changed during your experiment

- your bar graph showing the volume of liquid water you measured in each bag

- a claim about the factors that affect how much thermal energy is in water

  ◆ Use your answer to the last *Reflect* question to develop your claim.

  ◆ Your claim should be stated something like this:

    A factor that affects the amount of thermal energy in water is [*your factor*]. When [*factor*] is [*larger/higher/smaller/lower*], the water has [*more/less*] thermal energy.

- evidence to support your claim

- a comparison of your results to your predictions, what you know now that you did not know before this experiment, and any new questions you may have

As you look at other groups' posters, focus on two things:

- Notice the graphs on each of the posters. The measurements will not be exactly the same on all the posters, but the graphs should have similar shapes for each experiment. Notice if any of the graphs have different shapes from yours.

- Read the claims on each poster. How well do they match one another? Notice whether any other group stated any of your claims better than you did. Notice if any group made claims different from yours. Examine the evidence each group used to support their claims. Make sure you agree with the claims and evidence used to support each.

After you have had a chance to see the other posters, discuss the answers to the *Reflect* questions as a class. Make sure you understand the answers to each of the questions. When you get to the last question, develop a set of class claims about the factors that determine the amount of thermal energy an object possesses. Choose one or two sets of data from the posters to support those claims.

What Factors Affect How Much Thermal Energy an Object or Substance Has?

One factor that affects how much thermal energy a substance has is temperature. *Experiment 1* provided evidence of the effect of this factor. In *Experiment 1,* you observed that more ice melted in the warm water in Beaker A than in the cold water in Beaker B. The temperature of the warm water in Beaker A was higher than the temperature of the cold water in Beaker B. Therefore, Beaker A had more thermal energy than Beaker B. When two substances of equal mass have different temperatures, the substance with the higher temperature has more thermal energy.

Experiment 1 also showed you that even though the water in Beaker B was cold, it still had thermal energy. You know that because even though the water was cold, some of the ice that was placed into the beaker melted.

Another factor that affects how much thermal energy a substance has is its mass. Mass is a measure of how much of something there is. *Experiment 2* provided evidence of the effect of this factor. In *Experiment 2,* the water in both beakers was the same temperature. However, there was more water in one beaker than the other, and this made a difference. More ice melted in the water in the beaker with the greater mass of warm water than in the beaker with less water. The greater the mass of a substance of a given temperature, the more thermal energy it has.

Based on these results, you can clearly support claims about two factors that affect the amount of thermal energy an object or substance has—temperature and mass. The claims can be stated as follows:

- A factor that affects the amount of thermal energy in an object or substance is temperature. When temperature is higher, the object or substance has more thermal energy.

- A factor that affects the amount of thermal energy in an object or substance is mass. When the mass of an object or substance is greater (there is more of it), it has more thermal energy.

You also experienced one more factor that affects the amount of thermal energy in a substance. In *Experiment 1,* more ice in the bag of ice submerged in the cold water melted than in the bag of ice left on the table. Although the cold water was colder (had a lower temperature) than the air around the ice on the table, the ice in the cold water was able to absorb more thermal energy than the ice left on the table. How could this have happened? You will be able to answer this question after you read about how thermal energy raises temperatures in *Section 3.4.*

Reflect

1. Revise your *Energy Types* page. If you did not have thermal energy on your page before, add it now. Record indicators and factors that affect how much thermal energy an object or substance has.

2. What else do you still need to know about thermal energy in order to use thermal energy in the Rube Goldberg machine you are designing?

What's the Point?

Two factors that affect thermal energy are temperature and mass. The greater each factor, the greater the thermal energy a substance has. In the first experiment, the water in Beaker A was at a higher temperature than the water in Beaker B. You know that Beaker A had more thermal energy because it melted more ice. In the second experiment, the water in Beaker C and Beaker D both began at the same temperature. However, because there was more water in Beaker C, it had more thermal energy. The water in Beaker C melted more ice than the water in Beaker D.

Energy Types		0.0.1/1.2.2/2.5.2/2.6.2/ 3.2.2/3.6.2/4.5.2/5.1.3/5.5.1
Name: _____		Date: _____
Type of energy	Indicators that this type is being transformed	Factors that affect the amount of energy

© It's About Time

3.3 Explore

How Is Temperature Related to Thermal Energy?

You may have been surprised by the results of the experiment in *Section 3.2.* You may have thought that since the temperature of the water in Beakers C and D was the same, they would have the same amount of thermal energy. But the experiment showed something different. It showed that temperature and thermal energy are different. Two substances at the same temperature can have different amounts of thermal energy. To understand how this is possible, you will need to know more about temperature and thermal energy.

temperature: how hot or cold a substance or object is; a measure of the average kinetic energy of the particles in a substance.

When a car sits in the Sun, its surface feels hot. What is happening to the molecules of matter to make the temperature of the car's surface rise?

What Are Temperature and Thermal Energy?

When scientists need to think about abstract ideas, they often use a model. You will do that now to imagine the relationship between temperature and thermal energy.

First, however, you will need to know just a little bit about temperature and thermal energy. You know that temperature has to do with how warm something feels. However, you do not know what happens to matter as it gets warmer. Matter is made of many, many small particles, too tiny to be seen. These particles are always moving. The more energy they have, the faster they move. When thermal energy in the form of heat is transferred from a warmer substance to a cooler substance, the particles in the cooler substance begin to move faster. The average energy of motion of the particles of the substance increases. Therefore, the temperature of the substance increases. The average energy of motion of particles in a substance is its kinetic energy. Therefore, **temperature** is the measure of the average kinetic energy of the particles of a substance. The thermal energy of the substance is the total energy of the substance. You can think of it as the sum of the kinetic energy of the particles. The thought experiment coming up will help you better understand this.

Stop and Think

1. Temperature is the average kinetic energy of the particles that make up a substance. Why do you think temperature would affect how much thermal energy a substance has?

2. Mass is the total amount of stuff in a substance, and thermal energy is the total energy of the particles in a substance. Why do you think mass would affect how much thermal energy a substance has?

When you discuss the answers as a class, notice any disagreements among your classmates. It is probably hard to agree on an answer. This is why a model will help.

A Thought Experiment

In this model, marbles are used to represent particles of matter. In matter, the particles are always moving. Some move more slowly, and some move more quickly. But they are always moving. In this model, the speed of each particle in a substance is represented by the speed of one marble as it rolls across the floor. Temperature is the average kinetic energy of all the particles. So, in this model, average kinetic energy represents temperature.

Finally, in this model, more marbles is a model for more mass. The more mass, the more thermal energy there is. So, in this model, total kinetic energy is used to represent thermal energy.

Think about these relationships, and follow the procedure to imagine how temperature and thermal energy are related.

Procedure

1. Make a copy of the table below to record your data.

Model of Marbles as Particles			
Number of marbles (represents mass)	Kinetic energy of each marble (in energy units)	Average kinetic energy of marbles (represents temperature)	Total kinetic energy of marbles (represents thermal energy)
10 marbles	4, 4, 6, 5, 4, 7, 3, 4, 5, 4		
20 marbles	4, 4, 6, 5, 4, 7, 3, 4, 5, 4, 8, 4, 4, 7, 4, 7, 3, 2, 3, 4		

ENERGY

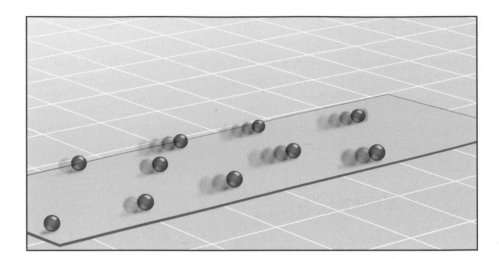

2. Begin by thinking about temperature. You will model that by averaging the kinetic energy of the marbles. Suppose that you have 10 identical marbles. They are all rolling across the floor at different speeds. The kinetic energy of each marble (in energy units) is given in the first row of the table. Calculate the average kinetic energy of the marbles. You can average the kinetic energy by dividing the sum of all the data values by 10. Record your data in the *Average Kinetic Energy of Marbles* column in the first row of the table.

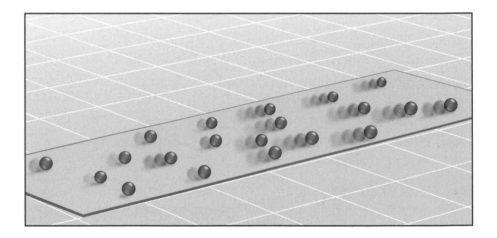

3. Now imagine that instead of 10 marbles, you have 20 marbles. Again, the marbles are identical, and each marble is moving across the floor at a different speed. Calculate the average kinetic energy of the marbles. You can find the average by adding all the data values in the second row of the table and dividing by 20. Record your data in the *Average Kinetic Energy of Marbles* column in the second row of the table.

4. Now consider thermal energy. Thermal energy is a measure of the total energy in a substance or object. In this model then, thermal energy is the total energy of the marbles, or their total kinetic energy. Which set of marbles do you think has more total energy—the set of 10 marbles or the set of 20 marbles? Why?

5. Calculate the total kinetic energy of the marbles in each set in the table. Record your data in the *Total Kinetic Energy of Marbles* column of the table.

Analyze Your Data

1. How does the average kinetic energy data in the two sets of marbles compare?

2. How does the total kinetic energy data in the two sets of marbles compare?

3. Why does the set of 20 marbles moving across the floor represent more thermal energy than the set of 10 marbles, even though the average kinetic energy of both sets of marbles is the same?

4. How do you think the thermal energy of a set of 40 marbles would compare to the thermal energy of the 10-marble and 20-marble sets if they all have the same average kinetic energy?

5. Think back to the experiment in the previous section. Imagine that Row 1 of your marble data table represents the water in Beaker D (the one with 200 mL of warm water). Imagine that Row 2 of the table represents the water in Beaker C (the one with 400 mL of warm water). How is the marble model like the water in those beakers?

6. Use this model to develop a statement about why the water in Beaker C melted more ice than the water in Beaker D.

The body temperature of each polar bear is 37°C (98.6°F). Which polar bear in the picture do you think has more thermal energy?

thermometer: an instrument for measuring temperature.

degrees Celsius (°C): a unit of measurement for temperature, abbreviated as °C. At sea level, water freezes at 0°C and boils at 100°C.

degrees Fahrenheit (°F): a unit of measurement for temperature, abbreviated as °F. At sea level, water freezes at 32°F and boils at 212°F.

kelvin (K): a unit of measurement for temperature on the Kelvin scale.

Kelvin scale: a temperature scale where absolute zero theoretically indicates that no thermal energy is present; 0 K = –273°C.

What Is Temperature?

The thought experiment on the preceding pages related thermal energy and temperature. Most people think about temperature as how hot something feels. When you touch an object to feel its temperature, you are actually feeling the impacts of particles in that object. The faster the particles move when they hit your hand, the hotter the object feels.

The speed of each particle in a substance depends on how much energy that particle has. Think of the people in a gym. Some people have lots of energy, and they are moving fast. Some are tired and have a low energy level. They are moving more slowly. Everyone is moving, so everyone in the gym has at least some energy. If many people in the gym are moving around quickly, the gym feels more energetic. If most people are moving more slowly, the gym feels less energetic. It is similar with the atoms and molecules that make up substances.

When a particle of a substance has less kinetic energy, it moves more slowly. When a particle has more kinetic energy, it moves faster. The particles in a substance are moving at many speeds. When more of the particles are moving fast, the substance has a higher temperature and feels warmer. When more of the particles are moving slowly, the substance has a lower temperature and feels cooler.

Temperature, then, is the average kinetic energy of the particles making up the substance. Some materials are made up of more than one substance, and their temperature is related to the average kinetic energy of all the different kinds of particles in the material. Temperature is measured using a **thermometer**. The most common units of temperature are **degrees Celsius (°C)** and **degrees Fahrenheit (°F)**. Scientists also use another unit, a **kelvin (K)**, to measure temperature. The **Kelvin scale** is a temperature scale where absolute zero is the temperature at which there theoretically is no thermal energy present. That is, theoretically, no particles are moving. Absolute zero is equal to approximately –273°C.

Temperature is an important factor that determines whether a substance is a solid, liquid, or gas. In a solid, the average speed of the particles is slow. The particles are close together and simply vibrate in place. As temperature rises, the average speed of the particles increases. At some point, the particles have enough kinetic energy that they begin to slide past one another while they are moving. The solid has become a liquid. As temperature rises even higher, the average speed of the particles increases even more. At some point, the fast-moving particles have so much energy that they literally bounce off the walls. They bounce around and fill all of the space in whatever container encloses them. The liquid has become a gas. The process of changing from solid to liquid to gas is endothermic. It requires heat. This process can be reversed. If a gas is cooled, the temperature drops, the particles slow down, and at some point, they form a liquid. Cooling further, the molecules slow even more, and the liquid becomes a solid. During the process of changing from gas to liquid to solid, the substance gives off heat. Cooling is an exothermic process.

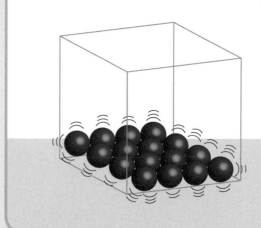

In a solid, the particles remain close together and simply vibrate in place.

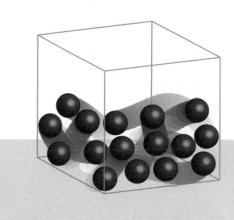

In a liquid, the particles have enough kinetic energy to slide fluidly past one another.

What Is Thermal Energy?

In your experiment in the preceding section, you observed that some of the ice in the bags melted and became a liquid. Ice is the solid form of water. The particles that make up ice are molecules of water. The water molecules in ice move slowly, so slowly that they merely vibrate in place. When the ice bags were put into the beakers, thermal energy from the water transferred to the ice. The thermal energy caused the molecules in the ice to move faster. Soon, the molecules moved around too quickly to stay in place as a solid. They began to separate from the solid ice and changed into a liquid.

ENERGY

Because thermal energy from the water in the beaker transferred to the bag of ice, the water in the beaker now had less thermal energy. The molecules in the water moved more slowly because they had less energy available. As a result, the temperature of the water dropped.

From this, you might suppose that thermal energy, like temperature, is related to kinetic energy. If you think that, you are right. The thermal energy in a substance is the total kinetic energy of all the particles in the substance. If you warm a substance or object, as each particle speeds up, the average speed of the particles (temperature) increases, and so does the total speed (kinetic energy) of the particles (thermal energy).

You use thermal energy to cook your breakfast.

If you think about thermal energy as the total kinetic energy of all the particles of a substance or object, then you can probably figure out why the mass of a substance affects its thermal energy. When a substance or object has more mass, it has more particles. This is why you found a difference in the amount of thermal energy in different amounts of water that were at the same temperature. Although the particles in both beakers were moving with the same kinetic energy, there are more particles in 400 mL of water than in 200 mL of water. At the same temperature, 400 mL of water has more thermal energy than 200 mL of water.

The relationship between thermal energy and kinetic energy is the reason that similar factors affect how much thermal or kinetic energy an object or substance has. Remember, from *Learning Set 2*, that the two factors that determine the amount of kinetic energy in an object are its speed and mass. The same factors determine the amount of thermal energy in an object or substance: the speed particles are moving and how many particles there are (mass).

This all means that temperature and thermal energy are related, but they are not the same thing. Temperature, the average kinetic energy of particles, tells you how warm something is. Thermal energy, the total kinetic energy of the particles, tells you the extent to which a substance or object can transfer heat or make something else warmer. If an object's temperature increases, its thermal energy increases also.

However, because thermal energy depends on both temperature and mass, two objects at the same temperature do not necessarily have the same thermal energy.

Temperature and thermal energy are related in another important way. Temperature determines the direction in which thermal energy naturally flows—from warmer objects (higher temperature) to cooler objects (lower temperature). When a warmer object is in contact with a cooler object, the particles at the boundary collide. In each collision, kinetic energy is transferred from one particle to another. In collisions, the faster particles of the warmer object tend to lose some speed, and the slower particles in the cooler object tend to gain some speed. As a result, the warmer object becomes cooler, and the cooler object becomes warmer.

Joules

Scientists measure energy and work in units called **joules**. A joule is the amount of work required to lift a 100-g mass a distance of about 1 m. The unit is named after James Prescott Joule, who was a nineteenth century English physicist. He studied the relationship between heat, work, and energy. A joule is abbreviated as "J."

All types of energy can be measured in joules. Part of Joule's research was studying the relationship between thermal energy and work. Different types of energy are related by the amount of work they can do. The amount of work required to lift a 100-g mass to a height of 1 m is about the same as the thermal energy required to raise the temperature of 1 g of air by 1°C. By calculating energy amounts in joules, scientists can compare different types of energy and keep track of the amount of energy present as it is transformed from one type to another.

joule: a unit of measurement for energy, abbreviated as J; the amount of work required to lift a 100-g mass a distance of about 1 m.

Joule used a device similar to this one to measure the mechanical equivalent of heat.

ENERGY

Reflect

1. How is kinetic energy related to thermal energy?

2. How is temperature related to thermal energy?

3. List two real-world examples of thermal energy from one substance being used to increase the temperature of another substance. What do you think affects how fast the second substance heats up?

4. List two real-world examples of substances or objects cooling. What do you think happens to their thermal energy as they cool?

5. Do you think thermal energy is a kind of kinetic energy or a kind of potential energy? Why?

Conference

You will now have a chance to apply what you learned about temperature and thermal energy. Your group will be assigned one of the pairs of objects on these pages. Your job will be to decide which of the objects in your pair has more thermal energy and why.

a) Pair 1:

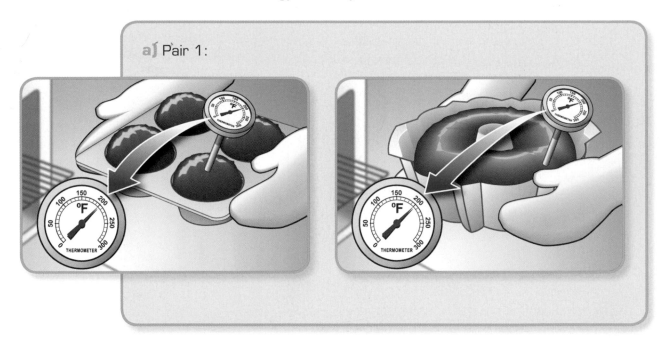

b) Pair 2:

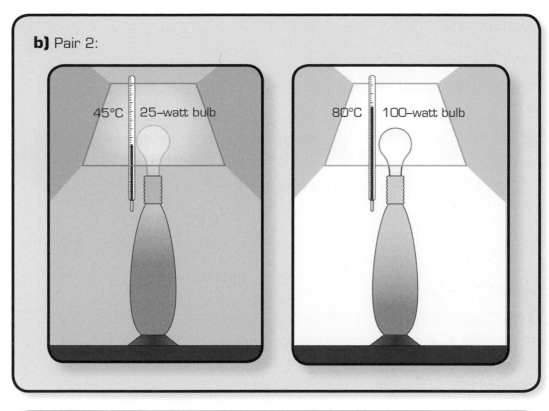

45°C 25–watt bulb

80°C 100–watt bulb

c) Pair 3:

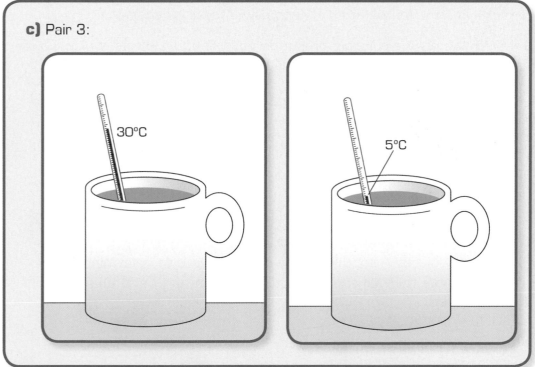

30°C

5°C

ENERGY

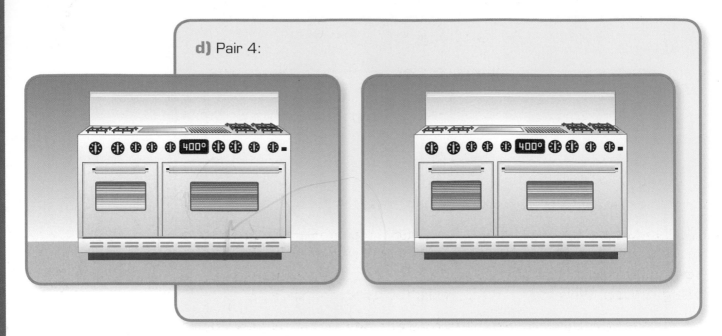

d) Pair 4:

Begin by describing what you know about the type of matter in the objects you were assigned. Then think about the number of particles in the two objects. With your group, write a description of the two objects, and describe the amount of thermal energy in each in terms of the number of particles and the temperature. Then answer these questions.

- If you put ice cubes in or next to each of your objects, which would melt the ice cubes more quickly? Why?

- Which object has more thermal energy? What evidence did you use to determine that?

Communicate

Share Your Ideas

Share your group's observations, reasoning, and conclusions with the class. As a class, prepare a chart like the one on the next page that lists the pairs of objects. Also, discuss the evidence used to determine which object has more thermal energy. Note any similarities or differences in the evidence used.

Thermal Energy Table		
Objects	More thermal energy	Less thermal energy
Pair 1		
Pair 2		
Pair 3		
Pair 4		

Then, as a class, take on a different challenge. You should have four objects in the *More Thermal Energy* column. Try to place these four objects in order of decreasing thermal energy, with the object with the most thermal energy on top. While doing this, consider the following questions:

- What evidence can you use to compare the thermal energy contained in objects made of different materials?

- Is it possible to compare the thermal energy of a cake with that of a light bulb? Why or why not?

- What additional information might you need in order to compare the thermal energy of objects made of different materials?

What's the Point?

Temperature is related to but not the same as thermal energy. Thermal energy and temperature both depend on the kinetic energy of the particles in a substance. The particles in a substance are moving at many different speeds. Particles moving at a slower speed have less kinetic energy. Particles moving at a faster speed have more kinetic energy. Temperature is a measure of the average kinetic energy of all the particles making up a substance. Temperature does not depend upon the mass of an object.

The thermal energy of a substance is a measure of the total kinetic energy of its particles. Therefore, the total number of particles contained in an object, or its mass, is a factor that determines how much thermal energy an object has. Thermal energy also depends on temperature: the higher the temperature of an object, the greater its kinetic energy. Thermal energy flows naturally from objects at a higher temperature to objects at a lower temperature. Energy is measured in units called joules.

ENERGY

3.4 Read

How Can You Compare the Thermal Energy of Two Different Types of Matter?

If two objects made of the same substance have different masses or temperatures, you can determine which has more thermal energy. If the objects have different masses but are otherwise the same, the one with more mass has more thermal energy. If the objects have different temperatures but are otherwise the same, the warmer one has more thermal energy. However, if two objects are made of different substances, you need more information to determine which object has more thermal energy.

The picture below shows a block of wood and a block of aluminum metal. Both blocks have been sitting on the table for some time and are at the same temperature. Both blocks also have the same mass. Up until now, mass and temperature are the only factors you have investigated for thermal energy. How can you decide whether the wood block or the aluminum block has more thermal energy?

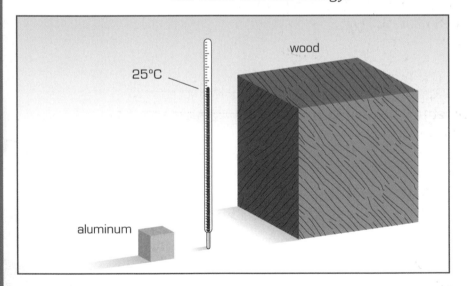

25°C

wood

aluminum

Identical masses of different materials can have different amounts of thermal energy, even at the same temperature. This means that *the material that makes up the substance* is a third factor that affects how much thermal energy a substance has. For example, 1 g of water at 25°C has about 10 times as much thermal energy as 1 g of iron at the same temperature.

Scientists use a measurement called **specific heat** to describe how much thermal energy is required to raise the temperature of different substances. The units for specific heat are joules per gram per degree Celsius (J/g•°C). The specific heat of water is 4.184 J/g•°C. This means it takes 4.184 J of thermal energy to raise the temperature of 1 g of water by 1°C.

Two important things to remember about specific heat are:

- The greater the specific heat of a material, the more thermal energy is required to raise its temperature.

- The greater the specific heat of a material, the more thermal energy it has compared to some other material with the same mass and temperature.

The specific heat of iron is 0.449 J/g•°C. This means that if you have some water and a piece of iron with the same mass and temperature as the water, the water has about 10 times as much thermal energy as the iron. Water also needs 10 times as much thermal energy as iron does to raise its temperature by 1°C. In fact, water's specific heat is greater than the specific heat of *every* type of metal.

specific heat: the heat required to raise the temperature of 1 g of a substance 1°C.

Because water has a high specific heat, it takes a lot of energy to heat water to boiling, but once water is hot, it will remain hot for a long time. The high specific heat of water makes it a good substance for storing thermal energy. This is one reason water is often used in cooking.

If you think about hard-boiling eggs, you may be able to better appreciate just how special water's specific heat is. Suppose you want to hard-boil an egg. All of the particles in the egg need to be heated completely to hard-boil it. You know from your experiment with the ice and water that thermal energy from warm water can transfer into a substance submerged in the water. The way people normally hard-boil eggs is to submerge the eggs in water, turn the heat up to boil the water, and then let the eggs boil in the water and absorb its thermal energy. People usually allow the water to boil for about 5 min to hard-boil the eggs. Then they remove the eggs from the water and cool them.

However, because water has such high specific heat, there is a way to hard-boil eggs using less energy. You can use the thermal energy from the burner to bring the water with the eggs to a boil, and then turn off the burner. The water will stay hot long enough to fully cook the eggs without extra energy from the burner.

ENERGY

The table below shows the specific heat of different materials with which you are familiar.

Specific Heat Table

Material	Specific heat (J/g·°C)
Air (nitrogen)	1.03
Aluminum	0.897
Diamond	0.510
Iron	0.449
Polyethylene (PET, a type of plastic)	1.79
Sand (quartz)	0.742
Water	4.186

Stop and Think

1. Which material listed in the table requires the greatest amount of energy for 1 g to be heated by 1°C?

2. You are choosing a material that can store a lot of thermal energy but not get very hot (not reach a high temperature). Would you choose a material with a low or high specific heat? Give reasons for your answer.

3. A container of water can be heated by adding hot water or a piece of hot metal. If the mass of the water is equal to the mass of the metal, which material will have the greater effect on the water's temperature? Justify your answer.

4. On a hot day, which would you expect to have a higher temperature, sand or water, if they have the same mass? Why?

5. Think back to the experiment you did with the water and ice. More of the ice submerged in cold water melted than the ice in the bag sitting on the table. The water was cooler than the air in the classroom. Why did the cold water melt more ice than the warm air?

How Specific Heat of Water Affects Climate

You may know that the climate near a large lake or near the ocean is milder than the climate farther inland. A milder climate means that it is less hot in the summer and less cold in the winter. Temperatures near a large lake or the ocean are milder because of the specific heat of the water compared to the specific heat of land. Water absorbs heat slowly and also releases heat slowly. Land absorbs heat more quickly, but it also releases its heat more quickly.

During the summer, when the weather is warmer, the land absorbs thermal energy from the air more quickly than the water does, so the temperature of the land rises faster than the temperature of the water. When the land temperature rises, air that is above land far from large bodies of water receives thermal energy from below and becomes warmer. Air that is above a large body of water receives less thermal energy from below. So air that is farther inland is generally warmer in the summer than air close to lakes or oceans.

In the fall when the air is cooler, less thermal energy is available. As the land and water cool in the fall, the water retains more of the thermal energy it absorbed during the summer. During cold weather, the land cools more quickly, so in winter it has less thermal energy to transfer to the air above it. Because its specific heat is lower than the water, the air above large bodies of water receives a larger transfer of thermal energy from below than air that is inland. So the air near lakes and oceans is generally warmer in the winter than inland air. The larger the lake, the more thermal energy it has stored up to heat the air around it. This keeps temperatures more moderate near large bodies of water.

Which will warm up faster, the water or the sand in this coastal area?

How Does Thermal Energy Raise the Temperature of a Substance?

In the experiment in *Section 3.2*, when you put bags of ice into the beakers of water, the ice began to melt. Thermal energy was transferred from the warm water to the ice. The thermal energy heated the ice, so some of it melted and became water. At the same time, the loss of thermal energy cooled the water in the beaker. How did this happen?

conduction: the transfer of thermal energy by direct contact.

Heat is thermal energy that is transferred from one object or substance into another object or substance. You have read that heat naturally flows from hotter objects to colder objects. This transfer of thermal energy can happen in three different ways—through *conduction, convection,* and *radiation.*

Recall that when two substances at different temperatures are in contact with each other, the faster-moving particles of the warmer object collide with slower-moving particles in the cooler object. After many collisions, the particles in the cooler object have speeded up, and the particles in the warmer object have slowed down. Eventually, the two objects end up at the same temperature. This process is called **conduction**. Conduction occurs when two objects are in direct contact with each other. In conduction, the colder object gains thermal energy. The hotter object loses the same amount of thermal energy.

When you hard-boil eggs, heat moves by conduction from the burner to the pot, then from the pot to the water, then from the water to the eggs.

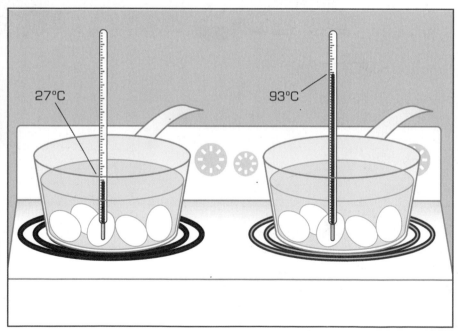

In the experiment in *Section 3.2,* the water in the beakers was not in direct contact with the ice. Thermal energy from the water was first transferred to the plastic bag. It was then transferred from the plastic bag to the ice, which was in direct contact with the bag. There are other familiar examples of conduction. When you hard-boil eggs on an electric stove, heat from the burner transfers by conduction to the pot, warming it up. The pot then transfers heat to water inside the pot. The water then transfers heat to the shells of the eggs, and the shells transfer heat to the insides of the eggs.

Another way to transfer thermal energy is through **convection**. You may know that warm air rises and cool air sinks. This is an example of convection. An electric space heater that is near the floor warms the air near it by conduction. This warm air rises, and cooler air rushes in to take its place. The cooler air is heated by the space heater, so it rises, and again cooler air takes its place. Eventually, the thermal energy released by the space heater is able to spread throughout a room by the rising and falling of air in the room. This movement of warmer air to cooler air is convection.

convection: the transfer of thermal energy by the movement of a fluid, such as water or air.

Convection will also occur in a beaker of water when an ice bag is placed in the water. The water near the ice becomes cooler by the transfer of thermal energy into the ice bag. This cooler water sinks toward the bottom of the beaker. It is replaced by warmer water rising from the bottom of the beaker. The entire beaker of water then cools off as it loses thermal energy to the bag of ice.

The oven in your kitchen is another example of convection. The food sits on racks near the center of the oven, while the heating elements are near the sides, top, or bottom. Thermal energy from the heating elements reaches the food by the convection of the air inside the oven.

Baking is usually done in a convection oven. In a convection oven, the heating element or flame warms the air near it. As that air warms, it rises, and cooler air takes its place. A fan speeds up the movement of the air.

Another way to transfer thermal energy is by radiation. Radiation occurs when some of the thermal energy in an object is converted into *electromagnetic waves* that spread outward from the object. You will learn more about electromagnetic waves in *Learning Set 4*.

Convection and conduction can transfer thermal energy only through matter, but radiation can transfer energy through matter or through empty space. This is why the Sun is able to transfer thermal energy to Earth. The Sun emits radiation in the form of electromagnetic waves. This radiation can travel through the empty space between the Sun and Earth. When matter absorbs radiation from the Sun, the particles of the matter move faster. When this happens, the thermal energy of the matter increases. Similarly, when matter emits radiation, the matter can lose thermal energy.

Another example of radiation is when you heat hot chocolate or popcorn in a microwave oven. Microwaves are a type of electromagnetic wave. The microwaves are generated in the oven and then absorbed by the food inside the oven. The thermal energy of the food increases when the absorbed radiation increases the speed of the particles that make up the food.

Microwave ovens use electromagnetic waves.

Your body warms up when the matter in your body absorbs radiation from the Sun.

Often, all three processes—conduction, convection, and radiation—occur at the same time. Remember the example of the oven in your kitchen. Thermal energy is transferred to air particles in contact with the heating elements by conduction. The movement of warmer air rising and cooler air sinking spreads thermal energy throughout the oven by convection. You can see the heating elements glowing because they are so hot. This glowing is an indicator of radiation. The heating elements are emitting electromagnetic waves, some of which are visible light that you can see. These electromagnetic waves also warm the air in the oven.

Reflect

List five different objects or machines that are used to transfer thermal energy from one place to another. Describe briefly the method by which each transfers thermal energy, and then classify each as using conduction, convection, radiation, or some combination of these. Be sure to cover each of these three processes at least once in your examples.

Thermal Energy from the Sun and Earth

You might appreciate the sunshine peeking through the clouds on a chilly day. But you might not appreciate how important that sunshine is. The Sun is the source of most of the energy used on Earth. The movement of air and water, the kinetic energy of living things and objects, light, and sound—all of these can be traced back to energy that originated in the Sun. This energy is transferred from the Sun to Earth by electromagnetic waves.

At the end of *Learning Set 1,* you read about chemical energy that is stored in fossil fuels. Remember that fossil fuels are the remains of plants that lived millions of years ago. Plants obtain the energy they need by transforming light energy from the Sun into chemical energy stored in starches. So even the chemical energy stored in fossil fuels can be traced back to the Sun.

geothermal energy: energy that comes from the natural internal heat of Earth.

While fossil fuels will run out someday, the Sun will fortunately shine in the sky for another five billion years. So not only is the Sun the ultimate source of all of Earth's energy, it is also the best source of renewable energy, energy that is continually resupplied. Many devices today, from calculators to electronic street signs, run on solar energy. Scientists are working on ways to make the transformation of radiation from the Sun into electrical energy more efficient so that more and more devices can rely on energy from the Sun alone.

The Sun is a source of renewable energy that is far from Earth. However, radiation from the Sun can be kept from reaching Earth's surface by clouds. And in the middle of winter, Earth receives less energy from the Sun than in the summer. However, there is a source of renewable energy that is much closer and is not dependent on the weather or climate. This is **geothermal energy** from Earth. The root word "geo" means Earth, and "thermos" means heat, so geothermal energy is literally "heat from Earth."

Hot springs are a source of geothermal energy.

Geothermal energy is thermal energy that comes from Earth's interior. This thermal energy is constantly being released at the surface, but it is released in greater amounts in certain locations. Volcanoes and hot springs are two examples of places that receive a large amount of geothermal energy.

This geothermal power plant in Iceland provides electricity to thousands of people.

In Iceland, where there are numerous cracks in Earth's crust, scientists have found ways to use the large amounts of available geothermal energy that is released through these cracks. Iceland is cold, but almost 90 percent of the energy needed to heat buildings and generate electricity in Iceland comes from geothermal energy. The geothermal energy is absorbed by water or steam in pipes far underground. The water or steam is then pumped to the locations that need to be heated.

In the United States, California uses the most of this clean, renewable energy source. Even so, geothermal energy today provides less than 1 percent of the world's population's energy needs.

Reflect

1. What are examples of the use of thermal energy in your home? What processes do these examples use to transfer thermal energy from one location to another?

2. What are the advantages of geothermal energy? Why is it not used everywhere to heat homes and generate electricity?

3. Do you think thermal energy is a kind of kinetic energy or a kind of potential energy?

Update the *Project Board*

It is time now to revisit the *Project Board*. Perhaps some of the questions you had about energy have been answered. Examine the questions in the *What do we need to investigate?* column. For which ones do you now know the answers? Record what you know now about thermal energy in the *What are we learning?* column.

You have a lot of evidence for what you know about thermal energy. Make sure you record evidence that supports what you have learned in the *What is our evidence?* column. If you have more questions, record them in the *What do we need to investigate?* column.

What's the Point?

Temperature, mass, and the type of material are factors that affect the thermal energy of an object. When two materials being compared are different, the temperature and the mass can be the same, but one material may contain more thermal energy than the other. Specific heat is a measure of the heat required to raise the temperature of one gram of a substance 1°C. Material with the higher specific heat will have more thermal energy than material with lower specific heat if they both have the same mass and temperature.

Thermal energy can be transferred from one place to another through conduction, convection, or radiation. Conduction is the transfer of thermal energy by objects or substances that are touching. Convection is the transfer of thermal energy by a moving fluid (liquid or gas). Radiation is the transfer of thermal energy by electromagnetic waves.

Two renewable sources of thermal energy are solar energy and geothermal energy. Solar energy is thermal energy transferred from the Sun through radiation. Geothermal energy is thermal energy that comes from Earth's interior.

3.5 Explore

How Do You Know When Chemical Energy Is Involved?

Indicators of chemical reactions can be found almost anywhere you look. Some reactions are very fast, such as an explosion of dynamite. But some can happen slowly, over days or weeks. The ripening of fruit is an example of a slow chemical reaction. Perhaps you have seen a green tomato on the vine. If you have ever eaten a green tomato, you know that more than color makes a ripe tomato. When a tomato is green, its odor, flavor, and texture are different from when it has ripened. A change in color or odor is evidence that chemical energy is involved.

In this section, you will carry out several investigations to look for other indicators of chemical energy. With this knowledge, you will be able to identify when chemical energy is involved in an energy transformation. Knowing the indicators will also help you investigate factors that determine the amount of chemical energy involved. You may find it challenging to involve chemical energy in an energy transformation in your Rube Goldberg machine. An understanding of the factors will help you control the amount of chemical energy released, so your machine operates properly.

The change of color and odor as a tomato ripens indicates that chemical energy is involved.

Each group in the class will be assigned one of four investigations. Each of these investigations shows one example of a chemical change. A chemical change occurs when one or more new substances form from the atoms or molecules present in the original substance or substances. Each group will do one of the activities and then share their understanding with others.

Before getting started, read the procedure for your investigation, and gather your materials.

Investigation 1: Vinegar and Baking Soda

Procedure

Materials

- **15 mL of vinegar**
- **10 g of baking soda (about 1 tsp)**
- **1 small flask**
- **1 graduated cylinder, 100 mL**
- **1 rubber balloon**
- **1 funnel**
- **paper towels**
- **1 plastic teaspoon**

1. Put 10 g (1 tsp) of baking soda into the balloon, using the funnel. Remove the funnel and clean the inside of the funnel with a paper towel.

2. Measure 15 mL of vinegar, using the graduated cylinder.

3. Using the clean funnel, pour the vinegar into the small flask.

4. While someone holds the small flask, stretch the opening of the balloon over the mouth of the small flask. Make sure that none of the baking soda gets into the flask.

5. Holding the flask and balloon upright, empty the baking soda from the balloon into the flask. Hold the balloon onto the flask tightly so it does not fall off.

Step 3

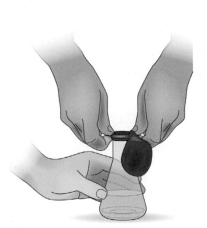

Step 4

Step 5

6. Observe the balloon and flask for the next 5 min. During this time, touch the outside of the flask from time to time to make observations of temperature changes. Record your observations. Make sure to record the differences you see in the flask and the balloon, as well as any temperature changes you might feel.

Materials

- 5 dull, stained pennies
- 25 mL of white vinegar
- 5 g of table salt (about ½ tsp)
- 1 graduated cylinder, 100 mL
- paper towels
- 1 plastic 10-oz cup
- 1 plastic teaspoon

Investigation 2: Vinegar, Copper, and Salt

Procedure

1. Examine the pennies and record your observations of their appearance.

2. Using the graduated cylinder, measure 25 mL of vinegar, and pour it into the plastic cup. Measure about 5 g (½ tsp) of table salt. Add it to the vinegar and stir with the spoon until the salt dissolves.

3. Place the coins in the salt-vinegar solution.

4. Observe the cup for the next 5 min. During this time, touch the outside of the cup from time to time to make observations of temperature changes. Record your observations. Make sure to record any changes you see in the liquid and the pennies, as well as any temperature changes you might feel.

5. Using the spoon, remove the coins from the salt and vinegar solution. Rinse them with water and place them on a paper towel to dry.

6. Examine the pennies, and record what they look like. Note any differences between the way the coins look now and the way they looked before they were put into the solution.

Materials

- 2 steel nails
- 2 steel screws
- 25 mL of white vinegar
- 10 g table salt (about 1 tsp)
- 1 graduated cylinder, 100 mL
- 20 stained pennies
- paper towels
- 1 10-oz plastic cup
- 1 plastic teaspoon

Investigation 3: Vinegar, Salt, and Metals

Procedure

1. Examine the nails and screws. Record your observations of how they look.

2. Using the graduated cylinder, measure 25 mL of vinegar, and pour it into the plastic cup. Measure about 10 g (1 tsp) of table salt. Add it to the vinegar and stir with the spoon until the salt dissolves.

3. Place 10 pennies in the salt-vinegar solution and wait 10 min.

4. Remove the pennies from the salt-vinegar solution, rinse them, and place them on a paper towel to dry. Compare the 10 pennies that were in the solution with the 10 pennies that were not treated. Record your observations.

5. Using the diagram as a guide, place the steel nails and screws into the same vinegar solution. Lean one of the steel nails against the side of the cup so only about one-half of it is in the solution. The other nail and the screws should be completely submerged in the liquid.

6. Observe the cup for the next 10 min. During this time, touch the outside of the cup from time to time to make observations of temperature changes. Record your observations. Make sure to record any changes you see in the liquid and the nails, as well as any temperature changes you might feel.

7. After 10 min, use the spoon to remove the nails and screws from the solution. Place them on a paper towel to dry.

8. Examine the nails and screws again, and record your observations. Touch the nails and screws, and record what they feel like. Note any differences in the nails and screws from before they were put into the solution and after they came out of the solution. Compare the bottom half of the nail that was in the solution to the top half of the nail that was not in the solution.

Investigation 4: Antacid

Procedure

1. Insert the antacid tablet into the balloon. You may have to break the tablet so the pieces fit through the opening in the balloon.

2. Measure 30 mL of water using the graduated cylinder.

Materials

- 1 effervescent antacid tablet
- 30 mL water
- 1 small flask
- 1 graduated cylinder, 100 mL
- 1 rubber balloon
- 1 funnel

ENERGY

3. Using the funnel, pour the water into the small flask.

4. Hold the balloon so that the tablet cannot fall out, and stretch the open end of the balloon over the top of the flask.

5. Holding the flask and balloon upright, empty the tablet from the balloon into the flask. Hold the balloon onto the flask tightly so it does not fall off. The illustration for *Investigation 1* may help you see how to do this.

6. Observe the balloon and the flask for the next 10 min. During this time, touch the outside of the flask from time to time to make observations of temperature changes. Record your observations. Make sure to record the differences you see in the flask and the balloon, as well as any temperature changes you might feel.

Analyze Your Results

Use the observations and results from your group's investigation to answer the following questions.

1. How did the appearance of the materials you worked with change? Describe any changes.

2. Did you observe any changes in heat, light, or sound? Describe any observed changes.

3. Which of the changes you observed do you think are indicators that chemical energy was used?

4. Do you think chemical energy is a type of kinetic energy or a type of potential energy? Why?

Communicate

Share Your Results

Each group will share the results of its investigation with the class. When it is your turn to present, begin with a brief description of your investigation, including the materials used. Then share your observations and results. If you have pennies, nails, or screws to show, show them to the class, and tell the class what they looked like before you put them into the liquid. Then report the indicators of chemical energy that you identified.

As you listen, make sure you understand what each group did, what their results were, and what indicators they identified. If you do not understand something, be sure to ask for more information.

After all of the presentations, make a class list of indicators of chemical energy. If there are questions about some of the indicators, discuss these questions. You may want to ask questions of the groups that suggested each indicator. Make sure there is agreement on the final list.

Then, as a class, answer these questions that relate to the *Big Challenge*:

- Which of the changes you observed can be used to provide energy to something else?

- How might one of these changes be used as a step in the *Big Challenge?*

- What else do you need to know about chemical energy to use chemical energy in the machine you are designing?

What Are Indicators of Chemical Energy?

The indicators for chemical energy are similar to indicators for a chemical change. The indicators include temperature change, change in color, giving off light and sound, formation of a solid from solution (precipitation), or formation of bubbles in a solution (gas formation). A fireworks display is a good example of chemical reactions giving off light and sound.

One indication of a chemical reaction is the formation of bubbles. In this model of an erupting volcano, baking soda and vinegar react to produce foamy bubbles.

Update the *Project Board*

In this section, you have started to learn about chemical energy. Add what you think you know about chemical energy to the *What do we think we know?* column for chemical energy. Update the *Project Board* with questions that have been raised from the investigations in this section. Add your questions to the *What do we need to investigate?* column.

Design a Rube Goldberg machine to turn off a light				
What do we think we know?	What do we need to investigate?	What are we learning?	What is our evidence?	What does it mean for the challenge or question?

What's the Point?

Indicators that a chemical change may have occurred include the formation of a gas, the formation of a solid, a change in color, or a change in temperature. Some of these indicators may also be present when other types of energy changes occur. A temperature change, for example, occurs when thermal energy is absorbed or released. The temperature change may or may not be related to a chemical change. When you see several indicators of chemical change occurring together, you can be more confident that a chemical change has occurred.

3.6 Investigate

What Factors Influence How Much Chemical Energy a Substance Has?

You now know several of the indicators of chemical energy. However, you do not yet know what factors affect how much chemical energy a substance has. In this section, you will vary the amount of antacid tablet used in a **chemical reaction** and measure how that affects the chemical energy that is released.

Each group will use a different amount of the antacid tablet—¼ tablet, ½ tablet, ¾ tablet, or 1 tablet. Each group will repeat the procedure multiple times and average their results. After each group has reported their results to the class, you will be able to see how changing the amount of one chemical in a reaction can change the chemical energy that is released.

chemical reaction: a process in which a new substance or substances are formed when atoms from the original substance or substances are rearranged.

Fireworks are grand displays of chemical energy. Think about what factors determine the amount of chemical energy released in each display shown here.

ENERGY

In this chemical reaction, the antacid will react with water to produce a gas. The reaction will occur in a film canister. You will be using the chemical energy released from the reaction to shoot film canisters into the air. It will be fun to watch, like fireworks. And, just as when you are watching fireworks, you will have to stay out of the way when the film canisters fall back to the ground. You will compare how much chemical energy was released by measuring how high and how far the film canisters travel.

Set up a launch site in your classroom. Everyone will need to stay outside the launch-site area except for the students who are launching a film canister. You will use a vertical scale to measure how high each film canister flies. Two students in each group will launch a film canister. The others in the group will observe its launch and measure how high and how far it travels.

Read through the entire procedure. Before you begin, you will make a prediction that relates the height and distance the canister flies to the amount of antacid used. You will need to connect this prediction to the amount of chemical energy that is used to propel the canister.

Materials

- **bubbling antacid tablets**
- **water**
- **1 film canister with cap**
- **paper towels**
- **1 tape measure**
- **1 graduated cylinder, 10-mL**
- **meter sticks**
- **saftey goggles**

Put your safety goggles on and leave them on for the remainder of this investigation.

Procedure

1. Prepare five samples of antacid tablet that are all the right size, according to the amount you have been assigned. You will use the samples in five trials.

2. Measure 10 mL of water in a graduated cylinder and pour it into a film canister. Wait until your group is called to the launch site.

3. Make your prediction about how high and far the canister will travel. Record it on your *Chemical Reactions* page.

4. When your group is called to the launch site, two of you should move quickly to the center of the site. One student will put the antacid in the film canister containing the water and move away. The other will quickly place the cap on the canister, turn it upside down, place it at the center of the "X" marked on the floor, and step back. A third group member will stand near the vertical scale and be ready to observe how high the canister flies.

5. When the canister lands, use the tape measure to measure the distance from the "X" to where the canister landed.

6. Record your data in the correct columns of the data table.

7. After your group has run all of your trials, calculate the average height your canister traveled by adding all the values for height and dividing the sum by 5, which is the number of trials. Repeat to calculate the average distance from the "X."

Stop and Think

1. What variables were changed, or manipulated, in this investigation? What variables were controlled?

2. As each group presents its data, what trends should you look for?

3. What indicator(s) of chemical energy did you observe in this investigation?

4. What factor that controls the amount of chemical energy did you investigate?

Chemical Reactions 3.6.1

Name: _____ Date: _____

For Your Group:

▢ = Your tablet size ($\frac{1}{4}$, $\frac{1}{2}$, $\frac{3}{4}$, or 1 tablet)

	Height	Distance	Your prediction:
Trial 1			
Trial 2			
Trial 3			
Trial 4			
Trial 5			

For your Class:

Film Canister Launches (Average Data)

	($\frac{1}{4}$ tablet)		($\frac{1}{2}$ tablet)		($\frac{3}{4}$ tablet)		(1 tablet)	
	Height	Distance	Height	Distance	Height	Distance	Height	Distance
Group 1								
Group 2								
Group 3								
Group 4								
Group 5								
Group 6								
Group 7								
Group 8								
Class average								

© It's About Time

ENERGY

Communicate

Share Your Results

The entire class observed the film canisters as they were launched. Now each group will share its data, including the averages they calculated. Make a poster that contains your data table and the average of all your data. Also, prepare a graph of the class averages. On the *x*-axis, plot the portion of the tablet used (¼, ½, ¾, 1). On the *y*-axis, plot either the height or the distance. As each group presents, record their data in the bottom chart of your *Chemical Reactions* page. When all groups have presented, discuss the following questions:

- What trends do you see in the data?

- What factor(s) did you identify that affect how much chemical energy a reaction releases?

- Did the data support your predictions? Why or why not?

- What do you think would happen if you used the same amount of substance in each canister but made the type of substance the variable? For example, if you tested equal amounts of antacid and aspirin against each other, what do you think would happen?

- What other factor(s) do you think affect how much chemical energy is released by a chemical reaction?

Chemical Energy

Almost all matter has the potential to react and release chemical energy. Matter is made of atoms, such as carbon, hydrogen, and oxygen. One way that atoms are arranged is in molecules. One of the most familiar molecules is water. Two atoms of hydrogen and one atom of oxygen are bonded together to form one molecule of water.

When the bonding between atoms or molecules changes in any way, a chemical reaction occurs. Bonds in the original substance or substances are broken, and the atoms form different combinations of atoms, with new bonds holding them together.

This is what happened in your investigations with the antacid tablets. The antacid tablet is made of sodium bicarbonate and an acid. Sodium bicarbonate is made of sodium, carbon, hydrogen, and oxygen atoms in a specific arrangement. When the solid tablet mixes with water, some of the bonds break, and new substances are formed. One of the new substances is a gas called carbon dioxide, which is made of one carbon atom and two oxygen atoms. The carbon dioxide that is formed builds up inside the canister, increasing the pressure. Finally, the top cannot withstand the pressure, and it pops off. The rest of the canister goes flying into the air.

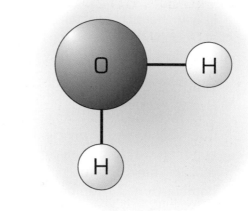

Two atoms of hydrogen and one atom of oxygen bond to form one molecule of water.

When a chemical reaction occurs, the substances that are produced are different from the original substances. Different bonds have formed between the atoms in the substances. If the new substances contain stronger bonds than the original substances did, energy is released into the surroundings as heat. The reaction is exothermic. One example of an exothermic reaction is the heat released by the hand warmer you read about in *Section 3.1.*

Sometimes less energy is released in forming the bonds in the new substances than was required to break the bonds of the original substances. When this happens, thermal energy from the surroundings is transformed into chemical energy. This type of reaction is an endothermic reaction. Some of the groups in your class observed an endothermic reaction when they mixed baking soda and vinegar. The outside of the flask felt cool to the touch.

Chemical reactions happen all the time. Some are slow, such as rusting, and others are fast, such as the explosion of fireworks.

In any chemical reaction, chemical energy is either released to the surroundings as heat, or heat is absorbed from the surroundings. Chemical energy is closely related to thermal energy. It is difficult to directly detect the chemical energy in the bonds of a substance. But the thermal energy produced from this chemical energy by breaking and forming chemical bonds can be observed.

Chemical energy is an important source of thermal energy. One common way to transform chemical energy is to burn fuels, such as fossil fuels. The burning of fuels or other substances is called **combustion**. All combustion reactions are exothermic. Some of the chemical energy stored in the fuel is released into the surroundings as heat. All combustion reactions need oxygen to happen.

Combustion reactions may also produce unwanted side effects, including noise, flames, and smoke. The smoke produced by burning fossil fuels includes **pollutants** that travel through the air. These pollutants have a negative impact on the environment or on people who breathe them in. Burning cleaner fuels or using solar or geothermal energy can reduce the amount of pollution produced. This will help keep the world a cleaner place. Many power plants now burn components of trash or sewage to reclaim the chemical energy stored in the trash.

Most fuel sources used today are nonrenewable, and the search is on for renewable sources that will not run out. Another problem is that most current sources of energy add pollutants to the environment during combustion. Ideal sources of energy are both renewable and nonpolluting, such as solar energy and geothermal energy.

If you now return to the energy-transformation cartoons, you will probably find even more examples of chemical energy being transformed. Notice that chemical energy not only can release thermal energy, but it also may give off light and sound.

combustion: any type of burning, usually a fuel with oxygen.

pollutant: a harmful substance that is added to an environment.

A lot of energy comes from the transformation of chemical energy in the burning of fossil fuels, such as coal, oil, and gas.

The thermal energy needed for cooking food on a camping stove comes from the combustion of propane.

Reflect

1. What are some indicators that chemical energy is released as thermal energy by a chemical reaction?

2. What are some factors that determine how much chemical energy an object possesses? How could you find out if there are more?

3. What are some good reasons for burning coal? What are some reasons to avoid burning coal?

4. Is chemical energy kinetic energy or potential energy? What is your evidence?

5. Add chemical energy to your *Energy Types* page. Record indicators that chemical energy is being used and factors that affect the amount of energy.

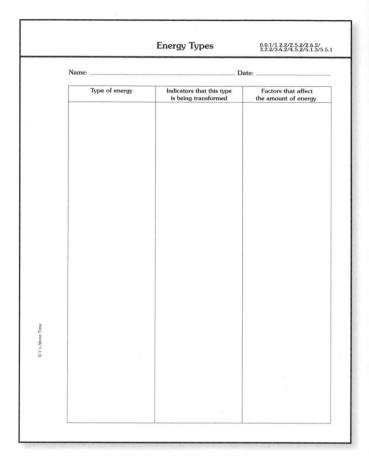

Energy Types		0.0.1/1.2.2/2.5.2/2.6.2/ 3.2.2/3.6.2/4.5.2/5.1.3/5.5.1

Name: _____ Date: _____

Type of energy	Indicators that this type is being transformed	Factors that affect the amount of energy

© It's About Time

Update the Project Board

Record what you have learned about chemical energy in the *What are we learning?* column. For each item you list, add evidence for it to the *What is our evidence?* column. Add any new questions you have to the *What do we need to investigate?* column.

What's the Point?

Chemical energy is stored in chemical bonds between atoms in a substance. During chemical reactions, a transformation occurs between chemical energy and thermal energy. In an exothermic reaction, chemical energy is transformed into thermal energy and released to the surroundings. In an endothermic reaction, some of the thermal energy in the surroundings is transformed into chemical energy. Light and sound can also be released in chemical reactions. A combustion reaction is one example of an exothermic reaction. It occurs when a fuel is burned.

More to Learn

Chemical Energy and You

You have probably heard about solar-powered cars and solar-powered batteries. Solar power is power from the Sun. But think about a solar-powered you! As a matter of fact, almost all living things on Earth are "solar-powered" in some way.

Light energy from the Sun is absorbed by plants. Through the process of **photosynthesis**, plants are able to transform the light energy into chemical energy stored in sugars. This is stored energy, which the plants can use at a later time.

Photosynthesis is a series of chemical reactions that absorb energy, so photosynthesis is an endothermic process. In these reactions, plants use water, carbon dioxide, and light energy to produce sugar and oxygen. The oxygen is released into the atmosphere and is used by organisms, such as plants and animals.

When a plant needs to release the stored chemical energy in the sugar, the reverse reaction, called **respiration**, is performed. This reaction combines sugar and oxygen to form carbon dioxide and water. Respiration is an exothermic process, which means it releases heat. The plant uses this released energy to perform functions it needs in order to survive, for example, to grow roots and leaves.

photosynthesis: the process by which plants transform the energy from sunlight, water, and carbon dioxide to form sugars and oxygen.

respiration: the process by which stored energy is released from sugar by combining with oxygen to form carbon dioxide and water.

Photosynthesis
carbon dioxide and water
sunlight energy
Cell Respiration
oxygen
sugars formed
oxygen released
carbon dioxide
mouse cells

Plants can perform both photosynthesis and respiration. Animals, including people, can perform only respiration. So animals must eat food that contains energy-rich substances such as sugars, and then breathe in oxygen. The cells inside the animal can then perform respiration to get the energy they need.

For example, when grass or corn is eaten by a horse, the food is ground up and mixed with saliva. The horse's stomach and other parts of its digestive system are designed to extract the nutrients and sugars from food and to separate out any unusable waste materials. In the intestines, the food is broken down into individual molecules, which can then be transported by blood vessels throughout the body. The unwanted waste is transported out of the body. Nutrients are delivered to where they are needed. And the stored chemical energy in sugars is kept for later use or transported to cells that release the chemical energy through respiration.

A horse's muscles get the energy they need by breaking down the molecules in food and using the stored energy.

Every cell in your body is constantly using the chemical energy from sugars to carry out life processes, such as growing, dividing, or doing work. Take for example your muscle cells. Inside the muscle cells, the process of respiration releases thermal energy. The muscle cells are able to further transform some of this thermal energy into kinetic energy by shrinking or expanding. This is how you use muscles to push things, pull things, run, and jump, and for all the other movements you make.

The chemical energy that is stored in food can be measured in **Calories**. A Calorie is about 240 times as much energy as a joule. If you consume more Calories of food than your body needs, the excess energy is stored, often as fat. This is why you gain weight if you eat more food than you need. If you do not eat enough food to provide the energy your body needs, then your body uses some of its stored energy to perform life processes. In this case, you will lose weight.

Calorie: a unit of energy used to describe the amount of energy in food, also called a kilocalorie.

The muscles in people also need the stored energy in food.

Climbing up a flight of stairs in your home uses only about one Calorie. Heavy exercise can use several hundreds of Calories an hour. Even when sleeping in your bed, your body uses about 60 Calories of energy per hour to perform necessary life processes.

Your body is really a living, breathing chemical factory. All of the functions your body carries out require the chemical energy stored in the food you eat. Your body contains stored chemical energy, the same way all living things, and the remains of living things, contain stored chemical energy. Part of what makes you alive is that your body can transform the chemical energy in food into thermal energy through respiration and then further transform that thermal energy to carry out various needs.

Learning Set 3

Back to the Big Challenge

Design a Rube Goldberg machine to turn off a light.

The *Big Challenge* you are working on in this Unit is *Design a Rube Goldberg machine to turn off a light.* You have ideas about the last step and about how to transfer energy to that last step. What about the other steps of your machine? You now know enough about thermal energy and chemical energy to imagine how they might help your Rube Goldberg machine turn off a light. Using what you now know, you will choose a way of transforming thermal energy or chemical energy to get a machine started, and you will design steps that will transform thermal energy or chemical energy into the energy your machine needs to turn off a light. But first you will think once more about whether thermal energy and chemical energy are kinetic energy or potential energy and how they can be transformed to do work. You will need to know these things to make your design successful.

Reflect

To help you think about thermal energy and chemical energy, you will examine the energy-transformation cartoons from the Unit *Introduction* again. Identify the steps that involve thermal energy and chemical energy in your group's cartoon. Record these on an *Energy-transformation Cartoon* page. Then for each of these steps, answer the following questions. Be prepared to share your answers with the class.

1. How do you know the step involves thermal energy or chemical energy? What are the indicators?

2. How does the step transform thermal energy or chemical energy?

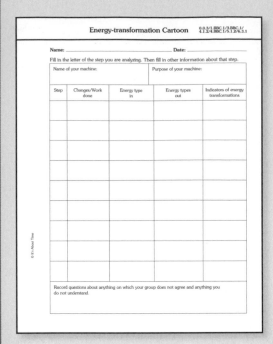

3. What are the effects of each step, and what kind of energy is produced by each step?

4. How could you change the effects of each step?

5. Does thermal energy act more like kinetic energy or potential energy? Which answers to the other questions support your answer?

6. Does chemical energy act more like kinetic energy or potential energy? Which answers to the other questions support your answer?

Explain

Working with your group, develop two claims and explanations. One claim should answer the question, "Is thermal energy kinetic energy or potential energy, and how does it do work?" The other should answer the question, "Is chemical energy kinetic energy or potential energy, and how does it do work?" Use a different *Create Your Explanation* page for each of your claims.

After you have recorded your two claims, work with your group to develop explanations. Remember that an explanation has four parts: a claim, evidence, science knowledge, and an explanation. The evidence in each of your explanations will come from the data collected earlier in this *Learning Set* and your analysis of the cartoons. The science knowledge in each will come from what you have been reading. Each of your explanation statements should tie together your claim, evidence, and science knowledge. Your explanations should help somebody reading them to understand how you came up with them.

Plan Your Design

With your group, consider how you can involve thermal energy or chemical energy in your design of a machine to turn off a light. You can revisit the energy-transformation cartoons to get ideas.

Design two sets of steps that involve thermal energy or chemical energy to turn off a light. One should begin with a step that transforms thermal energy or chemical energy into another form of energy. The other should begin with a step that transforms another form of energy into thermal or chemical energy. Both sets of steps should end with a step that turns off a light. You may use as few or as many steps in each of your designs as you want.

Sketch your steps on a *My Rube Goldberg Machine* page, and label your sketch to show what type of energy is transformed into what other type of energy in each step. If you borrowed any ideas from other groups, be sure to record which group you borrowed the ideas from. It is important to give credit for ideas you borrow from others.

You will need to think carefully through how the steps pass energy to each other. Each step has to be able to pass energy smoothly to the next step, and the separate pieces of your machine need to work together to complete the task.

Communicate

Plan Briefing

When it is time for you to present your designs to the class, show your sketches one at a time. For each, describe the steps, and tell the class how energy is transformed from one step to another step. Try to be brief. If you are unsure about how to describe some energy transformations in your steps, ask the class for help.

Observe everyone's designs carefully, and listen to their descriptions of how energy will be transferred from step to step. If you think a group has not described an energy transformation well, raise your hand and ask for more information or offer a more complete description. Remember to be courteous and respectful. If a group asks for advice, offer your ideas.

Notice all of the different ideas your classmates have about transforming energy and about involving thermal energy and chemical energy in their machines. You might want to borrow some of those ideas later. When you borrow ideas, you will need to remember which group you borrowed your ideas from and give them credit. Record ideas you might want to remember at the bottom of your *My Rube Goldberg Machine* page. Remember to record which group presented each idea.

ENERGY

Reflect

Discuss answers to these questions with your group. Be prepared to present your answers to the class.

1. Which two ideas for involving thermal energy or chemical energy in a machine to turn off a light do you like the best? Why?

2. For each of the ideas you like best, which type or types of energy transforms into chemical or thermal energy? Which type or types of energy does the transformation of chemical or thermal energy result in?

3. List two things you now know about addressing the *Big Challenge* that you did not know before these presentations.

4. What else do you need to know about energy and energy transformations to address the *Big Challenge* successfully?

Add the ideas you like best to a class list of favorite steps. For each, record the type or types of energy it begins with, the type or types of energy it results in, and which group suggested the step.

Update the *Project Board*

The *What are we learning?* column on the *Project Board* helps you pull together what you have learned. Share the things you think are important to add to the *Project Board* and your evidence for each. As a class, decide which of these things belong in the *What are we learning?* column. Remember to include evidence in the *What is our evidence?* column. You must fit the pieces together to help you address the challenge. Your *Big Challenge* is to *Design a Rube Goldberg machine to turn off a light.* The last column, *What does it mean for the challenge or question?* is where you should record how learning about chemical and thermal energy can help you complete the *Big Challenge*. Remember to keep a record of what was added to the class *Project Board* on your own *Project Board* page.

Design a Rube Goldberg machine to turn off a light				
What do we think we know?	**What do we need to investigate?**	**What are we learning?**	**What is our evidence?**	**What does it mean for the challenge or question?**

Learning Set 4

How Can Sound and Light Be Forms of Energy?

Sound and light energy are a big part of daily life for many living organisms. Sound energy makes it possible for many animals to communicate and to react to situations around them. Light energy brightens the day and illuminates the night. Light also provides the energy on which almost all life on Earth depends. In this *Learning Set,* you will find out what sound and light energy are and how they may be applied to the challenge for this Unit.

The sound you hear and light you see during lightning strikes are forms of sound and light energy.

The music you hear when you listen to a band is actually sound energy.

4.1 Understand the Question

Think About Sound Energy and Light Energy

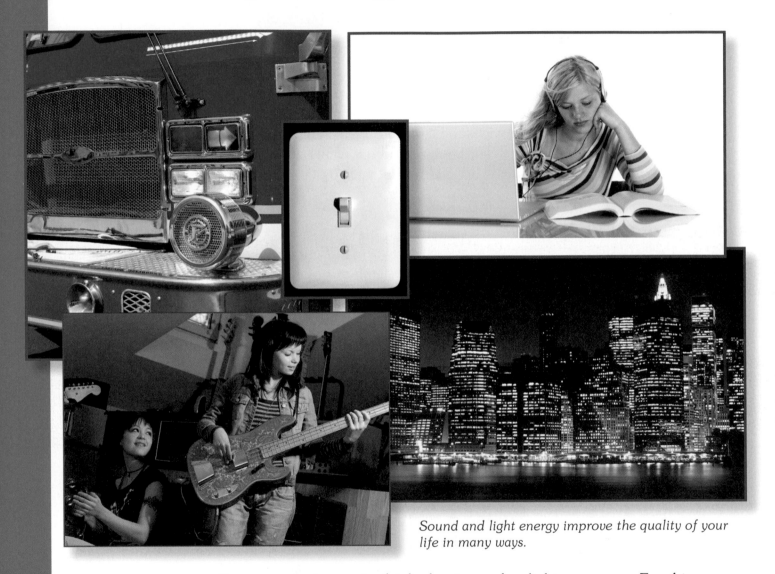

Sound and light energy improve the quality of your life in many ways.

It may seem strange to think about sound or light as energy. For this reason, you will begin your exploration of sound and light by thinking about your experiences with them. This will help you identify what you already know and help you feel more comfortable thinking about them as types of energy.

Get Started

One way to think about sound and light as energy is to think about ways sound and light change things. For example, earlier in this Unit you observed that light from a flashlight made the flags of a radiometer move. This is an example of light energy providing energy to move something.

vibrate: to move back and forth.

To begin to understand sound as energy, you might think about a time when you were very close to very loud music, perhaps at a concert, in a car, or at home. When the music is loud, you can feel the bass notes thump in your chest or stomach. The energy in the sound makes your eardrums and the things around you **vibrate**.

Where else have you seen light used to provide energy? What are other ways sound provides energy? With your group, list examples of light energy and sound energy in the first row of a *Sound Energy and Light Energy Explorations* page.

Then, using your examples, work with your group to fill in the rest of the chart. List indicators that can tell you whether light energy or sound energy is present. List anything you know about factors that affect how much light or sound is present. For example, you know you can flip a switch to make lights go on, and you can turn a dial to raise the sound level of a TV or radio. Also, record any questions that come up and any ideas you are not sure about.

Sound Energy and Light Energy Explorations   4.1.1

Name: _____   Date: _____

	Sound Energy	Light Energy
Examples of sound energy and light energy		
Indicators that energy is present		
Factors that affect how much energy an object possesses		
What I am not sure about		

© Its About Time

Communicate

Share Your Ideas

Briefly share your ideas with your class. Notice what your class agrees about and any disagreements. By the end of this *Learning Set,* you will know much more about both sound energy and light energy.

Mess About

In this activity, you will *mess about* to find out more about sound energy or light energy. You are going to explore either a set of sound sources or a set of light sources. After you have spent some time exploring your assigned items, you will share with the class what you observed.

Explore the items you have been given, and try doing different things with them. Explore how each item can be used to make something change. Look for indicators that energy is present. Imagine how each item might be causing changes. See if you can figure out how to increase or decrease the amount of sound energy or light energy. Be creative. Keep in mind the question for this *Learning Set: How can sound and light be forms of energy?*

Materials

Sound Groups:

- **2 tuning forks of different pitches**
- **small mallet**
- **bowl of water**
- **1 set of wind chimes with hollow tubes**
- **2 inflated balloons, two sizes**

Light Groups:

- **table lamp with 25-W bulb**
- **table lamp with 60-W bulb**
- **photovoltaic-powered device**
- **magnifying lens**
- **2 or 3 colored filters (red, green, or blue)**

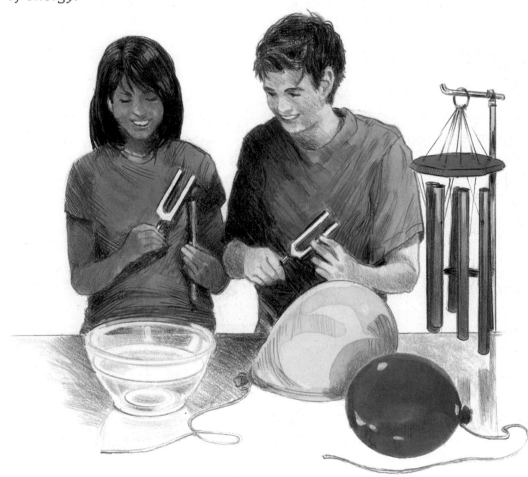

As you explore, work together to answer the following questions. Record your answers, and be prepared to share your answers with the class.

1. What do you think sound (or light) energy is? What are the indicators that sound (or light) energy is present?

2. How can you determine how much sound (or light) energy an object possesses?

3. If you can, sort the objects in order of increasing sound (or light) energy. What makes that easy or difficult?

4. How does your distance from the source of sound (or light) energy make it easier or harder to determine how much energy is present?

5. What do you think might be factors that determine how much sound or light energy is emitted by an object? How can you find out?

Communicate

Share Your Ideas

Since none of the groups explored both types of energy, you will need to share what you observed with the rest of the class. One of the *sound* groups will present to the class what they observed about sound energy. The other *sound* groups will add more detail as needed. Then one of the *light* groups will present to the class, and other *light* groups will add to their presentation.

When it is your group's turn to present, tell the class how you explored your objects, and share your answers to the questions. If your group is presenting, begin by presenting the objects you explored. Show how they operate and the changes they cause. Then, present what you did to change the energy of the object. Finally, share what you think the indicators are for your type of energy and the factors that affect how much energy is present.

If you are one of the groups adding to the presentation, tell the class which explorations you did that were the same as those already presented. Then present in detail other ways you explored your objects. Include the indicators and factors you identified and any disagreements you have with other groups.

ENERGY

As you listen, take notes on your *Sound Energy and Light Energy Explorations* page. Make sure you understand what other groups did to explore their type of energy. Listen, too, for anything that sound energy and light energy have in common. If you do not understand what a group did, or if you do not agree with their indicators or factors, ask a question. Remember to be respectful, even if you disagree.

When the presentations are done, discuss what light energy and sound energy might have in common. Then, identify questions you still have about sound and light energy and any suggestions you have about further investigations.

Reflect

Return to the energy-transformation cartoon your group analyzed previously in the Unit *Introduction*. Look at it again, and find energy transformations you think are caused by sound energy and light energy. On an *Energy-transformation Cartoon* page, record the steps that use sound energy and light energy, and fill in the boxes in the row beside each step. Then answer the questions on the next page. Be prepared to share your answers with the class.

1. In the cartoon, how do sound energy and light energy make things happen?

2. What are the indicators that sound energy is present? What are the indicators that light energy is present?

3. Suppose you were watching a television program with the mute button on. What indicators would tell you that sound energy was emitted in the action occurring in the program?

4. Suppose you were in another room, listening to a television program, but you could not see the screen. What indicators would tell you that light energy was emitted in the action occurring in the program?

5. What might be factors that determine how much sound energy or light energy is emitted by an object?

6. How do you think you can investigate an object to determine how much sound energy or light energy it emits?

Energy-transformation Cartoon	0.0.3/1.BBC.1/3.BBC.1/ 4.1.2/4.BBC.1/5.1.2/6.3.1

Name: _____ Date: _____

Fill in the letter of the step you are analyzing. Then fill in other information about that step.

Name of your machine:			Purpose of your machine:	
Step	Changes/Work done	Energy type in	Energy types out	Indicators of energy transformations

Record questions about anything on which your group does not agree and anything you do not understand.

© It's About Time

Update the *Project Board*

In the *What do we think we know?* column, record the indicators you have identified for sound energy and light energy and the factors you think affect how much sound or light energy an object possesses. In the *What do we need to investigate?* column, record questions about issues your class still disagrees about or that you are unsure about. Also, record any ideas you have about investigations that will help you better understand sound and light energy.

What's the Point?

Sound is an indicator for sound energy. Light is an indicator for light energy. However simple this may seem, it is also the case that both sound energy and light energy are complex.

4.2 Explore

What Factors Affect Sound Energy?

There are some sounds that are so soothing they can put you to sleep. Other sounds can actually be painful to your ears. Some sounds can make your whole body feel like it is vibrating. Although it may seem strange to think about sound having energy, it is the energy in sound that can make your ears hurt. When you observed a tuning fork striking the side of a bowl of water earlier in this *Learning Set,* you could clearly see that sound is associated with vibrations. In this section, you will explore the factors that influence the amount of energy in sounds, how sound energy is transformed from other types of energy, and how sound energy can do work.

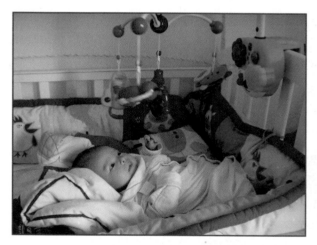

Lullabies and soothing sounds from nature can calm babies and help them go to sleep.

Some sounds are so loud they can harm the human ear if proper protection is not worn.

The most obvious indicator for sound energy appears simple. If you hear a sound, sound energy is present. However, the human hearing range is narrower than that of many other animals. Also, people tend to lose part of their hearing as they grow older, and some people are hard of hearing. This suggests that sometimes when sound energy is present, you cannot detect it with your ears.

You will begin with an exploration. Each group will carry out one of the following four explorations and then report to the class. Some groups will explore how different sounds have different effects. Some groups will explore what affects the loudness of sounds. Some will explore what affects the *pitch* of a sound—how high or low it is. Afterward, you will report to one another. As a class, you will be able to identify factors that affect how sound is produced and how sound travels. You will also identify factors that affect how much sound energy reaches your ears.

Exploration 1: Talking to Rice

Take a few pieces of rice and place them on the plastic cling wrap covering the top of the jar. Start by talking quietly near the jar. Be careful not to blow your breath on the rice. You might read this paragraph aloud if you cannot think of anything to say. Observe the rice as you are talking. Begin to talk more loudly, and then even more loudly, and continue observing the rice.

How does the movement of the rice change as the loudness of your voice changes? Each group member should have a chance to talk to the rice.

Repeat the procedure, this time talking to the rice through the funnel. On a piece of paper, record your observations of how each change you make affects the rice.

Materials

• **jar covered with taut plastic cling wrap**

• **5 grains of rice, raw**

• **8 x 11 paper curled into a funnel shape**

• **rubber band**

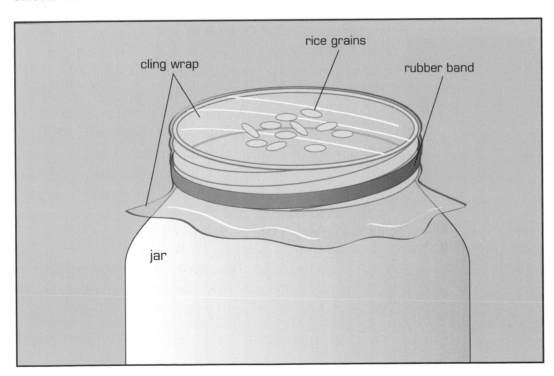

ENERGY

Exploration 2: Music from Rubber Band Cans

Materials

- **2 matching rubber bands, thick**
- **2 matching rubber bands, thin**
- **4 cans of different heights, open at one end**

Each member of your group should take a rubber band. Pluck the rubber band, and listen carefully to the sound it makes. Explore what happens to the sound of each rubber band as you change its tension from loose to tightly stretched. Record your observations. Then stretch each rubber band over the open end of a can and pluck it. Change the tension in the rubber band and pluck it again. Record observations on a piece of paper of all the ways you pluck the rubber band and the different sounds you hear.

Exploration 3: A Ruler as a Percussion Instrument

Materials

- **ruler**
- **desk**

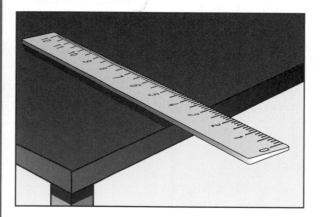

In this exploration, you will use a percussion instrument. A percussion instrument produces sound by the vibration caused by striking together two materials, such as drumsticks and a drum. Hold the ruler firmly on the top of the desk with one hand. Allow part of the ruler to extend beyond the edge of the desk. Lift the free end of the ruler, and release it so that it snaps against the desk. Identify factors that affect the sound of the ruler. You may think about lifting the end of the ruler higher (be careful not to break it) or changing how much of the ruler extends over the edge. Every group member should have a chance to snap the ruler. Record on a piece of paper all the different ways you snap the ruler and the different sounds you hear.

Analyze Your Data

Use the observations and results from your group's investigation to answer the following questions.

1. What did you observe with your senses of sight, hearing, and touch?

2. In what ways were you able to change the sound you were investigating?

3. In what ways did you observe sound changing?

4. What indicators for sound energy did you observe?

5. What type(s) of material was the sound traveling through?

6. What factors did you observe that affected the amount of sound energy? What is your evidence?

Communicate

Share Your Ideas

Each group investigated an object that made sound. Now, each group will share the results of its exploration with the class.

If yours is the first group to present an exploration, begin with a brief description, including the materials used. Then share your group's observations, reasoning, and conclusions with the class. Provide a summary for the class. Make sure you identify any factors you identified that affect the amount of sound energy.

If your group is adding to what was presented, begin by reporting your ideas about the indicators and factors that were different from those presented. Present any indicators and factors you identified that were not already presented.

Listen carefully as each group presents. If you do not understand something, be sure to ask for more information. As you listen, make sure you understand what each group did, what their results were, and what factors they identified. If there are questions about some of the factors, discuss those questions. You may want to ask questions of the groups that suggested each factor.

As a class, prepare a table like the one shown on the next page that lists the results of the explorations.

Sound Energy Chart			
Exploration	Description of sounds	Material sound travels through	Factors affecting sound energy
1. Talking to rice			
2. Music from rubber band cans			
3. A ruler as a percussion Instrument			

Reflect

1. What happens to sound vibrations when you hit or pluck something with more force? With less force?

2. Describe what happens to sound when the length of an object is changed. Why do you think this is so?

3. An object made a sound, and then you heard it. How do you think the sound traveled from the source to your ears?

4. If a flashlight were shining in your eyes, you could stop the light with your hand or a piece of paper. What happens when you try to stop sound with your hand or a piece of paper?

5. How do you think sound energy causes changes?

6. Do you think sound energy is a type of kinetic energy or a type of potential energy? Why?

Explain

You are now ready to try to explain how each factor you identified affects sound energy. Use a different *Create Your Explanation* page to record each of your claims.

Remember that a good explanation has four parts:

- your claim

- your evidence

- your science knowledge

- a statement connecting your claim to your evidence and the science you know

Start by making a claim about how a factor you identified affects sound energy. Try to state your claim this way:

When [*your factor*] [*increases/decreases*], sound energy [*increases/decreases/stays the same*].

Describe the evidence from the explorations that supports your claim. Write a statement that uses your evidence and science knowledge that supports your claim. This will be your explanation. Write your explanation statement so it tells why the factor you have chosen affects sound energy.

As you are working on your explanation, remember to use all of your science knowledge, as well as evidence from your investigations, explorations, and readings, to support your explanation. Science knowledge is knowledge about how things work. This knowledge can come through readings, discussion, talking to an expert, or other experiences. You may include information that you read in this *Learning Set* or knowledge you have gained in other classes. Do not worry if you cannot create a perfect explanation. Just work with the information you have for now. You will have opportunities later to revise your claims and explanations.

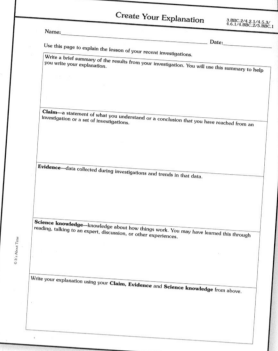

Conference

Share Your Explanations

When everyone is finished, you will share your explanations with the class. Record each group's explanation. As a class, come to agreement on an explanation about how each factor you have identified affects sound energy.

Update the *Project Board*

In this section, you explored sound energy. You identified indicators of sound energy and the changes caused by the involvement of sound energy. Update the *Project Board* by adding ideas from your explorations in the *What do we think we know?* column. Be sure to add to the *Project Board* the ideas your group agreed on and areas you are not sure about. You may have questions about the relationship between sound energy and vibrations. You may have ideas for investigations to find out more about sound energy. Record your questions and ideas for investigations in the *What do we need to investigate?* column.

Design a Rube Goldberg machine to turn off a light				
What do we think we know?	What do we need to investigate?	What are we learning?	What is our evidence?	What does it mean for the challenge or question?

intensity: the amount of electricity, light, heat, or sound energy per unit area per unit time.

decibel: a measurement used to compare the intensity of different sounds. Each increase of 10 decibels is a sound intensity 10 times greater.

Measuring Sound Energy

You may have heard loud sounds, such as a jet plane taking off, and soft sounds, such as a raindrop hitting a window. To compare different sounds, scientists measure sound **intensity**, the energy passing through a given area in a given time. One way to measure sound intensity is to compare sounds using units called **decibels**. A 50-decibel sound has an intensity 10 times greater than a 40-decibel sound. A 60-decibel sound has an intensity 10 times greater than a 50-decibel sound, or 100 times greater than a 40-decibel sound. For example, normal conversation has a sound intensity of about 60 decibels. This is 100 times greater than the intensity of sound in a quiet room, 40 decibels. In the front row of a rock concert, sound intensity can be 120 decibels, which is 1,000,000 times greater than the intensity of normal conversation.

Project-Based Inquiry Science

The louder a sound source is, the more sound energy it is emitting, and the greater the sound intensity. However, as you may have discovered, sound intensity also depends on your distance from the sound source. The farther you are from the source, the lower the sound intensity. You can think of the sound source as emitting its energy in all directions. Farther from the source, the same amount of energy is covering a bigger area, so the intensity decreases. This spreading out of the sound energy is called **dispersion**.

Sound Intensity Decibel Scale

Decibels	Example of sound
130	ambulance siren
120	loud rock music (front row); jet engine
110	symphony orchestra
100	power saw
90	subway train
80	vacuum cleaner
70	street noise
60	people talking
50	private office
40	quiet room in home
30	library
20	whisper
10	breathing
0	threshold of hearing

dispersion: the spreading out of energy as it travels away from the source of the energy. The decrease in intensity as distance from an energy source increases.

ENERGY

What's the Point?

Indicators for sound energy include sounds that are heard and vibrations. Additional indicators include seeing a sound source as it produces sound, for example, seeing contact between two objects. Most examples of motion are also indicators of sound energy.

The factors that determine the amount of sound energy include characteristics of the sound source and the substance through which the sound is traveling. To increase sound energy, you can increase the force being applied to make an object vibrate. It takes work to increase sound energy.

Sound intensity also depends on how loud the source is and on the distance from the source. The farther you are from a sound source, the lower the intensity of the sound you hear. You can compare intensity of different sounds using the decibel scale.

You can change the pitch of a sound by changing the length of the vibrating part of an object. The shorter the part that vibrates, the higher the pitch. You also can change pitch by changing only the tension in an elastic material that vibrates. For a given length, increasing the tension makes the pitch higher. Pitch can affect how sound energy is transmitted. Sounds can cause vibration of nearby objects, depending on their length or shape.

A police car is a source of both sound energy and light energy.

How Do You Hear Sound?

Ears are the sense organs that detect sound. In the ear, vibrations of air are transformed into nerve impulses that are transmitted to the brain for interpretation. Think about the outside of your ears. This is the part with which you are most familiar, because you can see it. The outer part is shaped like a funnel to direct sound into the smaller part and into a narrow tube. This narrow tube, called the **ear canal**, carries the sound inside the ear to the **eardrum**. The eardrum is a tightly stretched **membrane** like the surface of a musical drum. When sound energy reaches the eardrum, the membrane of the eardrum begins to vibrate. The vibrations are then transmitted to the middle ear.

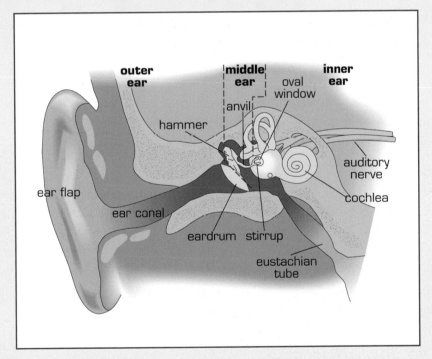

The middle ear starts at the inside of the eardrum. Inside the middle ear are the three smallest bones in the human body. They are the **hammer**, **anvil**, and **stirrup**. Each bone is named for its shape. The eardrum first transmits the vibrations to the hammer. The hammer then transmits the vibrations to the anvil, which, in turn, transmits the

ear canal: a tubelike structure connecting the external ear to the eardrum.

eardrum: the membrane separating the outer ear from the inner ear.

membrane: a layer of tissue that serves as a covering, connection, or lining.

hammer: the first in a series of three small bones in the middle ear.

anvil: the second in a series of three small bones in the middle ear.

stirrup: the third in a series of three small bones in the middle ear.

ENERGY

vibrations to the stirrup. Vibrations from the stirrup are transmitted to another membrane covering an opening called the **oval window.** The oval window separates the middle ear from the inner ear.

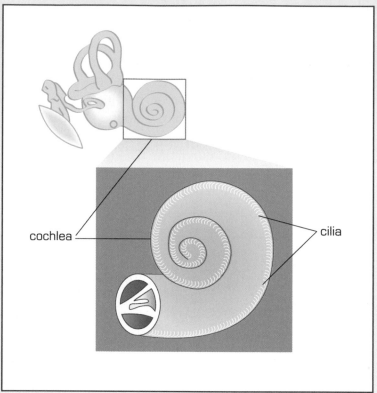

cochlea

cilia

oval window: an opening between the middle ear and the inner ear.

cochlea: a spiral tube that makes up the part of the inner ear responsible for hearing.

cilia: tiny hairs that line the cochlea and help turn vibrations into nerve impulses.

auditory nerve: a nerve that connects the inner ear with the brain and transmits sound, in the form of nerve impulses, to the brain.

The largest structure in the inner ear is called the **cochlea**. The cochlea is a fluid-filled tube that is spiral, like a snail's shell. The cochlea is lined with thousands of hairs, called **cilia**. These are much smaller than the hairs on your head. The vibrations in the fluid cause the cilia to move, sending nerve impulses along the **auditory nerve** to the brain.

This process inside the ear changes sound energy into electrical energy that is received by the brain. If you think of all the energy transformations, you might agree that this is one of nature's best examples of a Rube Goldberg machine!

4.3 Explore

How Are Sound and Light Energy Transmitted?

When you throw a ball, the kinetic energy of the moving ball is transferred along with the ball. If you throw a ball at a piece of paper, the paper will move when the ball strikes it. The movement of the paper indicates that the piece of paper now has some of the kinetic energy from the ball. You experienced this same phenomenon in the previous section when you held a vibrating tuning fork close to a dangling cork. The kinetic energy of the tuning fork made the dangling cork move. But something was different in the tuning-fork example. The tuning fork never touched the cork, yet the cork still moved. Somehow, the energy from the tuning fork was transferred to the cork without touching it.

How did the energy from the vibrating tuning fork travel between the tuning fork and the cork if they never touched one another? The answer is that the sound energy from the tuning fork traveled in **waves** toward the cork. When the energy in the waves was transmitted to the cork, the cork moved. Scientists use the idea of waves to describe how sound energy travels and is transferred. They also use the idea of waves to describe how light energy travels and is transferred. This means that everything you see and hear comes to you in the form of waves. So, to include sound and light energy in your Rube Goldberg machine, you must know something about waves.

Mechanical Waves—Off to the Races

Your group is going to hold races between a wave in a rope and a wave in a coiled spring. At the same time, you will explore factors that affect the speed of a **mechanical wave**. A mechanical wave is a transfer of energy without a transfer of material. The material a wave moves through is called a **medium**. In this case, the rope and coiled spring are the medium that your waves will travel through. As you do your exploration, pay attention to the direction each wave travels and the direction the rope and coiled spring travel. You will each have a chance to create waves.

wave: a disturbance that travels through a medium from one place to another.

mechanical wave: a transfer of energy through a medium without a transfer of the medium.

medium: the material through which a mechanical wave travels.

Materials

- **coiled spring**
- **rope that is longer than the coiled spring**
- **stopwatch with second hand**
- **small piece of paper about 1.5 cm by 5 cm (about 0.5 in. by 2 in.)**

Procedure

1. Two students in your group will each hold one end of the coiled spring. Hold the spring on the ground with some tension so there is a little space between the coils. One student will generate a wave in the spring. To do this, squeeze part of the spring by bringing a handful of coil edges together and then letting them go. This type of wave is called a *longitudinal* or *compressional wave.* The other student should hold the spring fixed in place on the ground. Have each student practice making a longitudinal wave travel the length of the coiled spring until you are ready to start the first race.

2. A third and fourth student will each hold an end of the rope. They will stand next to the students holding the coiled spring, and hold the rope in a straight line on the ground. One student will generate a wave with a rapid side-to-side motion. This type of wave is called a *transverse wave.* The other student should hold the rope fixed in place on the ground. Practice making a transverse wave until you are ready to start the first race.

3. A fifth student will be the starter, and a sixth student will be the recorder. Students will get a chance to change roles so all students can generate a wave. The starter will start the race by counting down: "Ready, set, go!" At the sound of "go," each team will generate its wave, and the starter will start the stopwatch.

   The starter can call a mis-start if the waves are not produced at the same time. When the first wave reaches the students at the other end, the starter will stop the stopwatch. The recorder will record the winner of the race and record the winning time in the *Race data* table on a *Mechanical Wave Investigation* page. For the first race, nothing is recorded in the *Factors changed* column.

4. After the first trial, discuss the waves you observed and summarize your observations about the waves in the *Other observations* column.

5. Continue with more trials. In each trial, the losing team may choose one factor to change to see if the change will make their wave go faster. For example, you may want to change the amount of side-to-side motion of the rope. Record the factor in the *Factors changed* column. Record the factor before the start of the race. Make sure that the factors changed will not cause any damage to the coiled spring or to the rope.

6. After all students have had one turn in each role, both teams in each race should change a factor. Record the factors changed before each race. Then run the race and record the results.

7. Repeat *Steps 5* and *6*.

8. After your group has completed two rounds of race trials, make a list of the factors you investigated in the *Summary of observations* table. Record the effect of each factor on the speed of a wave.

Mechanical Wave Investigation 4.3.1

Name: _____ Date: _____

Race data

Race Number	Winner	Winning time	Factors changed	Other observations
1				
2				
3				
4				
5				
6				
7				
8				

Summary of observations

Wave speed	Wave reflection

© It's About Time

9. Fold a small rectangle of paper in half and place it over one of the coils of the coiled spring near the fixed end. Also place a small piece of paper on the rope near the fixed end. Send a wave down the coiled spring and the rope. Notice what happens to the paper as the wave pulse goes by. Observe what happens to the wave when it reaches the fixed end of the coiled spring or rope. Record your observations in the *Wave reflection* box in the *Summary of observations* table on the *Mechanical Wave Investigation* page.

Stop and Think

1. In what direction did the coils of the spring move as the wave moved from one end of the coiled spring to the other?

2. A dictionary definition of compressional is "the state of being compressed." A dictionary definition of longitudinal is "placed or running lengthwise." Explain why compressional or longitudinal wave is a suitable name for the type of wave you made on the coiled spring.

3. In what direction did the rope move as the wave moved from one end of the rope to the other?

4. A dictionary definition of transverse is "in a crosswise direction." Another definition is "at right angles (perpendicular) to the long axis." Why is transverse a good name for the wave you generated and observed on the rope?

5. Does the speed of the wave depend on how much you moved the rope sideways to generate the wave? Use evidence from your investigation to answer this question.

6. Does the speed of the wave depend on how many coils you squeezed together? Use evidence from your investigation to answer this question.

7. You observed that the paper attached close to the fixed end of the spring or rope "jumped" as the wave went by. At first, the paper was at rest and had no (kinetic) energy. When it started to move, you know that it had gained kinetic energy. Where did this energy come from?

8. What happened to the wave pulse when it reached the fixed end of the spring or rope?

Characteristics of Waves

You will learn more about sound waves and light waves later in this *Learning Set.* However, before learning about the specifics of sound waves and light waves, there are some characteristics of waves you need to know.

How Waves Transfer Energy

In this investigation, you observed two types of mechanical waves— **longitudinal (compressional) waves** and **transverse waves**. In longitudinal waves, the vibrations move in a direction parallel to the direction in which the wave travels. These were the type of waves you made with the coiled spring. Sound waves are longitudinal waves. The waves you made with the rope are transverse waves. You may know that the prefix "trans" means across. Transverse waves have vibrations that are across, or perpendicular to, the direction in which the wave travels. Light waves are transverse waves.

Whether a wave is a transverse wave or a longitudinal wave, it transfers energy the same way. The wave carries energy through the medium, and the energy is transferred to whatever the wave touches. You saw this when you observed the way the pieces of paper you attached to the coil and the rope moved with the wave. You saw the pieces of paper move up and down or side to side with the wave. You also saw another important property of a wave when you observed the pieces of paper. The pieces of paper returned to where they were at the start after the wave passed through.

longitudinal (compressional) wave: a wave that causes a medium to vibrate in a direction parallel to the direction in which the wave travels.

transverse wave: a wave that causes a medium to vibrate in a direction perpendicular to the direction lin which the wave travels.

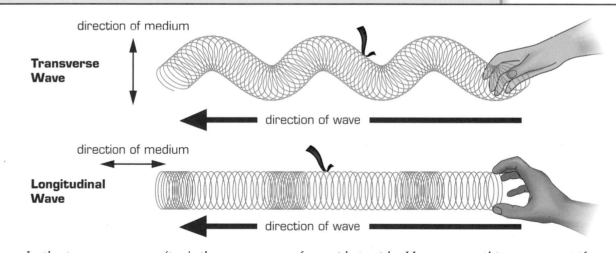

In the transverse wave (top), the wave moves from side-to-side. You can see this movement if you watch the ribbon tied to the coiled wire. In the longitudinal wave (bottom), the wave moves back and forth. You can see this movement if you watch the ribbon tied to the coiled wire.

ENERGY

What you observed was that the wave transferred energy, but it did not transfer matter. The pieces of paper you attached to the coiled spring and the rope did not move from where you attached them. However, the wave moved from one end of the spring or rope to the other. Another example of this phenomenon is what happens when you throw a pebble into a pond. When you throw a pebble into a pond, the kinetic energy from the pebble is transferred to the water and produces a small wave. The wave moves away from the location where the pebble hit the water. After the wave passes, the water was where it was before. It is the same for sound waves and light waves. After a wave passes through a medium, the matter in the medium returns to where it was before the wave passed by.

Features of Waves

During the race, you changed several factors to see how they affected the speed of the wave. Some of the factors you may have changed were *wavelength,* wave *period* or *frequency,* and wave **amplitude**. Understanding what each of these terms means will be important when you read about sound waves in the next section.

Wavelength

When scientists study length of a wave, they begin by measuring the rest position of the medium. Think back to the waves you made with the rope. You started with the rope in a straight line; this was the rest position. The vibration caused the rope to move left of the line, then right of the line, then left again in a repeating pattern. The wave looked a bit like this:

amplitude: the height of the crest in a transverse wave; a measure of how compressed the compressions are in a longitudinal wave.

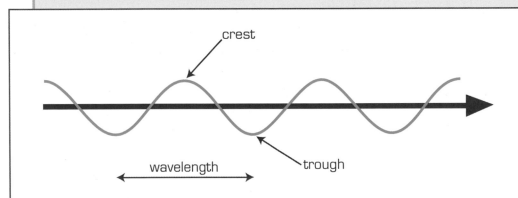

A wave has a crest (high point) and a trough (low point). In a transverse wave, the wavelength is the distance from crest to trough.

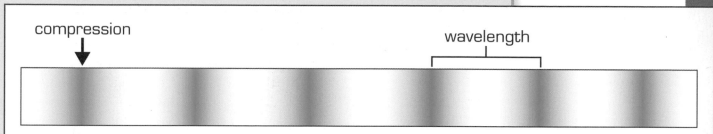

In a longitudinal wave, a wavelength is the distance between one compression and the next compression.

The high point in a wave is called a **crest**. The low point is called a **trough**. One complete wave is the distance from crest to crest. The length of one complete wave is called the **wavelength**. You can also measure one complete wave from trough to trough, or between any two points that correspond.

In longitudinal waves, there are **compressions** in the wave instead of crests. In the coiled spring, you could see the compressions traveling the length of the spring. The distance between one compression and the next compression is the wavelength of a longitudinal wave.

Wave Period and Frequency

Imagine you are sitting at the end of a long boat dock, watching the waves in the water move toward the shore. You watch the crests as they pass you. You find that it takes two seconds for each crest to pass you. This is the **period** of the wave, the time it takes to complete one cycle of the wave—crest, trough, crest. The **frequency** of the wave is the number of cycles each second. In this case, the frequency of the wave is $1/2$ cycle per second. Every second, one half of the wave passes by. The period and the frequency are inversely related to one another.

Now suppose the waves slow down. You see one wave crest pass by you every five seconds. The period of the wave is now five seconds. The frequency of the wave is $1/5$ cycle per second. Scientists use a special name, hertz (Hz), for frequency. One hertz is one cycle per second.

Wave Amplitude

The point of greatest movement away from the rest position is called the amplitude of a wave. In a transverse wave, the amplitude is the height of a crest. In a longitudinal wave, amplitude is a measure of how compressed the compressions are. The amplitude of a wave is a measure of how much energy is used to produce the wave.

crest: the highest point of a transverse wave.

trough: the lowest point of a transverse wave.

wavelength: the distance between two successive crests or troughs in a transverse wave or between two successive compressions in a longitudinal wave.

compression: region of a longitudinal wave where the particles of the medium have the highest density.

period: the time required to complete one cycle of a wave.

frequency: the number of crests or compressions in a wave that pass a point per unit time; for sound waves, measured in hertz (hz).

ENERGY

Perhaps you tried to make a wave go faster by shaking the rope harder or pushing and pulling harder on the spring toy. If so, you probably increased the amplitude of the wave.

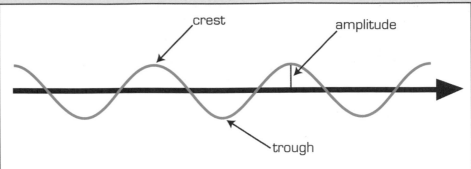

In addition to crest and trough, a wave also has amplitude. In a transverse wave, amplitude is the height of a crest. In a longitudinal wave, amplitude is how compressed the compressions are.

speed of a wave: the distance a wave travels (crest, trough, crest) in a given period of time. Speed of a wave can be calculated by multiplying wavelength by frequency.

Wave Speed

Now that you know something about wavelength and wave frequency, you can think about what the **speed of a wave** might mean. The speed of a wave is measured the same way the speed of anything is measured. Speed, you know, is the time it takes to travel some distance. To calculate speed, divide the distance traveled by the time taken. The unit used for the speed of waves is the same as the speed of anything. Often, wave speeds are given in meters per second (m/s).

Now think about what the speed of a wave means in terms of wavelength and wave frequency. The distance from one crest to another of a wave is the wavelength. The time it takes for the wave to travel this distance is the period. So, to find wave speed, you can divide the wavelength by the period. Mathematically, this is the same as multiplying by the frequency. So, the speed of a wave can be calculated by multiplying wavelength and frequency.

As you may have discovered, neither frequency, wavelength, nor amplitude affected the speed of the waves you created with the ropes and coils. Waves tend to travel at one speed through a medium. If you vibrated the spring or rope faster, you made more crests or compressions per second, but the wave speed did not change. This fact will be important when you look at the relationship between the frequency and wavelength of sound waves in the next section.

Reflection of Waves

One more important characteristic of waves is **reflection**. When you throw a ball at a hard wall, the ball will bounce back. The ball **reflects** off the wall. Reflection means to turn back from a hard surface. You observed the same thing happening with the waves you created. When a wave reached the end of the coiled spring or rope, you saw that the wave was reflected back. Because waves carry energy, when a wave reflects back, the energy in the wave is also reflected. This is what happened with the waves you made in the ropes and coils. When each wave reached the fixed end of the rope or coil, the wave was reflected back, and so was the energy in the wave.

reflection: when the medium and energy in a wave is turned back from a hard surface.

reflect: to turn back from a hard surface.

Stop and Think

1. Draw a series of transverse waves. Label the wavelength, amplitude, trough, and crest of one of the waves.

2. What is the difference between wave speed and wave frequency? Use the examples of water waves in your answer.

3. What factor or factors affect the speed of a wave?

What's the Point?

Energy can be transferred by mechanical waves. When energy is transferred in this way, there is no transfer of matter. Two types of mechanical waves are longitudinal waves and transverse waves. In a longitudinal wave, the medium vibrates parallel to the direction in which the wave is traveling. In a transverse wave, the medium vibrates perpendicular to the direction in which the wave is traveling. Waves are described by the properties of wavelength, frequency, and amplitude. However, the speed of a wave does not depend on any of these factors. The speed of a wave depends on the medium through which it is traveling. Reflection is another important property of waves. Reflection is what happens when a wave meets a hard surface and bounces off of it. The reflected wave carries its energy with it as it reflects off the hard surface.

More to Learn

Seismic Waves

Other forms of energy also travel as mechanical waves. One type of energy that travels as mechanical waves is **seismic** energy, the energy of earthquakes. Seismic waves can travel quickly through Earth or along Earth's surface. The waves can be recorded on **seismographs** thousands of miles away. A seismograph is an instrument used to detect and record seismic waves.

An earthquake generates several types of seismic waves. Two of these, P waves (primary waves) and S waves (secondary waves), travel at different speeds. P waves are longitudinal waves like sound waves. In solids, they travel faster than S waves. They arrive at a seismograph station before the slower-moving transverse S waves. The difference in arrival times of the P waves and S waves tells you how far away the earthquake occurred. By using readings from three or more seismographs, geologists can pinpoint the location of an earthquake.

Seismic waves travel differently through the different parts of Earth's interior. This allows scientists to use seismic-wave readings to make detailed maps of Earth's interior. S waves do not travel through liquids, so scientists have been able to use these waves to deduce that part of Earth's core is liquid.

seismic: caused by an earthquake or vibrations inside Earth.

seismograph: an instrument used to detect and record seismic waves.

Seismic energy can cause great destruction to property.

4.4 Read

How Does Sound Energy Travel?

Think of the ripples of water in a pond when you toss in a pebble. The ripples start at the point where the pebble hits the water. The ripples spread out from this point in all directions. The ripples are small waves, and they keep making larger and larger circles as they spread out. The waves can travel for quite a while after the pebble enters the water.

Now imagine people standing around the pond. Could they all hear the pebble when it goes into the water? No matter where you stand, you should hear the splash. Could the sound also be a kind of wave, like the ripples in the pond?

Scientists often use models to help visualize things that cannot be seen. A model that shows sound traveling as waves can help you to understand many of the characteristics of sound. Sound travels from one place to another in the form of longitudinal waves, similar to the waves you made with the coiled spring. Recall that in longitudinal waves, the vibrations move in a direction parallel to the direction in which the wave travels.

Sound can travel through all forms of matter, but it travels better through most solids than liquids, and better through most liquids than gases. Most of the sounds you hear result from sound waves that travel to your ear through air, which is a mixture of gases.

A pebble dropped into a pond will make concentric circles of waves.

Speed of Sound

You already know that when a wave moves through a medium, it does not carry the matter in the medium with it. It is the same with sound waves. When a sound wave moves through a medium, it does not carry the medium along with it. Sound waves start with a vibration in matter. The waves travel when the kinetic energy of the vibration is transferred from particle to particle of the matter.

Think back to the Newton's cradle you explored in *Learning Set 2*. The balls in the middle hardly move at all, yet kinetic energy is transferred from one end to the other. In much the same way, a mechanical wave can carry energy through a medium without moving matter through the medium.

The speed of sound is 343 m/s (meters per second) in air at room temperature. You may have read about aircraft that go faster than the speed of sound. They are called *supersonic*. However, there is no single speed of sound. Sound travels more slowly in cold air and faster in hot air. Sound travels even faster through water, at 1443 m/s. The speed of sound is different in different materials.

pitch: how high or low a sound is.

The speed of sound depends on the particles of the medium the sound wave is moving through. Because the particles in a solid are tightly packed together, sound waves can quickly transfer energy from particle to particle in a solid. The particles in liquids are less tightly packed, so the sound travels more slowly than in most solids. Gas particles are farther apart, so the speed of sound is slowest when it moves through gases.

The arrangement of particles in solids, liquids, and gases affects the speed of sound through the media. Sound travels slowest through gases and fastest through solids. This is because in solids, the particles are closest together, and in gases, they are farthest apart.

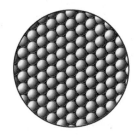 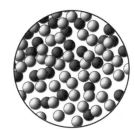 

Relating Characteristics of Sound to Wave Characteristics

One characteristic of sound is its **pitch**. Pitch is how high or low a sound is. The pitch of a sound is related to the sound wave's frequency. When you hear a high-pitched sound, you are hearing sound waves with a high frequency. A low-pitched sound is from a wave that has a low frequency. The human ear can hear sounds from about 100 Hz (hertz) up to about 18,000 Hz. Other animals are able to hear lower- and higher-frequency sounds.

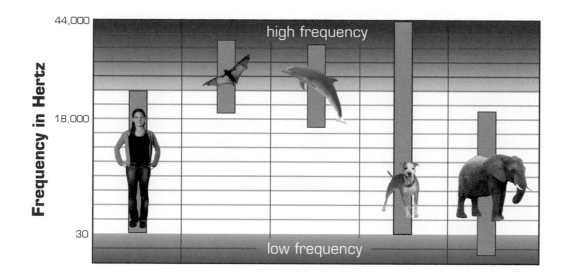

Different animals can hear a range of different frequencies of sound. Look at the graph to see which animal hears the greatest range of sound and which hears the smallest range.

As you observed in your mechanical-wave race in the previous section, the speed of a wave is not affected by the frequency of the wave. In air, high-frequency sound waves and low-frequency sound waves both travel at 343 m/s. How is this possible? The speed of any wave depends on both its frequency and wavelength. The longer the wavelength, the lower the frequency. The shorter the wavelength, the higher the frequency. With higher-frequency waves, more compressions pass by you each second, but the distance between compressions is smaller. You can see in the diagram that a higher frequency wave has a shorter wavelength than a lower frequency wave.

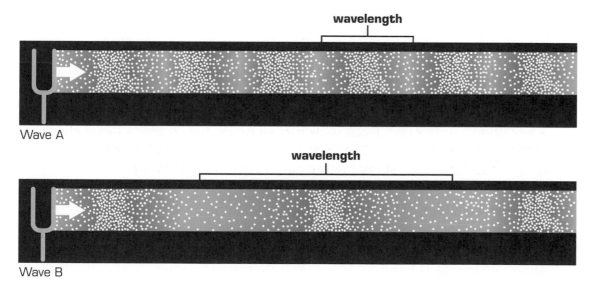

Which of the two longitudinal waves has the higher frequency? How do you know?

ENERGY

You read earlier that sound energy and intensity depend on how loud the source is. You compared intensity of different sounds using the decibel scale. The wave model can be used to explain the loudness of a sound. The louder the sound, the greater the energy. When you generated the waves in the rope, the more you moved the rope away from the rest position, the greater the amplitude of the wave you generated. It required more energy from you to move the rope the greater distance, so you transferred more energy to the rope. The amplitude of the wave was related to the energy transferred to the rope. The same is true for sound. The greater the amplitude of the sound wave, the greater the energy carried by the wave. Therefore, the louder the sound is.

Have you ever heard an echo? If you yell loudly in an empty gymnasium, you will hear the yell repeated shortly after. What you hear is the reflection of the sound off the hard walls of the gymnasium. Just as the wave you generated in the coiled spring or rope reflected from the fixed end, sound waves reflect off hard surfaces.

Stop and Think

1. Why does sound travel better through a solid than through air?

2. How is the pitch of a sound related to the frequency of a sound wave?

3. How is the loudness of a sound related to the amplitude of a sound wave?

4. Use the wave model of sound to describe what happens when you hear an echo.

Revise Your Explanation

With your group, revisit the explanations you wrote in *Section 4.2*. Use what you have learned about waves to revise or add to your claims about the factors that affect sound energy. Then use what you have read to revise the science knowledge and your explanation statement.

Conference

Share Your Explanations

When everyone is finished, share your claims and explanations with the class. As each group shares their revised claims and explanations, record the explanations. Revise the classroom poster that has the full set of claims and explanations.

Update the *Project Board*

Think about the results of your explorations in *Sections 4.2* and *4.3,* as well as what you have read about waves in this section. Record what you learned about sound waves in the *What are we learning?* column of the *Project Board.* Every time you add something to this column, remember to add supporting evidence in the *What is our evidence?* column.

Again, it is important to recognize any questions you may have. Well-developed questions can guide your learning. Any questions you have about sound energy should be recorded in the *What do we need to investigate?* column.

Design a Rube Goldberg machine to turn off a light				
What do we think we know?	**What do we need to investigate?**	**What are we learning?**	**What is our evidence?**	**What does it mean for the challenge or question?**

What's the Point?

Sound waves are longitudinal waves that can travel through many kinds of matter. Sound waves, like other mechanical waves, are described by the properties of wavelength, frequency, wave speed, and amplitude. Amplitude is a measure of the energy used to create the wave. The greater the amplitude, the greater the energy of the wave and the louder the sound. The pitch of a sound is related to frequency. When you hear a high-pitched sound, the frequency of the wave is greater than that of a low-pitched sound. The speed of sound is generally fastest in solids and slowest in gases. A wave model can account for reflection of sound waves and why the speed of sound in a medium is the same for waves with different frequencies.

4.5 Investigate

What Factors Affect the Intensity of Light Energy?

It may seem odd to you to think about light as energy. However, you did see that when a flashlight was held close to a radiometer, the flags moved more than when the flashlight was held farther away. So, clearly, the light somehow provided energy to the radiometer. You may be wondering how light can provide energy and how light from the Sun can heat Earth. You may also be wondering how light can power devices such as a calculator. Like sound, light energy can travel in waves. In this section, you will investigate light energy and identify factors that affect the amount of light energy emitted by a light source. Your investigations will also help you understand the relationship between light that you see and light energy.

Demonstration

Watch as your teacher shines the light from a flashlight on a classroom wall. The beam will make a circle of light on the wall. The teacher will move the flashlight closer to the wall and away from the wall. Work in groups to discuss what is happening during the demonstration.

Analyze Your Data

In your group, discuss the following questions:

1. What do you think is happening when the circle of light becomes larger? What about when it becomes smaller?

2. Do you think the light energy emitted by the flashlight changes at any point in the demonstration? If so, how?

3. When a flashlight is close to the wall, the illuminated area is a small circle. How do you think the intensity of the light in the small circle compares with the intensity when the light makes a big circle? In other words, how does the intensity of light striking the wall relate to the distance of the flashlight from the wall?

4. How can you use the area illuminated by a flashlight at different distances to determine how the intensity of light at the wall is related to distance from the source?

5. Suppose you repeat the demonstration, using two flashlights, one of which is brighter and more powerful. Describe the circles of light that will be produced if both flashlights make circles of light that are the same size. How do you think the brightness of the light source will affect light intensity at the wall?

How Does Distance Affect Light Intensity?

The data from the demonstration suggest that as light energy spreads out over a larger area, it decreases in intensity. But you do not know for sure, because you have observed this using the light of just one flashlight. What if the light source was different? Would the same thing happen? You are going to investigate to find the answers.

In this investigation, three lab stations will be set up around the classroom, each using a different light source. Your group will have a chance to run the procedure at least once at one of the lab stations. You will watch as other groups run the procedure at other lab stations. It will be important for you to record observations at all three lab stations. Record your data in an *Effect of Distance and Source Brightness on Light Intensity* page.

Procedure

Materials

- one light source: flashlight, table lamp with 25-W bulb, or table lamp with 60-W bulb

- 1 poster board with a 2 cm x 2 cm opening in the center

- 1 poster board, laminated and with 2 cm x 2 cm grid

- 1 washable marker

- masking tape

1. When it is your turn to set up a station using one of the three light sources, start by taping to the wall your group's laminated poster board with the grid. Make sure you know which light source you are using so you will record your data in the proper place on your *Effect of Distance and Source Brightness on Light Intensity* page.

2. Position a desk so a light source on it is 100 cm from the wall. One student in the group will hold the poster board with the square hole vertically on the desk. Position it so the hole is right in front of the light source.

3. A second student will turn on the light source and hold it up to the board so the light shines through the hole and strikes the laminated poster board on the wall.

4. A third student will use a marker to outline the illuminated area on the laminated plastic. Estimate the area by counting the grid squares contained inside the outline. Label the area "Produced by source at 100 cm. Area = _____ cm². " Write the area you estimated on the blank line.

5. Notice the intensity of the light striking the laminated poster board. You will not be able to rank the intensity until you have seen other illuminated areas. Until then, look at the center of the illuminated area, where the light intensity is greatest, and notice how intense it is.

6. Repeat *Steps 2–5,* but this time, move the desk so the light source and the poster board with the hole are 50 cm from the wall. Record your data. Notice if the intensity of light in the illuminated area is greater or smaller than it was when the light was held 100 cm from the poster board.

7. Repeat *Steps 2–5,* but this time, move the desk so the light source and poster board are 25 cm from the wall. Record your data. Notice if the intensity of light in the illuminated area is greater or smaller than it was when the light was held 50 cm from the poster board.

8. Record the relative intensity of the illuminated areas. Which was most intense? Which was least intense? Which was in the middle?

Watching the Procedure

When your group is watching another group carry out the procedure, you will not get to set up the station. However, you will need to record the data that group is collecting and judge the relative intensity of the illuminated areas.

1. Make sure you know which light source the group is using, and make sure you always know how far away from the laminated board they are positioning the light source.

2. Each time the group running the procedure creates an illuminated area, notice how large it is, and make sure they tell you how many square centimeters they measured. If you cannot hear the size, ask them to repeat it. Record the size of each illuminated area.

3. Notice the intensity of the light in each illuminated area. Observe how the intensity changes as the distance from the light to the laminated board changes. Notice, too, the differences in intensity between the illuminated areas created by the different light sources. Make notes so you will remember these differences.

Effect of Distance and Source Brightness on Light Intensity 4.5.1

Name: _____ Date: _____

Light source	Distance to wall (cm)	Area illuminated at wall (cm²)	Intensity rating (scale of 1 to 10)
25–W bulb	25		
	50		
	100		
60–W bulb	25		
	50		
	100		
flashlight	25		
	50		
	100		

4. You will need to rank the intensity of the illuminated areas produced by each of the light sources at each distance from the laminated board. So, if you need to, go back and observe a procedure a second time so you can be more exact about the intensity of light at different distances and using different light sources.

Analyze Your Data

1. Begin by doing your best to rank the intensity of the light in the illuminated areas you observed, and graph the results. Which light source and distance produced the most intense illumination? Which produced the least intense illumination? Which ones were very similar to each other? Assign a number between 1 and 10 to the intensity of the light in each illuminated area.

2. What relationship do you see between the size of the illuminated area and the distance of the light source from the wall?

3. What relationship do you see between the size of the illuminated area and the intensity of the illuminated area when the light source is the same?

4. What relationship do you see between the brightness of the light source and the size of the illuminated area?

5. What relationship do you see between the brightness of the light source and the intensity of the illuminated area when the light sources are the same distance from the illuminated area?

Communicate

Share Your Results

Although all of the groups did the same investigation, different groups may have analyzed the results differently.

When it is your group's turn to present, show the class your data table. As you show your data table and graph, tell the class how you ranked the intensity of the illuminated areas, and point out the trends you see.

As you listen to the other groups, notice ways in which each group's data are similar to yours and ways in which their data are different. Notice the relationships groups are proposing between distance and area, area and light intensity, or distance and light intensity. For each presentation, decide if you agree. As always, if you do not understand what is being presented, ask questions. If you think the data are not trustworthy, also ask questions about that. Remember to be respectful, even if you disagree with a group.

Reflect

Discuss the following questions as a group. Be prepared to share your answers with the class.

1. How do the graphs of different groups compare? What are the similarities and differences?

2. Based on the graphs, develop a statement about the relationship between the distance from the light source and the intensity of light at the poster board.

3. Based on the graphs, develop a statement about the relationship between the brightness of the light source and the intensity of light at the poster board.

4. Develop a statement about the relationship between the amount of illuminated area and the intensity of light at the poster board.

5. Develop a statement about the relationship between the amount of illuminated area and the distance from the poster board.

6. Now think back to the radiometer. As the flashlight was brought closer to the radiometer, the flags moved faster. Based on what you observed in this experiment and on your observations of the radiometer, what do you think is the relationship between light intensity and light energy?

7. What are two factors that determine the available amount of light energy?

8. Do you think light energy is a type of kinetic energy or a type of potential energy? Why?

photon: a tiny
particle or packet
of light energy.

Why Does Light Intensity Decrease With Distance From the Source?

You observed that light travels in a straight line. Even though the wave model of light can be used to explain how light travels, some characteristics of light are easier to understand using another model. One model scientists use to describe the behavior of light is a particle model. You can think about a beam of light as a stream of tiny particles, or packets of energy, called **photons**. Photons do not lose energy as they travel.

Like sound, light spreads out as it moves away from the source. The explosion of fireworks sends out material in all directions. In much the same way, as photons travel away from a light source, the photons disperse, or spread apart from one another. This dispersion of light is the reason that as you move a light source away from a wall, the illuminated area increases. At the same time, intensity decreases because as the photons spread apart, each square centimeter on the wall has fewer photons striking it every second.

If you think about light as packets of energy, then you can better understand how light intensity affects the speed of the flags in a radiometer. When a flashlight is close to the radiometer, the photons emitted by the flashlight are concentrated close together, so a large number of photons hit each flag every second. The more photons that hit each flag every second, the greater the kinetic energy that results when light energy of the photons is transformed into kinetic energy of the flags.

Reflect

Think about what you have learned about photons and intensity of light. Answer these questions and be prepared to discuss the answers with your class.

1. In *Learning Set 1,* you messed about with a device powered by photovoltaic cells. What do you think would happen if you were to shine a brighter light on the device? What if you used a dimmer light? Why?

2. Light does not pass through some materials. What do you think happens to the energy of photons when photons strike a surface and are absorbed? What indicators would tell you that the energy of the photons has been transformed?

3. How do you know that light travels faster than sound? (Hint: Give an example of something that produces sound and light at the same time.)

4. Why do you think light is sometimes called "visible light?" What other kinds of light have you heard about or read about?

Explain

It is time to update your *Energy Types* page or use a new *Energy Types* page to record what you know about light energy.

You are also ready now to try to explain how each factor you identified affects light energy. Use a different *Create Your Explanation* page to record each of your claims.

Start by making a claim about how a factor you identified affects light energy. Try to state your claim this way:

When [*your factor*] [*increases/decreases*], light energy [*increases/decreases/stays the same*].

Describe the evidence from the explorations that supports your claim. Record science knowledge from what you have read. Then develop a statement that uses your evidence and science knowledge and tell why the factor you chose affects light energy. This will be your explanation.

As you are working on your explanation, remember to use all your science knowledge, as well as evidence from your investigations, explorations, and readings, to support your explanation. Science knowledge is knowledge about how things work. This knowledge can come through readings, discussion, talking to an expert, or other experiences. You may include what you read in this *Learning Set* or knowledge you have gained in other classes. Do not worry if you cannot create a perfect explanation. Just work with what you know for now. You will have opportunities later to revise your claims and explanations.

Energy Types 0.0.1/1.2.2/2.2.2/2.5.2/2.6.2/ 3.2.2/3.6.2/4.5.2/5.1.3/5.5.1

Name: _____ Date: _____

Type of energy	Indicators that this type is being transformed	Factors that affect the amount of energy

© It's About Time

Create Your Explanation 3.BBC.2/4.2.1/4.5.3/ 4.6.1/4.BBC.2/5.BBC.1

Name:_____ Date:_____

Use this page to explain the lesson of your recent investigations.

Write a brief summary of the results from your investigation. You will use this summary to help you write your explanation.

Claim—a statement of what you understand or a conclusion that you have reached from an investigation or a set of investigations.

Evidence—data collected during investigations and trends in that data.

Science knowledge—knowledge about how things work. You may have learned this through reading, talking to an expert, discussion, or other experiences.

Write your explanation using your **Claim, Evidence** and **Science knowledge** from above.

© It's About Time

ENERGY

Conference

Share Your Explanations

Share your explanations with the class. As a class, come to agreement on explanations about why each factor you have identified affects the amount of light energy.

electromagnetic radiation: radiant energy that can travel through a vacuum and through matter in the form of waves.

vacuum: space that contains no matter.

Solar Energy

Solar energy is energy from the Sun. It travels from the Sun to Earth in the form of **electromagnetic radiation**. Electromagnetic radiation is energy that moves as waves through a **vacuum** and through matter. Vacuum is any space that contains no matter. The space between the Sun and Earth's atmosphere is a vacuum. Because energy from the Sun is a form of electromagnetic radiation, it is able to travel through the vacuum to reach Earth's atmosphere. Then it travels through the layer of gases that make up Earth's atmosphere.

Solar radiation accounts for most of the renewable energy on Earth. Finding ways to harness it better would lead to less dependence on the nonrenewable sources of fossil fuels. Electrical energy and heat for homes would cost less, and there would be less pollution.

There are several ways in which solar energy can be made usable. Buildings can be designed so that in cold weather, solar energy can readily enter and heat the buildings. Windows and awnings can be placed in such a way that permits solar radiation to enter in the cold, winter weather and not enter during hot, summer weather. In some parts of the world, solar energy is used to heat water in tanks on the roofs of houses. Using solar energy to heat water reduces the amount of nonrenewable resources needed to heat water for showers, baths, and cleaning.

Light energy from the Sun can also be transformed into other types of energy. For example, light striking solar cells on the roof of a house can be transformed into electrical energy and then stored as chemical energy in batteries until it is required.

Solar energy can also be used in an indirect way. Wind, waves, and hydroelectricity result from energy that came from the Sun. All of these are sources of renewable energy.

Even the nonrenewable sources come from solar energy. Solar energy is transformed by plants into chemical energy through the process of *photosynthesis.* The energy stored in fossil fuels comes from the chemical energy stored in plants or eaten by animals millions of years ago.

Reflect

Answer the following questions in your group. Be prepared to share your answers with the class.

1. Why do you think a house that uses solar energy needs to store chemical energy in batteries?

2. What is the source of almost all energy on Earth? Justify your answer.

Update the *Project Board*

Think about the results of the demonstration and the investigation, as well as what you have read. Record what you learned about light energy in the *What are we learning?* column of the *Project Board.* Do not forget to add supporting evidence to the *What is our evidence?* column.

Again, it is important to recognize any questions you may have. Well-developed questions can guide your learning. Any questions you have about light energy should be recorded in the *What do we need to investigate?* column.

What's the Point?

Light intensity depends mainly on two factors: the strength (brightness) of the light source and distance from the source. Close to the source, the intensity is greatest. As you move farther away from the light source, intensity decreases. This can be explained with a particle model of light in which photons emitted by the light source travel outward in all directions. As the photons move farther from the source, they spread apart, and fewer photons pass through each unit area. A brighter light source emits more photons. This is what makes it brighter.

More to Learn

Why Is It so Much Warmer Near the Equator Than at the North Pole and South Pole?

The same Sun strikes all parts of Earth, but different parts of Earth have very different climates. Do you know why?

In February, the Arctic Circle is a frozen mass of snow and ice. To the south, there may be four feet of snow in Vermont and New York. Meanwhile, in southern Florida, people are swimming in the warm waters of the Atlantic Ocean or the Gulf of Mexico. Traveling even farther south, at the Equator, it is hot and steamy, with tropical plants and animals thriving in the rain forests. All of these locations are warmed by the same Sun at the same time. Why are there such extreme differences in the heating of Earth? The answer to this question has to do with intensity of light from the Sun and its duration.

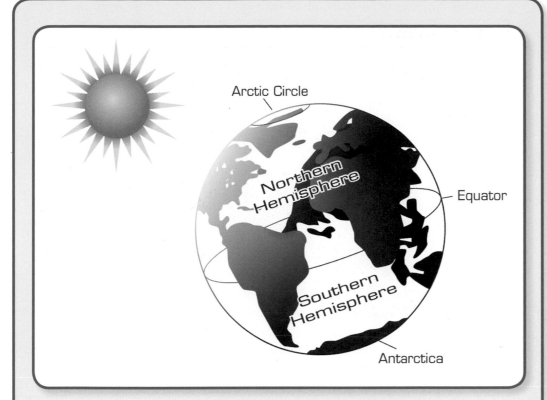

Different locations on Earth experience differences in climate depending on the intensity of sunlight that reaches each region.

Demonstration

Earth is heated by light energy from the Sun. The amount of light energy emitted by the Sun is constant, yet there are places on Earth that receive more intense light energy than other places and also for a longer time duration each day. In this demonstration, a flashlight and a round sphere are used to model what happens as sunlight hits Earth at noon. Watch the demonstration carefully, and record your observations of changes in the area illuminated as light strikes different parts of the sphere.

To model how the Sun's light energy affects places on Earth differently, the model must be set up so that the placement of the Sun and Earth are similar to their placement in the solar system. In this model, the sphere represents Earth, and the flashlight represents the Sun. The sphere is marked with lines representing Earth's latitude lines. The sphere must be tilted so that the top half is leaning toward the flashlight. This models how Earth tilts toward the Sun when it is summer in the Northern Hemisphere.

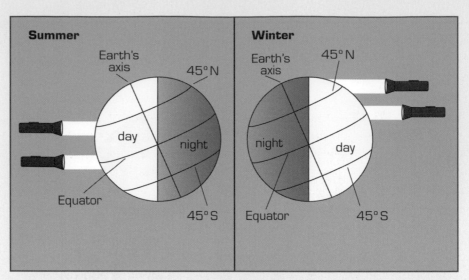

Your teacher will hold the flashlight horizontally so the light strikes the sphere at the Equator. Have someone in the class use a ruler to make sure the flashlight is 30 cm (about 1 ft) from the sphere. That same person should measure the length of the oval of light cast by the flashlight. Record this data on a table like the one below, in the column *Equator summer*.

Sunlight Model Data

	Equator summer	45° N summer		Equator winter	45° N winter
Length of oval, cm					
Area of light					

The flashlight will next be pointed at the line at 45° N latitude. This is where Portland, Oregon, is, halfway between the Equator and the North Pole. Note that the flashlight will still be held horizontally to model how photons from the Sun arrive at Earth, traveling in nearly parallel paths.

Someone should measure to make sure the flashlight is still 30 cm from the sphere and then measure the length of the oval of light. Record this number in the *45° N summer* column of your table.

Analyze Your Data

1. Use the equation for calculating the area of a circle to calculate the approximate area of the ovals of light from the flashlight. Although they are ovals, you can get a good enough approximation of the relationship of their sizes by treating them as circles. Divide the length of the oval by two to get the radius. Square that and multiply it by pi (π): 3.14. Record the approximate area of each oval in its column.

2. What do you notice about the relationship of the area of each oval? Which has a larger area? Which has a smaller area?

3. What does that tell you about the light intensity at the Equator versus Portland, Oregon? Which receives more light energy from the Sun?

Demonstration

The flashlight will now be moved to the other side of Earth. This models the relationship between Earth and the Sun in the Northern Hemisphere in the winter. Repeat the measurements you did earlier. First, measure the oval produced at the Equator and then at 45° N latitude. In both cases, use the ruler to make sure the flashlight is 30 cm from the sphere. Measure the length of the oval in each case. Record the measurements in the *Equator winter* and the *45° N winter* columns of your table.

Analyze Your Data

1. Calculate the approximate area of each oval of light from the flashlight, and record the area of each in its column.

2. Compare the areas of the winter and summer Equator ovals. How do they compare? What does this tell you about the amount of light energy they receive from the Sun in the summer and winter?

3. Compare the areas of the ovals produced at 45° latitude in the summer and the winter. What does this tell you about the light intensity at 45° N latitude in the summer and the winter? When does Portland, which is at 45° N latitude, receive more light energy from the Sun, in the summer or in the winter?

4. Why it is warmer in the summer than in the winter in Portland? Include what you understand about the tilt of Earth and its relationship to the Sun in the summer and winter.

5. To calculate how much more light energy Portland gets in the summer than in the winter, calculate the ratio of the area of the 45° N latitude in the summer to the area of the 45° N latitude in the winter.

6. Now do the same for the two Equator measurements.

7. Why is the temperature near the Equator about the same all year? Use what you know about light energy to answer this question.

8. Why is it so much colder at the North and South Poles than it is at the Equator?

Reflect

Answer these questions with your group, and be prepared to discuss them with the class.

1. Suppose you stay outside from noon to 3:00 PM on a sunny day in winter. Compare this to staying outside from noon to 3:00 PM on a sunny day in summer. In which case would you be more likely to get a sunburn? Why?

2. You are asked to make measurements of the oval of light hitting the model Earth at 45° S latitude in the Southern Hemisphere. Estimate from the data already collected what you would expect the length of the oval to be at 45° S latitude when it is summer in the Northern Hemisphere. What will the length of the oval be at 45° S latitude when it is winter in the Northern Hemisphere?

3. The demonstration showed how the Sun's rays strike Earth at around noon. In a single day, however, the sun rises low in the East, moves across the sky, and sets low in the West. At what time(s) of day is the intensity of sunlight the greatest? At what time(s) of day is the intensity of sunlight the least?

4.6 Explore

How Does Light Behave Like a Wave?

Your experience with light energy has suggested that light travels from point A, a source, to point B, a surface, in a straight line. You have learned about two factors that affect the light intensity at the surface: the brightness of the source and the distance of point B from the source. Light spreads out as it travels away from the source, and this can be modeled using a particle model of light.

However, this particle model is not a perfect model of light energy. Other factors exist that can be modeled only by thinking of light as a wave. The intensity of light can be affected by the characteristics of those waves.

When you place a straw in water, it looks like the straw is broken. Why do you think it looks that way?

Demonstration

You will observe as your teacher inserts a pencil into a cup in a variety of situations. Record your observations on paper at each step.

1. The pencil is inserted into the cup and pulled out. Record your observations of the pencil.

2. The cup is filled with water. The pencil is inserted into the water, pulled out of the water, and finally inserted back into the water. Record your observations.

3. The cup is covered with a cloth. After the cloth is removed, record your observations of how the pencil has changed.

4. While still in the water, the pencil is moved slowly, tipped from left to center to right and back again several times. Record your observations of how the pencil appears in the left position, the center position, and the right position.

5. Record your observations of the pencil after it is taken out of the cup of water.

Analyze Your Data

1. How does your eye see the pencil when the teacher first shows it? Make a sketch showing the path of light rays from the pencil to your eyes.

2. How did the pencil appear when placed into the empty cup?

3. How is the path the light takes different after the pencil is placed in the water? Make a sketch showing the path of light rays from the pencil to your eyes that would match your observations.

4. Identify factors that affected the pencil's appearance.

5. Why do you think the pencil appeared to change and then was restored to its original form?

Communicate Your Results

Share Your Ideas

As a class, share your observations. Discuss any differences in observations. If you do not understand what a person is presenting, or if you disagree about the observations, ask a question. Remember to be respectful.

Make a class list of the factors that affect the pencil's appearance. Note any disagreements. Later you will have a chance to put questions on the *Project Board* that will help you settle those disagreements.

The squares on the bottom of a swimming pool look crooked when water is in the pool.

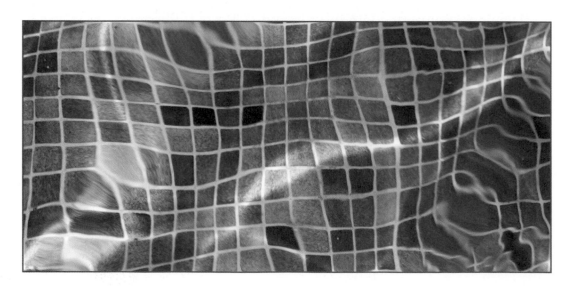

How Are Light Waves Similar to Sound Waves?

Before you can understand what happened in the demonstration, you need to think about light energy traveling as waves. Recall that sound waves are longitudinal waves. Light waves are transverse waves, which means that the vibrations are at right angles to the direction in which the wave travels. Like sound waves, light waves have the characteristics of wavelength, frequency, and amplitude.

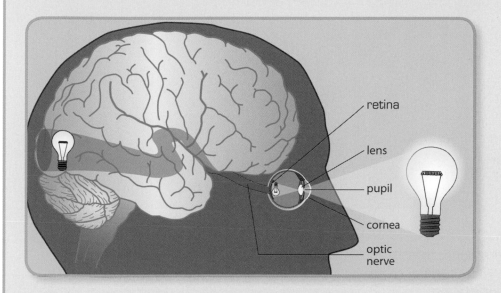

retina
lens
pupil
cornea
optic nerve

speed of light: the speed at which light travels in a vacuum, approximately 300,000 km/s.

Sound waves are emitted by a sound source and then move outward in all directions. The sound energy disperses, so the farther you are from the source, the lower the intensity of the sound. The same thing happens with light. Light waves are emitted by a source and then move outward in all directions. The farther you are from the source, the lower the intensity of the light.

Light waves are a form of radiation. Sound energy can travel only through matter, but light energy can travel through a vacuum, where no matter is present. Energy that can move in waves through a vacuum is called electromagnetic radiation.

The Speed of Light

All light waves move very fast, covering short distances almost instantly. Light waves from the Sun, which is about 150 million kilometers away, take about 8 min to reach Earth. The **speed of light** is about 300,000 km/s. This is about 1 million times faster than

ENERGY

the speed of sound through air. You can easily experience the difference between the speed of sound and the speed of light when lightning flashes several kilometers away. You see the flash almost instantly, and then seconds later, you hear the thunder, which is carried by the much slower-moving sound waves.

During a thunderstorm, you often see the lightning before you hear the thunder. Why do you think this happens?

scatter: to bounce off or deflect in different directions.

The Reflection of Waves

Both sound waves and light waves can reflect off surfaces. The reflection of sound waves is why you hear echoes. Since most objects do not generate their own light, you see almost all objects because of reflection. Light shines on objects and reflects off of them. If you are looking in the direction of the object, the reflected light enters your eye. Reflected light is what shines into your eyes and allows you to see objects around you.

When waves reflect, they can **scatter**. You have experienced this with echoes. Usually the sound of an echo is fuzzy compared to the original sound. This is because the sound scatters. The sound waves are bouncing off a surface that is not perfectly smooth. This causes the sound to reflect in many different directions and to reach your ear at slightly different times.

The same kind of scattering happens with light. A polished mirror shows a very clear reflection. But the reflection in a car's fender is scattered in many directions because the surface is not as smooth. Some of the reflected light does not enter your eye, so the reflection you see is dim. The light that does enter your eye may have been shifted because it was reflected off a rough surface, and this makes the reflection fuzzy.

When light waves reflect off a smooth surface like a mirror, they produce a clear reflection. When light waves reflect off a surface that is not as smooth, they can scatter, producing a fuzzy reflection.

Diffraction of Waves

Waves can also change direction when they pass through an opening or around something in their path. This wave phenomenon is called **diffraction**. Sound waves can move around corners in a way similar to ripples in a pond moving around a rock jutting out of the water. You probably know that sticking your hand in the way of a sound does not prevent the sound from reaching your ears. Even covering your ears allows some sound to pass through.

Light seems to be different. You cannot see around corners without a mirror, and you can block light from your eyes by holding your hand out in front of you. In fact, light waves do change direction, but not enough to be easily noticed.

diffraction: the ability of a wave to spread out or change direction as it passes through an opening or around an obstruction.

Waves can change direction as they go around something in their path, such as a rock or a duck.

Refraction of Waves

Waves can also bend when they pass from one medium to another. The bending of waves is called **refraction**. One way to make the bending of light easier to see is to pass light through different materials, such as glass or water. When you saw the shape of the pencil appear to change in the demonstration, you knew the pencil did not bend. But you did see light rays bend as they passed from water through glass and into the air.

> **refraction:** the change in direction of a wave when it enters a new medium with a different wave speed.

Light bends, or refracts, as it passes through a glass prism. A prism can separate the colors of the rainbow because each color bends a different amount.

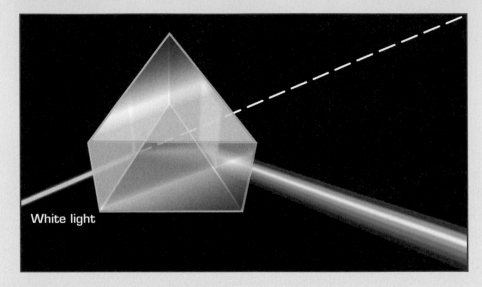

White light

Why does light bend when it goes from water into glass or from glass into air? Remember that waves move at different speeds in different materials. The speed of light is 300,000 km/s in a vacuum, but light travels more slowly through air, and even more slowly through water. It is the change in speed that causes light waves (and sound waves, too) to refract, or bend, when they pass from one material into another.

Stop and Think

1. Describe three similarities and three differences between light energy and sound energy.

2. You can sometimes hear a series of echoes as sound waves reflect back and forth off the walls of two buildings. How could you make light produce a series of "echoes"?

Project-Based Inquiry Science

Revise Your Explanations

Earlier, you made claims about the factors that affect how much light energy is available. But you did not know how to think about light as waves when you did that. You now know more about light, and you know some additional factors that affect how much light is available. Revise the claims and explanations you made previously using what you now know about light energy, and develop claims about new factors that affect how much light is available. Then using your evidence and science knowledge as support, work with your group to create an explanation of how these factors affect light energy. Use a separate *Create Your Explanation* page for each of the factors you make a claim about.

For each factor that affects light energy, start by making a claim about the way the factor you identified affects light energy. Try to state your claim this way:

When [*your factor*] [*increases/decreases*], light energy [*increases/ decreases/stays the same*].

Describe the evidence from the explorations that supports your claim. Then record science knowledge that supports your claim. Develop an explanation statement that connects your claim to your evidence and science knowledge in a way that tells why the factor in your claim affects light energy the way it does. As you are working on your explanation, remember to use all your science knowledge, as well as evidence from your investigations, explorations, and readings, to support each explanation.

Create Your Explanation 3.BBC.2/4.2.1/4.5.3/ 4.6.1/4.BBC.2/5.BBC.1

Name:_____ Date:_____

Use this page to explain the lesson of your recent investigations.

Write a brief summary of the results from your investigation. You will use this summary to help you write your explanation.

Claim—a statement of what you understand or a conclusion that you have reached from an investigation or a set of investigations.

Evidence—data collected during investigations and trends in that data.

Science knowledge—knowledge about how things work. You may have learned this through reading, talking to an expert, discussion, or other experiences.

Write your explanation using your **Claim, Evidence** and **Science knowledge** from above.

electromagnetic spectrum: a continuous range of wavelengths that includes all of the types of electromagnetic waves.

Electromagnetic Radiation

So far, all of the examples you have examined have involved visible light. However, visible light is just one type of electromagnetic radiation. You are probably familiar with many other types of electromagnetic radiation, such as X-rays, microwaves, and ultraviolet light. In fact, all of these, along with visible light, are simply different parts of the **electromagnetic spectrum**, a continuous range of wavelengths that includes all of the types of electromagnetic waves.

ENERGY

wave-particle duality: light energy can at times show particle properties and at other times show wave properties.

At one end of this spectrum are radio and television waves, then microwaves, infrared rays, visible light, ultraviolet rays, X-rays, and, finally, gamma rays. All of these carry energy. The major difference between these types of waves is the wavelength of each type of wave. Radio and television waves have long wavelengths, while X-rays and gamma rays have short wavelengths. Shorter wavelengths are associated with greater energy. This means that X-rays and gamma rays carry more energy than radio and television waves.

Because electromagnetic waves all travel at the speed of light, increasing the wavelength means the frequency must decrease. This is because fewer complete waves can pass by a point in the same amount of time if the wavelengths are longer. So radio waves have long wavelengths and a low frequency. Gamma rays have short wavelengths and a high frequency. Either wavelength or frequency can be considered a factor in the amount of electromagnetic energy available. The higher the frequency of an electromagnetic wave, the greater is the energy.

Scientists have found that it is sometimes easier to think of electromagnetic radiation as particles called photons. At other times, it is easier to think of electromagnetic radiation as waves. This dual nature of electromagnetic radiation is called the **wave-particle duality**.

The electromagnetic spectrum ranges from radio waves to gamma rays. As wavelength decreases, energy increases. Visible light is only a narrow band in the middle of the spectrum.

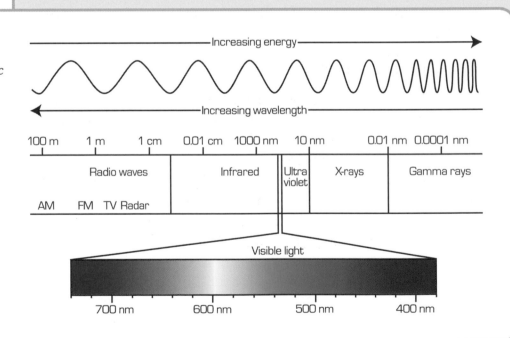

Conference

Share Your Explanations

Share your claims and explanation statements with the class. As you listen to other groups, notice how well their claims match your claims. Notice whether any other group stated any of your claims better than you did. Notice if any group made claims different from yours. Examine the evidence each group used to support its claims. Make sure you agree with the claims and evidence used to support each. Notice the explanation statements of other groups. You may notice that some groups expressed their explanations better than your group did.

Revise Your Explanations

As a class, revise the set of claims and explanations about light energy. Make sure everybody agrees with each claim and understands each explanation statement.

Update the *Project Board*

The question for this section of the Unit is *How does light behave like a wave?* Add what you now know about light as a wave to the *What are we learning?* column. Do not forget to add evidence to the *What is our evidence?* column for every entry.

What's the Point?

Light refracts, or bends, when it passes from one material into another material because the speed of the waves changes. Electromagnetic waves are transverse waves that can travel though a vacuum. Visible light is a small portion of the electromagnetic spectrum. All the waves in the electromagnetic spectrum travel at the speed of light (300,000 km/s in a vacuum). The waves in the electromagnetic spectrum differ in wavelength and frequency. As wavelength increases, frequency decreases. If other factors are the same, electromagnetic waves with lower frequency have less energy than electromagnetic waves with higher frequency.

More to Learn

How Do You See Light?

pupil: the circular opening in the center of the iris that controls the amount of light that enters the eye.

iris: a flat, colored, ring-shaped membrane with an adjustable circular opening at the center.

lens: a structure in the eye that changes shape to focus light and images onto the retina.

retina: the layer at the back of the inside of the eye containing cells that respond to light and color.

optic nerve: cells that transmit electrical signals from the retina to the brain.

cones: cells that respond to bright light, responsible for color detection and sharpness of vision.

rods: light-sensitive cells responsible for vision in dim light.

Eyes are the sense organs that detect light waves. In the eye, light energy and color information are transformed into nerve impulses (electrical energy). This energy is sent to your brain for interpretation. Think about the front of your eyes. This is the part that you are most familiar with, since you can see it. In the center is the **pupil**, which is an opening that allows light to come into the eye. The **iris** is a membrane that surrounds the pupil. The iris is the part that determines the color of your eyes. The iris also controls the size of the pupil and the amount of light that comes into the eye. Just behind the pupil and iris is the **lens**, which focuses light into the back of the eye. In the back of the eye is the **retina**, which is made of cells that receive the light energy and react to its intensity by sending an impulse to the brain. The signals are sent to the brain along the **optic nerve**.

The retina is the place in the eye where light energy is transformed into chemical energy. The retina is made up of **cones** and **rods**. The rods respond to the overall intensity of light coming into the eye. The rods are more sensitive to light than the cones, so they are used in night vision. Cones are primarily responsible for identifying color differences in light.

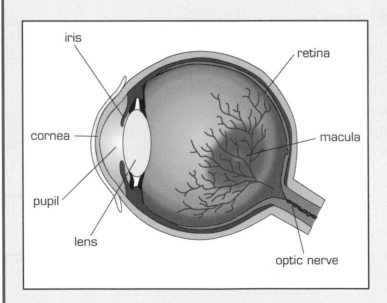

Light energy enters the eye, is converted into chemical energy in the retina, and then transformed into electrical energy in signals sent to the brain. The eye is another example of one of nature's Rube Goldberg machines.

Learning Set 4

Back to the Big Challenge

Design a Rube Goldberg Machine to Turn Off a Light

The *Big Challenge* you are working on for this Unit is *Design a Rube Goldberg machine to turn off a light.* You have considered how thermal energy and chemical energy might be involved in a Rube Goldberg machine that will turn off a light. You now know enough about light energy and sound energy to imagine how light energy or sound energy might be involved in your machine. You will soon be designing a set of steps that transform light energy or sound energy into another form of energy. However, before doing that, you will think once more about whether light energy and sound energy are kinetic energy or potential energy and how they do work.

Reflect

To help you think about light energy and sound energy, you will examine the energy-transformation cartoons again from the *Introduction* to this Unit. Identify the steps that show light energy and sound energy transformations in your group's cartoon, and record them on an *Energy-transformation Cartoon* page. Fill in the blocks in the row for each step you identify. Then for each step, answer these questions. Be prepared to share your answers with the class.

1. How do you know the step involves light energy or sound energy transformations? What are the indicators?

2. How does the step transform light energy or sound energy?

Energy-transformation Cartoon	0.0.3/1.BBC.1/3.BBC.1/ 4.1.2/4.BBC.1/5.1.2/6.3.1

Name: _____ Date: _____

Fill in the letter of the step you are analyzing. Then fill in other information about that step.

Name of your machine:			Purpose of your machine:	
Step	Changes/Work done	Energy type in	Energy types out	Indicators of energy transformations

Record questions about anything on which your group does not agree and anything you do not understand.

© It's About Time

3. What are the effects of each step, and what kind of energy is produced by each step?

4. How could you change the effects of each step?

5. Does light energy act more like kinetic energy or potential energy? Which answers to the other questions support your answer?

6. Does sound energy act more like kinetic energy or potential energy? Which answers to the other questions support your answer?

Explain

Working with your group, develop two claims and explanations. One claim should answer the question, "Is light energy kinetic energy or potential energy, and how can it do work?" The other should answer the question, "Is sound energy kinetic energy or potential energy, and how can it do work?" Use a different *Create Your Explanation* page for each of your claims.

After you have recorded your two claims, work with your group to develop explanation statements. Remember that an explanation has four parts: a claim, evidence, science knowledge, and an explanation statement. The evidence in each of your explanations will come from the data collected earlier in this *Learning Set,* the data recorded on your *Energy Types* pages, and your observations of the energy-transformation cartoons. The science knowledge in each will come from what you have been reading. Each of your explanation statements should tie together your claim, evidence, and science knowledge. They should help somebody reading them to understand how you came up with your explanation, and why light energy or sound energy is a type of kinetic energy or potential energy.

Communicate

Share Your Explanations

Share your explanations with the class. As a class, come to agreement on an explanation about how each factor you have identified affects light energy.

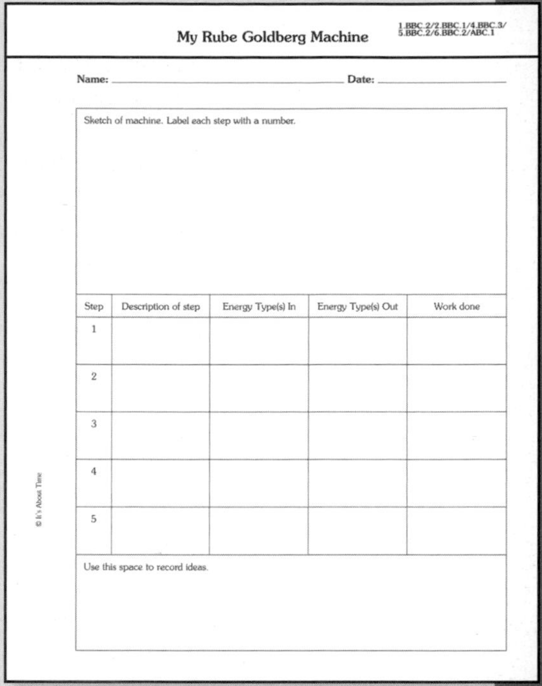

Plan Your Design

With your group, consider how you can use light energy or sound energy in your design of a machine to turn off a light. You can revisit the energy-transformation cartoons if you have trouble coming up with ideas.

Design two sets of steps that transform light energy or sound energy to turn off a light. One should begin with a step that transforms light energy or sound energy into another form of energy; the other should begin with a step that transforms another form of energy into light energy or sound energy. Both sets of steps should end with a step that turns off a light. You may use as few or as many steps in each of your designs as you want. Sketch your steps on one or more *My Rube Goldberg Machine* pages, and label your sketch to show the type of energy being transformed in each step and the type of energy that it is being transformed into. If you use any ideas you got from another group, record where you got your ideas. It is important to give credit for ideas you borrow from others.

You will need to carefully think through how the steps transfer energy to each other. Each step must be able to transfer energy smoothly to the next step, and the separate pieces of your machine need to work together to complete the task.

The sidebar shows a worksheet titled "My Rube Goldberg Machine" with fields for Name and Date, a sketch area labeled "Sketch of machine. Label each step with a number." and a table with columns: Step, Description of step, Energy Type(s) In, Energy Type(s) Out, Work done, with rows numbered 1 through 5, and a note "Use this space to record ideas."

Communicate

Plan Briefing

When it is time for you to present your designs to the class, show your sketches one at a time. For each, describe the steps and tell the class how energy is transformed from one step to another step. Try to be brief. If you are unsure about how to describe some energy transformations in your steps, ask the class for help.

Carefully observe everyone's designs, and listen to their descriptions of how energy will be transferred from step-to-step. If you think a group has not described an energy transformation well, raise your hand and ask for more information, or offer a more complete description. Remember to be courteous and respectful. If a group asks for advice, offer your ideas.

PBIS

Notice all of the different ideas your classmates have about transforming light energy and sound energy in their machines. You might want to borrow some of those ideas later. Record which group came up with each idea so you can give them credit.

Record ideas you might want to remember the bottom of your *My Rube Goldberg Machine* pages. Remember to record which group presented each idea.

Reflect

Discuss answers to these questions with your group. Be prepared to present your answers to the class.

1. Which two ideas for involving light energy or sound energy transformations in a machine to turn off a light do you like the best? Why? Which type or types of energy does each transform? Which type or types of energy is each transformed into?

2. List two things you know now about addressing the *Big Challenge* that you did not know before these presentations.

3. What else do you need to know about energy and energy transformations to address the *Big Challenge* successfully?

Add the ideas you like best to the class list of favorite steps. For each, record the type or types of energy it transforms, the type or types of energy it is transformed into, and which group suggested the step.

Update the *Project Board*

The *What does it mean for the challenge or question?* column on the *Project Board* is where you should record how learning about light energy and sound energy can help you complete the *Big Challenge*. Share what you know about light energy or sound energy that you think are important to add to the *Project Board* and your evidence for each. As a class, decide what belongs in the *What are we learning?* column. Remember to include evidence in the *What is our evidence?* column. Add any recommendations you have for addressing the *Big Challenge* to the *What does it mean for the challenge or question?* column. You must fit the pieces together to help you address the challenge. Remember to keep a record of what was added to the class *Project Board* on your own *Project Board* page.

Learning Set 5

How Do Electricity and Magnetism Provide Energy?

You may have experienced a power failure in your home. If you have, then you know what it is like getting around with the aid of a flashlight, trying to save frozen foods in the freezer and having no heat, computer, or television. If it was a long power failure, you experienced what life was like for humans for most of the past several thousand years on Earth.

Perhaps you have come to take electricity for granted. Do you know how a motor works? Would you be surprised to find out it has magnets inside? Did you know that power plants all over the world use magnetism to generate electrical energy? Would it be strange to hear a power failure called a magnetic power failure?

Electricity will be an important part of your Rube Goldberg machine. In the last step you will turn off a light. You may also have some steps that include magnetism or electricity. In this *Learning Set,* you will be conducting investigations of how electrical energy and magnetic energy are related. You will also explore indicators of electrical and magnetic energy and factors that affect how much of these types of energy are available.

5.1 Understand the Question

Think About Electrical and Magnetic Energy

When you were very young, you probably played with windup toys. These toys used elastic potential energy. You wound them up, and they moved across the floor, made sounds, or flashed lights. Many of your "toys" today are electronic. You do not have to do any work to power these devices. But think about what happens when you use an electronic device. Eventually the battery runs down. You have to plug it into a charger before you can use it again. The energy needed to recharge (more correctly, reenergize) is provided by the wall outlet.

electromagnet: a magnet that runs on electricity.

You just read that the electrical energy that comes from your outlet required magnets to generate it. You have probably used a magnet to attract a metal, but you probably did not realize that the magnet could be involved in energy transformation. You can use magnets to lift and move things, but they do not run out of energy. Have you ever played with an **electromagnet**? An electromagnet is like a magnet, but it runs on electricity.

In this *Learning Set,* you will explore electrical and magnetic energy and the connection between the two. You will begin by exploring arrangements of batteries, wires, light bulbs, and magnets. Record your observations and indicators on an *Electricity and Magnetism Observations* page.

You need electricity every day to operate devices such as computers.

When you wind up a toy, you supply the energy.

A toy that gets its electrical energy from batteries can run out of energy unless the battery is recharged.

Investigation 1: Assembly Required

Procedure

1. Examine the battery. Locate the positive (+) and negative (–) terminals of the battery. The terminals are at either end of the battery. The positive terminal has a projection, and the negative terminal has a flat base. These ends line up with metal strips or springs in a battery holder.

2. Sketch the battery on an *Electricity and Magnetism Observations* page, noting the difference in the (+) and (–) terminals. Use masking tape to label other parts of the battery you think may be important.

3. Assemble the materials so the light bulb lights up. If you are not successful at first, keep trying different arrangements of the materials until the light comes on.

Electricity and Magnetism Observations		5.1.1/5.2.1
Name: _____		Date: _____
	Electrical energy	Magnetic energy
Sketch		
Observations of forces that can do work		
Observations related to distance		
Observations related to direction		
Indicators		

© It's About Time

ENERGY

4. When you succeed in making the light bulb light up, sketch your setup on your *Electricity and Magnetism Observations* page. Label the battery terminals and how the parts are arranged.

5. Record your observations on your *Electricity and Magnetism Observations* page. Then discuss and answer the following questions with your group. Be prepared to share what you are learning with the class.

Stop and Think

1. What is the purpose of the battery in your setup?

2. What is the purpose of the wire in your setup?

3. What indicators of electrical energy did you notice?

4. What indicators of other types of energy besides light energy and electrical energy did you notice?

5. How did you know which battery terminal to connect to each wire?

Investigation 2: Testing, Testing, 1, 2, 3

Procedure

1. Place one magnet near a second magnet until you can make them repel. To repel means to force away. Use two small pieces of tape to mark the ends of the magnets that are near each other.

2. Push the magnets 1 cm closer together. Record your observations. How does it feel? Let every member of your group have a turn pushing these two ends of the magnet together.

3. Reverse one of the magnets so the unmarked end is near the marked end of the other magnet. Bring the ends of the magnets within 1 cm of each other and let go. Record your observations on another *Electricity and Magnetism Observations* page. Every member of your group should have a chance to do this.

4. Bring the marked end of one magnet near the paper clips. Observe how many paper clips can be lifted.

5. Remove the paper clips and bring the unmarked end of the magnet near the paper clips. Observe any differences.

6. Make an electromagnet by winding one of the wires around the nail. Attach one free end of the wire to the positive (+) battery terminal. Use masking tape to mark this end of the wire. Leave the other end of the wire unattached to make it easy to connect and disconnect to the negative (−) terminal. Use masking tape to mark one end of the iron nail.

7. Mess about with the electromagnet. See what it can do. Sketch what you make it do on the *Electricity and Magnetism Observations* page. Disconnect one wire from the battery when the electromagnet is not in use.

8. Reconnect the electromagnet wires to the battery, but this time, connect the marked wire to the negative (−) terminal. Try using the electromagnet again. How does what it can do now compare to what it could do in *Step 7?*

9. Record your observations on the *Electricity and Magnetism Observations* page. Then discuss and answer the following questions with your group. Be prepared to share your answers with the class.

Materials

- **2 magnets**
- **20 steel paper clips**
- **masking tape**
- **1 D-cell battery holder**
- **1 D-cell battery**
- **2 wires with alligator clips**
- **1 iron nail, 4 in.**

Stop and Think

1. How do the magnets interact with each other? To the paper clips?

2. How does the distance between the magnets affect how they interact with each other?

3. How does the distance between a magnet and the paper clips affect how they interact with each other?

4. What indicators of magnetic energy could you observe?

5. In what ways is the electromagnet like a magnet? In what ways is it different?

6. In what ways does changing the battery terminal connected to the marked wire affect the electromagnet?

Communicate

Share Your Ideas

Each group will present its observations. Show your sketches of a successful light-bulb setup. Then present your sketches of the magnets. List the indicators you found for electrical and magnetic energy. If you disagree with or do not understand another group's presentation, ask questions. Make sure you ask respectfully.

Add any new observations or indicators to your *Electricity and Magnetism Observations* page. Keep a class list on the board of the observations and indicators.

Look at the list on the board. Discuss which you think are indicators of electrical energy and which are indicators of magnetic energy. As a class, come to agreement on at least two indicators for each kind of energy.

Reflect

1. How do you think your battery, wires, and light bulb compare to the operation of a lamp connected to a wall outlet?

2. How do you think you could measure the amount of electrical energy used by the bulb?

3. What do you think electricity is?

4. What do you think magnetism is?

5. How do you think electricity and magnetism are related?

What Are the Indicators of Electrical and Magnetic Energy?

The study of electricity dates back to 600 BCE when the Greek philosopher Thales explored the properties of amber. The Greek name for amber was *elektron*. Thales wrote about rubbing wool on amber, a hardened tree sap, and then using the amber to attract feathers. Perhaps you have seen something similar. If you run a plastic comb through your hair, it can attract bits of paper.

If you walk across a room and then touch a doorknob, you sometimes see a spark jump. Early on, scientists recognized a spark as an indicator of electrical energy. They experimented with different ways of making bigger sparks. One German scientist, George Bose, used sparks from a hidden machine to shock his dinner guests! Other indicators of electrical energy they recognized were lightning, a shock from an electric eel, or the movement of a magnetized needle. However, it took quite some time for scientists to realize how these indicators might be related.

In the eighteenth century, scientists began to connect these indicators. One of the most famous achievements was Benjamin Franklin's experiment with a kite, key, and lightning. Franklin wondered if the sparks he could produce in his laboratory were related to lightning. To test this idea, he flew a kite with a key attached to it during a thunderstorm. After the thunderstorm had passed, he moved his hand near the key and received a shock. Despite what many people believe, Franklin did recognize the dangers involved, and he did take safety precautions. He held onto the kite with a length of silk and took cover in a nearby barn.

In your electricity investigation, you found that to light the bulb, it was necessary to have a complete loop with wire connecting the battery to the bulb and back again. The loop in an electric circuit must be made of material that conducts electricity, such as metal wire. A material that can **conduct electricity** allows electricity to flow through it. When two wires correctly connect the battery terminals to the two parts of the base of the bulb, the bulb lights up. You most likely discovered that it does not matter which terminal (+ or −) is connected to each wire.

conduct electricity: allow electricity to flow through a material.

You probably also found that the bulb got hot when it was connected to electricity, and you saw that the electromagnet could do work when both ends of the wire were connected to the battery. Indicators for electrical energy include light, heat released by wires, sparks, and the work done by an electromagnet. Another indicator of electrical energy is that an appliance that is running is connected to a battery or to an electrical outlet.

Indicators of magnetic energy include the ability to do work by lifting steel or iron objects, or by pushing or pulling on other magnets. In an electromagnet, thermal energy (the wires heating up) is an indicator that magnetic energy is being transformed. Another indicator that magnetic energy has been used is a battery running down when an electromagnet has been connected to it for a long time.

Magnets can attract or repel each other, depending on which way each magnet is facing. If two magnets attract, and you turn one to face the opposite way, the magnets will then repel. Both ends of a magnet will attract steel paper clips.

In June, 1752, Benjamin Franklin, along with his son William, experimented with a kite and key to see if lightning was electrical.

Magnets do not attract all metals. For example, they do not attract the copper wires. Magnets can attract through some materials, such as paper or even your finger.

Magnets can do work by lifting an object. There is a limit to how much weight a magnet can lift. This is an indicator that the magnetic energy of a magnet is not unlimited.

An electromagnet can lift paper clips only when the wires are connected to the terminals of the battery. The electromagnet behaves like a magnet because it can repel or attract other magnets. It does not attract the copper wire, and it will attract paper clips. When the wires connecting the electromagnet to the battery are reversed, the marked end changes so that it will now repel the end of a magnet that it had previously attracted.

Reflect

1. In the electrical setup of your investigation, why do you think it was important to have a complete loop with wire connecting the battery to the bulb and back again?

2. What are some indicators of the presence of electrical energy?

3. What are some indicators of the presence of magnetic energy?

4. How is an electromagnet similar to a handheld magnet you might use in your classroom? How is it different?

Conference

With your group, return to the sketch of the energy-transformation cartoon you analyzed before. Look at all of the energy sources and energy transformations. How is electrical energy shown in the cartoon? How is magnetic energy shown?

Make a list of the steps that you think might involve electrical energy or magnetic energy. Describe them on an *Energy-transformation Cartoon* page.

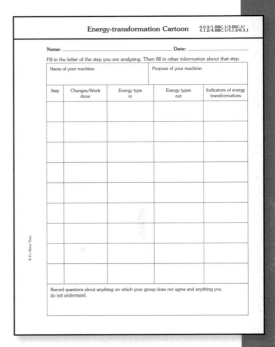

Reflect

1. What indicators have you identified for electrical energy?

2. What factors do you think affect how much electrical energy is available?

3. Do you think electricity is more like potential energy or kinetic energy? Why?

4. What indicators have you identified for magnetic energy?

5. What factors do you think affect how much magnetic energy is available?

6. Do you think magnetic energy is more like potential energy or kinetic energy? Why?

7. Add indicators for electrical energy and magnetic energy to your *Energy Types* page. You might also want to add examples. Do not add factors yet. You will add factors after you know more about what factors affect how much electrical and magnetic energy are available.

ENERGY

8. What else do you need to learn about electrical energy and magnetic energy to be able to include electricity and magnetism in the machine you are designing to turn off a light?

Update the *Project Board*

The question for this *Learning Set* is *How do electricity and magnetism provide energy?* You are just beginning to build your understanding of electrical energy and magnetic energy. Add what you think you know about these types of energy to the *What do we think we know?* column of the *Project Board*. Your class probably has some disagreements about these energy types. You may have identified some things you do not yet understand about electrical and magnetic energy. For example, you might not agree about whether electrical energy can be used to do work if no magnets are used. Add questions you need to answer to resolve those disagreements to the *What do we need to investigate?* column of the *Project Board*. Also, add questions you need to answer to include electricity and magnetic energy in your Rube Goldberg machine to the *What do we need to investigate?* column.

What's the Point?

In your investigations, you explored how electrical energy is transformed to light a bulb or to make an electromagnet. You explored the forces that magnets can exert on each other and materials that contain iron. Electrical energy and magnetic energy seem to be very closely related, but there are some differences. It is very easy to observe a magnet doing work. It is not easy to see work done when a battery is used to light a bulb.

Indicators of electrical energy include light, heat released by the wires or by a light, sparks, and work done by the electromagnet. Indicators of magnetic energy include work done to push or pull other magnets and to attract paperclips, and heating up of wires in the electromagnet.

Indicators of magnetic energy include the ability to do work by lifting steel or iron objects or by pushing or pulling on other magnets. In an electromagnet, thermal energy (the wires heating up) is an indicator that magnetic energy is being transformed. Another indicator that magnetic energy has been transformed is a battery running down when an electromagnet or some appliance has been connected to it for a long time.

5.2 Explore

What Factors Allow You To Control Electrical Energy?

One great advantage of electricity is that it enables you to precisely control devices. When you turn the volume knob on a radio to very low, you know the music will not wake a baby in the next room.

When you turn the volume knob on a radio to very low, you know the music will not wake a baby in the next room.

You may know exactly how many seconds to set the microwave for to perfectly warm a mug of cocoa. In this section, you will start to explore ways that you can control electrical energy in your Rube Goldberg machine. For your machine to function properly, you may need to carefully control the amount of electrical energy transformed in some step. You also might want to find ways to start or stop the transformation of electrical energy. The better you understand factors that affect electrical energy, the better you will be able to control it.

You may know exactly how many seconds to set the microwave for to perfectly warm a mug of cocoa.

Investigation 1: More Intense Light

Now you will try to make the light from a light bulb more intense. You may use any of the materials you have been given. You may have some left over and unused when you are finished. Record your observations on a new *Electricity and Magnetism Observations* page.

Procedure

1. Look at your successful sketch of a working battery and light-bulb setup from the previous investigation. Assemble the materials again the same way so the bulb lights up.

2. Now consider how your materials list is different here than it was for the earlier investigation. Then explore ways to make the light more intense. You may not be successful at first, but keep trying until you succeed.

3. When you succeed in making the light more intense, sketch a diagram of your setup on your *Electricity and Magnetism Observations* page. Label the battery terminals and how the parts are arranged.

Materials

- **2 D-cell battery holders**
- **2 D-cell batteries**
- **3 wires with alligator clips**
- **1 flashlight bulb**
- **1 flashlight bulb holder**
- **1 switch, SPST**
- **3 steel paper clips**
- **2 rubber bands**
- **2 magnets**
- **1 iron nail, 4 in.**

Stop and Think

Discuss and answer the following questions with your group. Be prepared to share answers with the class.

1. Why do you think the bulb is emitting more light energy this time?

2. What indicators of other types of energy besides light energy and electrical energy did you notice?

3. How does the arrangement of the battery terminals make a difference?

4. What factor affects the available amount of electrical energy?

5. How do you think you can wire the light and battery so that you can easily turn the light on and off? Why?

Investigation 2: Take Charge

Now you will try to turn the light on and off. You may use any of the materials you were given in *Investigation 1*. You may have some left over and unused when you are finished with this investigation. Record your observations on an *Electricity and Magnetism Observations* page.

Procedure

1. Reassemble your simplest battery and light setup so the bulb lights up. This will be the setup you used at the beginning of the previous investigation and earlier in the *Learning Set*.

2. Examine the materials you have available. Add items that allow you to turn the light on and off. If you are not successful at first, keep trying until you succeed.

3. Sketch a diagram of your successful setup on your *Electricity and Magnetism Observations* page. Label the battery terminals and how the parts are arranged.

4. Now disconnect your setup and try a different setup in which you use an electromagnet to turn the light on and off. If you are not successful at first, keep trying. (Hint: You might have the iron nail attract a paper clip into an "on" position. When the electromagnet is disconnected, a rubber band could return the paper clip to the "off" position.)

Stop and Think

Discuss and answer these questions with your group. Be prepared to share your answers with the class.

1. You have made a light switch. What other places have you seen switches being used?

2. What other ways might there be to make a light switch?

3. A pile driver is a machine that is used to hammer piles, or long pieces of wood, steel, or concrete, vertically into soil. To do this, a heavy rod is raised and then held in place. When the gravitational potential energy is needed, the rod is released and dropped on the head of the pile to do work. How is this similar to a light switch that stops the flow of electrical energy? What does the operation of a light switch tell

A pile driver does work by transforming gravitational potential energy.

you about whether electrical energy can be considered to be a type of kinetic energy or a type of potential energy?

Communicate

Share Your Ideas

Share with the class the way you made your light bulb glow more intensely in the first investigation. Notice how many different ways your classmates came up with for making a bulb glow more intensely. Make a class list of factors that seem to affect the intensity of light emitted by the light bulb.

Share your switches with the class. Show how your electrical switch operates and describe how your electromagnetic switch operates. Discuss your ideas about what happens when you use the switch. Share what you think about whether electrical energy is a type of kinetic energy or potential energy and why.

Reflect

1. In your home, you may have a light with a "dimmer" switch. This allows you to make the light brighter or dimmer. How do you think this switch operates?

2. In your home or at school, you may have turned on a light that has two switches, one at either end of a room. This light can be turned on or off from either switch. How could you put another switch in a third location that will also turn the light on and off?

What Is Electricity?

Electrical energy is the energy associated with charged particles such as electrons. In certain materials, usually metals, charged particles are free to move from one place to another. The flow of charged particles is called an **electric current**.

Electric current comes into a room through the electrical wires to an electrical outlet.

Electricity for a house flows from a power plant along electrical wires, through insulators and transformers, and into the house.

A current in a wire exists only if charged particles can move freely in a complete path. This pathway is called an **electric circuit**. An electric circuit is a closed path through which charged particles may flow. The circuit you built used wires to provide a path along which the charged particles could move. Any break in a circuit, no matter where it is located, will stop the flow of charged particles. If the charged particles cannot move around the path, the light bulb does not emit light.

electric current: the flow of charged particles.

electric circuit: a pathway where charged particles can move freely in a complete path.

ENERGY

The lights are part of a circuit that provides a closed path along which charged particles can flow.

electric force: the push or pull that moves charged particles.

attraction: a pulling together.

repulsion: a pushing apart.

repel: to push apart.

A switch is a simple way to open or close a circuit. When the switch is closed, the path is made complete, and charged particles can flow through the circuit. Opening the switch breaks the pathway, leaving the circuit incomplete, and the charged particles can no longer flow.

Think back to what you learned about kinetic energy. It takes work to increase an object's kinetic energy. It also takes work to start charged particles moving. The charged particles need a push (or a pull) to get going. A battery can provide this push or pull.

The push or pull that moves charged particles is called an **electric force**. An electric force is an **attraction** or **repulsion** between charged particles. The charged particles can have negative charges (–), such as electrons, or they can have positive charges (+), such as protons. Charges that have the same sign are called like charges. These like charges **repel**, or push apart. Opposite charges attract, or pull together.

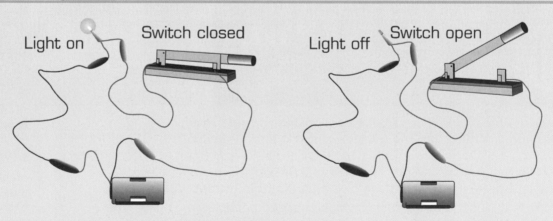

When a switch is in the "off" position (left), the circuit is open and allows electricity to flow to the light bulb. When a switch is in the "on" position (right), the circuit is closed, and the flow of electricity is stopped. The light bulb will not light.

Think back to Thales and his exploration of amber. The amber attracted the feathers. This could happen only if the charges in the amber were opposite to the charges in the feathers. One had to be positive and the other negative. A battery provides electric force in a similar way. In a battery, you can think of the positive terminal as attracting, or pulling on, the negatively charged particles. The negative terminal is repelling, or pushing away, the negatively charged particles. This is how a battery supplies the push and pull to move electric charges in a circuit.

You may have observed a number on each battery followed by a "V." This number is the **voltage**. Voltage is a measure of how much electrical energy is supplied to each charged particle. As an electric charge moves around a circuit, it picks up energy at the battery and loses or "drops" its energy at devices like light bulbs. You can compare this to eating food to obtain the energy you need to use your muscles. Just like blood carries energy to your muscles, an electric charge carries energy in a circuit. Also, note that the blood does not get used up, only the energy. In an electric circuit, the electric charge does not get used up, only its energy.

voltage: a measure of the energy for an amount of charge.

Legend	
Battery	⊣⊢⊢
Switch (open)	⌐⟋ ∘
Switch (closed)	∘—∘
Resistor	⩗⩗⩗
Wire	——

Sometimes, when you are not ready to use the energy from the food you eat, your body stores the energy as chemical energy. This gives you the potential to use the energy later. An electric charge can do that too. A battery stores electrical energy by turning it into chemical energy. When the battery is attached to a circuit, the chemical energy is turned back into electrical energy. Electric potential energy is the energy of the charge waiting to be used. In a circuit, as stored electrical potential energy is used, the stored electrical energy decreases, and the battery "runs down." A battery is just one type of voltage source. You will learn about other voltage sources later in this Unit.

ENERGY

There will be other opportunities in this *Learning Set* to build electric circuits. You will be asked to draw these circuits using specific symbols to represent the components. Examine the symbols in the picture and refer to them when you draw any electric circuits. By using a consistent set of symbols, everyone will be able to interpret your drawings and use them to build their own circuits. You have seen everything in this diagram before except the **resistor**. A resistor is an electronic device that can control the current in a circuit.

There are a few more terms that you need to be familiar with so that you can explain the electric circuits you build to others. Charged particles move better in some materials than others. These materials are called **conductors** of electricity. In a conductor, electrical charge can flow freely. The wires (inside the rubber coating) that you used in your investigations to build electric circuits are copper. This is because copper is a very good conductor of electricity.

Materials that limit the flow of electrons are called **insulators**. Some materials, like rubber, are very good insulators. For your protection, electrical cords are coated with rubber or other insulators. Materials that are good insulators are poor conductors.

Opposition to the flow of electric charge is called **resistance**. Resistance limits or reduces the current in a wire. The light bulbs in the circuits you built provide resistance to the flow of electricity. They are a type of resistor.

resistor: an electric device that can control the current in a circuit.

conductor: a material that allows free charged particles to move easily from one atom to another.

insulator: a material that limits the flow of charged particles.

resistance: opposition to the flow of electrical current.

Another factor that affects resistance in a circuit is the material used in the wiring. For example, iron has more resistance than copper. Copper is a much better conductor of electricity. A circuit that uses copper wire is more efficient than a circuit with iron wire. More charged particles will flow through the copper wire.

Porcelain and fiberglass are two materials that are used as insulators for high-voltage transmission wires. They prevent the wires carrying electricity from touching one another and causing sparks or fires.

Stop and Think

1. What is the relationship between an electric current and an electric circuit?

2. How does a switch affect the flow of charged particles in an electric circuit?

3. What is the relationship between batteries and voltage?

4. Why are copper wires in an electrical circuit often coated with rubber? Use the terms "conductor" and "insulator" in your answer.

Reflect

1. What additional indicators have you identified for electrical energy?

2. What additional factors do you think might be used to control electrical energy?

3. In what ways are electric charges similar to the opposite ends of magnets? In what ways are they different?

4. How do you think a circuit could be used to turn another circuit on and off?

Update the *Project Board*

Record what you know about electric circuits in the *What are we learning?* column of the *Project Board*. Record evidence that supports what you have learned in the *What is our evidence?* column. Record what you think about the factors that might be used to control electrical energy in the *What do we think we know?* column. If you have more questions about electrical energy, record them in the *What do we need to investigate?* column.

What's the Point?

In this section, you set up an electric circuit that allowed electricity to flow through a battery, wires, and light bulb, and back to the battery. You found that as long as the circuit is complete, or closed, the light bulb would light. The battery provided the energy for the electric charges to move in the circuit and light the bulb. The measure of the energy for a given amount of charge is called voltage. When the circuit was opened by a switch, the flow of electrical charges was interrupted, and the light bulb did not light.

5.3 Explore

How Can You Measure Electrical Energy?

In the last section, you read about several factors that can be used to control an electric current: whether a circuit is complete and the voltage. You could see whether electrical energy was being transformed by observing indicators, such as whether or not the light bulb was lit. You could estimate the amount of electrical energy present by observing the intensity of light emitted by the bulb. However, you do not know yet how to measure electrical energy.

A galvanometer measures small electric currents.

Electric current is another factor that determines the amount of electrical energy present. For a given circuit, the greater the electric current, the greater the electrical energy present.

You can measure electric current using another indicator of electrical energy that was discovered in 1819 by the Danish scientist Hans Oersted. While teaching his students about electricity, Oersted observed that a current in a wire caused a nearby compass needle to move. Within months, the first **galvanometer** was built. A galvanometer is a device used to measure small electric currents. If you insert a galvanometer into an electric circuit, you can measure the electric current in the circuit. You will be building on the work of other scientists as you build and use a simple galvanometer.

galvanometer: a device for detecting or measuring small electric currents.

Build Your Own Galvanometer

You will build a simple galvanometer and test it in an electric circuit.

Procedure

1. Take a 4-m length of #24 copper magnet wire and sand the two ends to remove any coating of paint or varnish.

2. Tape the wire about 15 cm from one end to the back of the compass.

3. While holding the compass with one hand, wrap the wire around the compass face over and over until you have about 30 turns of wire. Leave about 15 cm of the wire free at both ends.

4. Secure the other end of the wire to the back of the compass with a second piece of tape.

5. Build a circuit using the switch, battery and battery holder, wires with alligator clips, and the wires wrapped around the compass. Leave the switch open.

6. Turn the compass so that the 30 turns of wire are in line with the compass needle.

7. Close the switch and observe the compass needle. Record your observations and sketch the compass as it looks before and after the switch is closed. If the needle fails to move, it is likely that the circuit is open. Check all connections to make sure they are secure.

Materials

• **1 magnetic compass**

• **1 D-cell battery**

• **1 D-cell battery holder**

• **spool of copper magnet wire, #24, enamel-coated (4 m)**

• **1 SPST switch**

• **3 wires with alligator clips**

• **masking tape, 4 pieces, 10 cm**

• **1 piece sandpaper**

ENERGY

Stop and Think

1. What happened when you closed the switch and completed the circuit? What indicators did you observe for the presence of electrical energy in the wires?

2. You built an electromagnet earlier in this *Learning Set.* How is a galvanometer related to an electromagnet?

3. Why is it important to have a switch in the galvanometer circuit? What do you think would happen if the galvanometer were connected directly to the battery without the switch?

Reflect

1. Earlier in the *Learning Set,* you had the opportunity to observe whether a magnet might be affected by an electric circuit, but you could not observe any effect. Why do you think the effect of an electric circuit on a magnet is more observable with the setup in this investigation? What does this tell you about interpreting the results of experiments?

2. How do you think your galvanometer would react if you reversed the battery-terminal connections?

3. How do you think your galvanometer would react if the electric current were greater?

magnetic force: the force a magnet exerts on iron or another magnet.

How Does a Galvanometer Operate?

A galvanometer is a sensitive instrument that can detect and measure small amounts of electric current in circuits. It does this by responding to the magnetic forces that are generated by the electric current. The wire windings in the galvanometer become an electromagnet when there is a current.

When you explored magnets and electromagnets, you were told that the opposite ends of a magnet are called poles. You observed that either pole of a magnet could attract materials that contain iron. You also observed that a magnet can push or pull another magnet, depending on which way the poles are facing. The force that a magnet exerts on iron or another magnet is called **magnetic force**. A magnet's magnetic force is strongest near the poles of the magnet. The force becomes weaker as you move away from the poles and is weakest near the middle of the magnet.

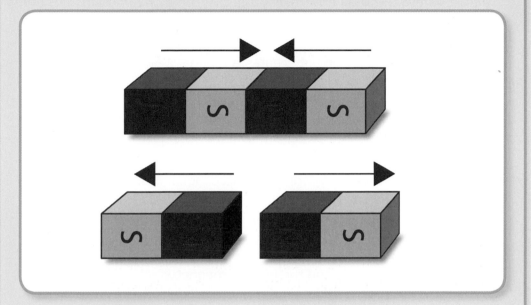

magnetic field: the strength and direction of the magnetic force a magnet exerts at each point in space; the magnetic field grows weaker as distance from the magnet increases.

If a magnet is allowed to swing freely, as in a compass, one pole will always point north. This is the north pole of the magnet. The other end, which points south, is the magnet's south pole. When two magnets are brought together, opposite poles will attract and like poles will repel. A north pole and a south pole attract. Two north poles repel, and two south poles also repel.

Although magnetic forces are strongest near the poles, they are all around the magnet and form the magnet's **magnetic field**.

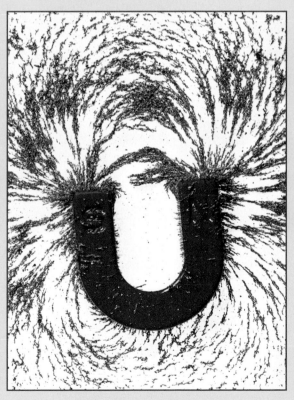

If you were to place some iron filings on a piece of paper and then placed that on top of a magnet, you could easily see the lines of the magnetic field.

ENERGY

**electro-
magnetism:**
the relationship
between
magnetism and
electricity.

If you were to place some iron filings on a piece of paper on top of a magnet, you could easily see the lines of the magnetic field. The force is greatest where the lines are closest together, near the poles.

By now you have discovered that magnetism is closely related to electricity. This relationship is called **electromagnetism**. As Oersted discovered, an electric current creates a magnetic field. When there is an electric current in a loop of wire, it acts as a weak magnet. The more loops of wire, the stronger the magnetic field. The magnetic field produced by the electric current in your galvanometer makes the magnetized needle of the compass move, indicating that electrical energy is being used.

Electromagnetism has many everyday applications. In a speaker, whether it is in your television, your headphones, or your phone, there is an electromagnet connected to a wire carrying an electric signal. The stronger the signal, the more the electromagnet responds and the louder the sound you hear. In an electric motor, electrical energy is used to make a magnet move, and the moving magnet is attached to a shaft that can do useful work. Most doorbells have an electromagnet. When you press a doorbell button, the electromagnet causes an iron rod to strike a chime.

Electromagnetism has many everyday applications, including use in telephones, electric motors, and doorbells.

Stop and Think

1. What is the role of a magnetic force in a galvanometer?

2. Why will a simple galvanometer not tell you much about the strength of the current?

3   How does electromagnetism help you understand the relationship between electricity and magnetism?

4. What additional indicators, if any, do you now know for magnetic energy?

5. What factors do you think might be used to control magnetic energy?

6. In what ways are magnetic poles similar to electric charges? In what ways are they different?

7. How do you think an electromagnet could be used to open and close a circuit?

8. What are some ways that you might use an electromagnet in a Rube Goldberg machine?

What's the Point?

Magnetic forces are similar to electric forces in many ways. Opposite poles of a magnet attract, and like poles of a magnet repel. The strength of the magnetic force exerted by a magnet decreases as distance from the magnet increases. You can observe this magnetic field by using iron filings.

The movement of the needle of a magnet by an electric current is an indicator that magnetic energy is being transformed. In building and using your own galvanometer, you experienced the relationship between electricity and magnetism. The magnetic field produced by the electric current in the galvanometer caused the compass needle to move. The ability of an electric current to produce a magnetic field is an important concept and has many practical applications in everyday life.

5.4 Investigate

Which Battery Provides More Electrical Energy?

You probably use batteries every day, and you may decide to use batteries in your Rube Goldberg machine. AAA, AA, C, D, and 9-V—these are only a few of the types of batteries you can find in a store. TV remotes, game controllers, alarm clocks, cell phones, flashlights, toys, and many other electronic devices all require different sizes of batteries. You might wonder why different devices need different batteries and what the differences are among all of these types of batteries.

Remember that batteries are a type of voltage source that gives charged particles the push they need to move through a circuit. You will now have an opportunity to use the galvanometer you made in the last section to test whether different batteries with different voltages provide different amounts of electrical energy. Your observations will help you identify some factors that determine the amount of electrical energy available from a voltage source. Knowing this will help you include electricity in your Rube Goldberg machine.

Batteries come in a variety of sizes, from tiny hearing-aid batteries to large car batteries.

Predict

Observe both of the batteries in the picture. Think about what might determine how much electrical energy a battery uses to do work on electrons in the wire. Which battery do you think will provide more electrical energy? Why?

Procedure

1. Assemble a circuit that includes your galvanometer, the D-cell battery, the resistor, and a switch. Leave the switch in the open ("off") position.

2. Move the compass so that the wire windings of the galvanometer line up in the same direction as the compass needle (in the north–south direction).

3. Close the switch to the "on" position. Record your observations of the movement of the compass needle. Make a drawing of the galvanometer showing how far the needle moved. Label the drawing as "1.5-V D-cell battery." Open the switch to the "off" position after 30 seconds because the resistor becomes hot.

4. Remove the D-cell battery from the circuit and replace it with the 6-V dry-cell battery. Leave the switch in the open ("off") position.

5. Check that the wire windings of the galvanometer line up in the same direction as the compass needle (in the north–south direction).

6. Close the switch to the "on" position. Record your observations of the needle in the galvanometer. Make a drawing of the galvanometer showing how far the needle moved. Label the drawing as "6-V dry-cell battery." Open the switch to the "off" position after 30 seconds because the resistor becomes hot.

Do not touch the resistor. It can become hot.

Materials

- galvanometer
- D-cell battery
- D-cell battery holder
- 6-V dry-cell battery
- SPST switch
- 4 wires with alligator clips
- 15 ohm, 10-W resistor

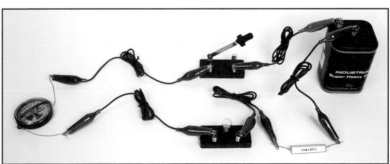

ENERGY

Analyze Your Results

Use the observations you recorded and your drawings to answer the following questions with your group. Also, read the information recorded on each battery. That information will help you answer some of these questions.

1. Which battery caused the greater movement of the compass needle?

2. Which characteristic(s) of the batteries do think are responsible for the movement of the needle in the galvanometer? Why do you think these characteristic(s) are important?

3. What one characteristic do you think is responsible for one battery causing the needle to move more than the other?

4. What other factors in the circuit may be important?

Communicate

Investigation Expo

Share the results of your investigation with the class. Everyone did the same investigation, so you will only discuss your results rather than presenting them with a poster. It will be important to make sure that all groups observed the same results. If any groups have results that conflict with yours, you should ask questions about their procedures. Make sure you ask respectfully. Discuss the reasons why their results might be different.

After sharing results, discuss the different features of each type of battery. Share the characteristics that your group thought might be responsible for the difference in how far the compass needle moved.

Each group should then contribute one characteristic they think is a factor that affects the current in a circuit. Record on the board each group's contribution.

How Does a Voltage Source Store and Provide Energy?

You already know that energy is the ability to do work. When a boulder sitting at the top of a hill is given a push, it will roll down the hill and eventually stop rolling. Where did the energy go? At the top of the hill, the boulder had gravitational potential energy. This potential energy was transformed into kinetic energy as the boulder moved down the hill. After it stopped rolling, the boulder had neither potential energy nor kinetic energy. How can this be?

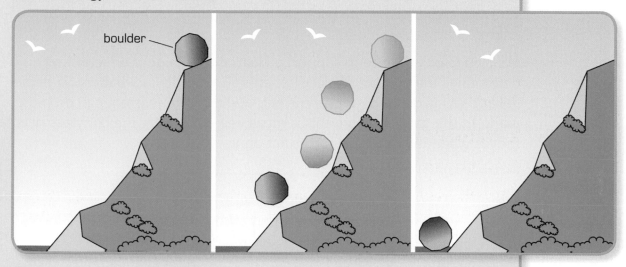

As the boulder bounced down the hill, it did work. Perhaps the work was not useful, but it fits the scientific definition of work. You could also hear the boulder, so you know that some kinetic energy was transformed into sound energy. Everything—the boulder, the ground, and the tree—was slightly warmed from collisions and friction. This is where the rest of the energy went. It was transformed into thermal energy.

A fully charged battery is like the boulder at the top of the hill. It has potential energy. As electric charges move around a circuit, they pick up energy at the battery. The greater the voltage of the battery, the more energy the charges will pick up. The voltage of the battery is a factor that controls the amount of energy the charges carry as they flow through the circuit. The rate of flow of the charges is the current.

A "dead" battery is like the boulder at the bottom of the hill. All the energy has been transformed. All of the stored energy did work or was transformed into other forms of energy, such as light energy or thermal energy.

ENERGY

Stop and Think

1. How is a fully charged battery like a boulder sitting on the top of a hill?

2. How is a "dead" battery like a boulder sitting at the bottom of a hill?

What's the Point?

There are many different batteries available for all kinds of uses. They vary in size, shape, color, and voltage. The voltage of the battery determines how much electrical energy is delivered to each charged particles by the battery. The size and shape of the batteries have no effect on how much electrical energy is available.

You collected evidence to support a claim that voltage is a factor that determines the amount of electrical energy available in a battery. A higher voltage will produce a greater current, and a greater current can do more work. In the galvanometer, this is measured by how far the compass needle moves when the magnetic forces act on it.

A historical galvanometer.

5.5 Explore

How Can One Voltage Source Light More Than One Light Bulb?

At the beginning of this *Learning Set,* you assembled an electric circuit. You were able to produce a flow of charged particles from one terminal of a battery, through the wires and the light, and back to the opposite terminal of the battery. This worked just fine for you. But what if you had to light a whole string of lights? They would look quite unattractive if every bulb had to have its own battery! In this section, you will investigate how to light a whole set of devices from one source of energy. When you can do this, you will understand something about how electricity is used in buildings. A source of electrical energy is brought to the building, and it is used to operate everything in the building. This may be useful in building your Rube Goldberg machine.

It would not be very efficient if every light on this bridge had to have its own source of energy!

Predict

Using what you know about electric currents and circuits, draw a sketch showing what you think a circuit would have to look like to light more than one light.

Light Two Bulbs With One Voltage Source

Imagine that you are given the task of designing lighting for a school dance. You must use one voltage source to light a whole string of decorative lights. How will you do it?

Materials

- 2 D-cell batteries
- 2 D-cell battery holders
- 2 small light bulbs
- 2 light-bulb holders
- 5 wires with alligator clips
- SPST switch

Procedure

1. Using the available materials, assemble a circuit that will light two light bulbs using only one voltage source. You may not need to use all of the materials to assemble a circuit that will work.

2. When you have a circuit that lights two light bulbs, make a sketch of your circuit.

3. Now turn the circuit off, remove one of the bulbs, and turn it back on again.

4. Observe what happens to the other bulb, and record your observations.

Analyze Your Data

1. In your circuit sketch, add arrows to indicate how you think the charged particles are moving. The arrows should start from one battery terminal, pass through the wires and bulb, and end up at the opposite battery terminal.

2. What do you think happens to the electric current when you remove one bulb?

3. What changes did you observe in the bulb that remains in the circuit? Suppose the removed bulb were put back into the circuit. What do you think would happen?

4. How much of the current do you think goes to each of the bulbs in your circuit? Why?

Communicate

Investigation Expo

When it is your group's turn, demonstrate the circuit you assembled. Then describe how you assembled the circuit and the path of the electric current. Your sketches should make this easy to show.

Make sure you answer all the following questions in your presentation:

1. How would you describe the circuit you built?

2. What are some advantages to using your circuit? What are some disadvantages?

3. How might your circuit be useful in an everyday application?

As you are watching the presentations, notice the intensity of the lights. How many types of circuits has the class built? How is the intensity of the lights different in each type of circuit?

Reflect

1. How many different types of circuits did the groups build? Sketch each one. Draw arrows to show how the current moves through each one. You might want to construct the types of circuits you did not construct previously.

2 For each type of circuit, what are its advantages and disadvantages?

3. How might each be useful in different everyday applications?

4. Why do you think the intensity of the lights differs in each type of circuit? The arrows you sketched for each one might help you answer this question.

series circuit: a closed circuit in which all parts are connected end to end to provide a single path for the current.

parallel circuit: a closed circuit in which the current divides into two or more paths before recombining to complete the circuit.

Series and Parallel Circuits

Perhaps you eat lunch in the school cafeteria. Some cafeterias have a single serving line that everyone must go through one by one. If even one person is slow, the entire line slows down. Some of you built this type of circuit. The two light bulbs were connected in a single pathway. The charges must flow from the battery to one light bulb, then through the other, and then back to the battery. This type of circuit is called a **series circuit**.

In a series circuit, as long as electrical energy is available and the circuit is complete, the charged particles keep flowing, and both bulbs remain lit. When one bulb is removed, the circuit is not complete, and the bulb that remains in the circuit is no longer lit.

In many cafeterias, there are two food lines so people can choose which path to take. Both lines move independently. A slow person in one line does not affect the flow of people in the other line. This is like the other type of circuit that some groups built, called a **parallel circuit**. In a parallel circuit, both bulbs are attached directly to the battery. Each bulb has its own pathway, and charged particles can leave the battery, flow through the bulb, and then return to the battery without going through the other bulb. When one pathway is broken by the removal of one bulb, the other pathway still provides a complete circuit, so the second bulb remains lit.

In a parallel circuit, the devices all receive the same amount of voltage. That is why the bulbs were not dimmed in your parallel circuits. In a series circuit, some of the energy is transformed as it passes through each bulb. The electrical energy the charged particles started with is divided equally between the two lights, so the lights are less bright than in a parallel circuit.

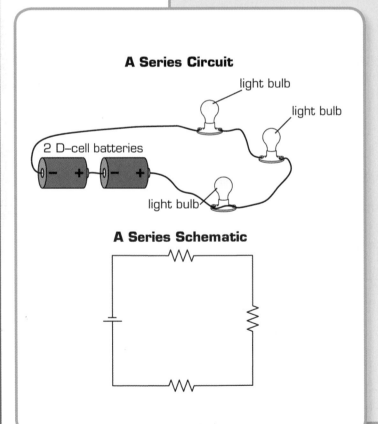

A Series Circuit

light bulb

light bulb

2 D–cell batteries

light bulb

A Series Schematic

In nearly all homes, offices, and schools, the electric outlets and lights are connected in parallel circuits. This way, outlets that are not being used will not break the path for charged particles flowing to outlets that are in use.

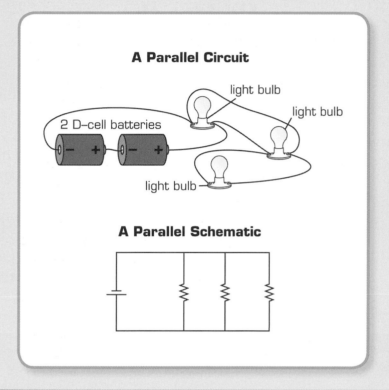

A Parallel Circuit

light bulb

light bulb

2 D–cell batteries

light bulb

A Parallel Schematic

Stop and Think

1. What is the difference between a parallel circuit and a series circuit?

2. What are the advantages of each type of circuit?

3. What are the disadvantages of each type of circuit?

4. How does the type of circuit you use affect the amount of energy available to devices powered by the circuit?

5. Add what you know about indicators for electrical energy and factors that affect how much electrical energy is available to the appropriate spaces in your *Energy Types* page.

Energy Types	0.0.1/1.2.2/2.2.2/2.5.2/2.6.2/ 3.2.2/3.6.2/4.5.2/5.1.3/5.5.1

Name: _____ Date: _____

Type of energy	Indicators that this type is being transformed	Factors that affect the amount of energy

© It's About Time

6. What do you still need to know about electrical energy to be able to include it in your Rube Goldberg machine?

Update the Project Board

You now know a lot about electrical energy and electric circuits and how to control the amount of electrical energy available to a device connected to a circuit. Record what you know about electrical energy in the *What are we learning?* column of the *Project Board.* Don't forget to add evidence to the *What is our evidence?* column. If you have new questions about electrical energy, add them to the *What do we need to investigate?* column. Add the new entries on the class *Project Board* to your own *Project Board.*

Design a Rube Goldberg machine to turn off a light				
What do we think we know?	What do we need to investigate?	What are we learning?	What is our evidence?	What does it mean for the challenge or question?

What's the Point?

Your investigations showed that there are different ways the parts of a circuit can be connected. A series circuit has only one path for charged particles to take. A parallel circuit has more than one path for the charged particles to take. How a circuit is connected is another factor that determines the electrical energy available to a device.

5.6 Explore

How Is Electrical Energy Produced?

It can be frustrating to be talking on a cell phone, listening to your favorite song, or playing a fun game when your battery goes dead. Think about what that means. It means that the battery runs out of energy. That might make you think about how the battery gets energy in the first place.

When batteries run out, usually there is another voltage source you can use to operate your electronic gadget, or you might have a device you can use to recharge (reenergize) the battery. Either of these requires an *AC* adapter that can be plugged into an electrical outlet. You know that an electric outlet can be counted on to deliver all the energy you need to run your gadget or reenergize its batteries. But where does the energy in an electric outlet come from, and what happens to this energy when there is a power failure?

Electricity in the electrical outlets in your home and other buildings is produced by a **generator**. A generator transforms mechanical energy into electrical energy, using the motion of a magnet inside a coil of wire. Both the electric outlet in a wall and a battery are sources of voltage. You already know that the amount of voltage in a voltage source determines how much electrical energy is available. To help you better understand voltage sources, your group will make a battery. Then you will observe a demonstration showing the construction and operation of a simple generator.

> **generator:** a device that converts mechanical energy into electrical energy using the motion of a magnet inside a coil of wire.

Wires come into your house and into an electric outlet.

ENERGY

Build a Battery

You will make your battery from lemons and two different metals. Then you will test the battery with a galvanometer and with headphones. One metal you will use is copper. The other is a galvanized nail. A galvanized nail is a steel nail coated with the metal zinc.

Materials

- 2 large, fresh lemons
- 2 galvanized nails, 2 in.
- 2 pennies
- 1 galvanometer
- 1 set stereo headphones
- 3 wires with alligator clips
- 1 plastic knife
- safety glasses

Procedure

1. Put on your safety glasses. Using the plastic knife, make two slits in one of the lemons, about 2.5 cm (about 1 in.) apart.

2. Push a galvanized nail about halfway into one of the slits. Insert the penny into the other slit, about halfway in. It is very important that the nail and the coin do not touch.

Insert the zinc nail in this slit   Insert the penny in this slit

3. To test your lemon battery, you will use the galvanometer that you built earlier. Using the alligator clip wires, connect one wire from the galvanometer to the penny. Connect the other galvanometer wire to the galvanized nail. Observe and record the movement of the needle in the galvanometer. Then disconnect the galvanometer. Record your observation.

4. Put on the headphones. Using the two wires with alligator clips, connect the headphone plug to the lemon battery. Typically, there are three sections on the plug. Try various combinations until you hear a click through the headphones. This click indicates the presence of electrical energy. Once you hear the click, remove the headphones from the circuit.

5. Increase the voltage of your circuit by using two lemons, two coins, and two nails. Connect the first lemon battery in series with the second lemon. Test this two-battery combination with your galvanometer. Observe how much the needle in the galvanometer moves. Then disconnect the galvanometer, and record this observation.

Stop and Think

1. What indicators of the presence of electrical energy did you observe?

2. What do you think would happen if you used two nails to make the battery instead of a nail and a penny? Why do you think this?

3. How did the galvanometer move when you connected the two lemon batteries in series as compared to when you used only one lemon battery?

4. What factors affected the amount of electrical energy available?

5. What do you predict would happen if you connected the two lemon batteries in a parallel circuit rather than in a series circuit? Why do you think this? If you have time, you may try this out.

Demonstration: Build a Generator

A generator transforms mechanical energy into electrical energy. You can make a generator by moving a wire through a magnetic field. Electric current will be generated from work done by kinetic energy. Your teacher will build a generator in class. As you observe the generator being built and what it does, think about the purpose of the magnet-wire coil.

Observe

Note the parts and placement of parts as your teacher builds a simple generator.

Materials

- 1 small, open-ended cardboard box, 13 cm x 9 cm
- 8 Alnico magnets
- 1 large iron nail, about 10 cm (4 in.)
- sandpaper
- masking tape
- 1 compass galvanometer
- 300 ft enamel-coated magnet wire, #30
- optional: 2 alligator clips
- 1 student galvanometer, +/- 500 µA

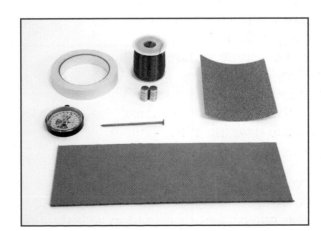

ENERGY

Procedure

1. The generator will be housed in a small cardboard box. Draw a large "X" from corner to corner on the two wider sides of the cardboard box. In the center of one "X," push the nail through the box and through the center of the other "X." It should go completely through the box, passing through two walls. Wiggle the nail around to make the hole slightly bigger. Hold the nail and spin the box. The box should be able to spin freely around the nail.

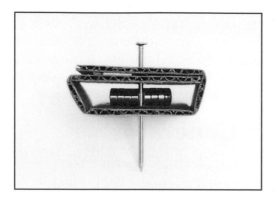
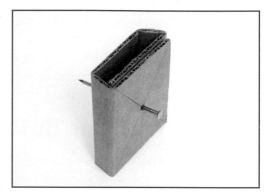

2. With the nail through the box, stack four magnets and attach them magnetically to the nail inside the box. Attach the other four magnets in the same way on the exact opposite side of the nail. The eight magnets should form a straight line and should be as close as possible to the inside walls of the box without touching the box.

3. Spin the nail with the magnets on it. The nail and magnets should be able to spin freely without the magnets hitting the walls of the box. Keep the nail and magnets inside the box during the next step.

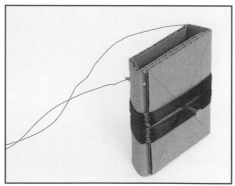

4. Leaving a 1-m wire lead, tape one end of the magnet wire to the outside of the box. Wind the remainder of the magnet wire (about 200 turns) around the center of the box, leaving a 1-m length hanging. Tape this end to the box also. You will have about 200 turns of wire with two 1-m leads hanging off. The nail with magnets should still turn freely inside the box.

5. Sand about ½ in. on both ends of the magnet wire to remove the enamel coating. Attach the two leads from the generator to the two leads from the compass galvanometer by twisting them together. The distance between the generator and the galvanometer must be at least 3 ft so the magnets do not affect the compass galvanometer.

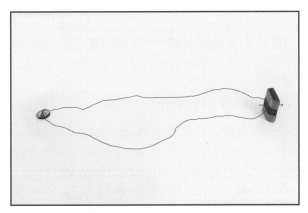

6. Spin the nail so the magnets are moving. Spin the nail fast and then slow. Observe and record the movement of the needle in the galvanometer.

7. As an option, a student galvanometer may be introduced to the circuit, using two alligator clip leads. This tool will provide a more sensitive and more accurate measuring device.

8. When the generator is completed, it will be connected to a galvanometer like the one you built and spun slowly. Record your observations on paper.

9. Next, the generator will be spun very fast. Record your observations on paper.

10. The generator will then be connected to a compass galvanometer. As the generator is spun slowly, record your observations on paper.

11. The generator will be spun fast. Record your observations on paper.

ENERGY

Stop and Think

1. What is the purpose of the magnet-wire windings in the generator?

2. What did you observe on the student galvanometer when the generator was spun slowly? What did you observe when the generator was spun quickly?

3. What did you observe on the compass galvanometer when the generator was spun slowly? What did you observe when the generator was spun quickly?

4. What factors do you think affect the amount of electrical energy in a generator?

5. How do you think you might generate more voltage, or electrical energy, to move the galvanometer even more? Why?

Reflect

With your group, make a list of factors that affect the amount of available electrical energy on your *Lemon Battery and Generator Exploration* page.

Also list any features that the battery and generator have in common, and the advantages and disadvantages of each device.

Then answer these questions. Be prepared to discuss the answers with the class.

1. How are a battery and a generator different? How are they similar?

2. How is the lemon battery similar to batteries you use in everyday devices? What are some disadvantages of your lemon battery compared to batteries you buy in a store?

3. What are some advantages and disadvantages of a generator compared to a battery?

Lemon Battery and Generator Exploration   5.6.1

Name: _____ Date: _____

	Lemon battery	Generator
Factors affecting amount of energy generated		
Construction difficulties		
Advantages		
Disadvantages		
Common features		

© It's About Time

How Do Batteries and Generators Compare?

Up until now, you probably did not have any experience that would help you understand how batteries store chemical energy. The batteries that you are most familiar with, such as AA, C, or D batteries, are made with **electrochemical cells**. An electrochemical cell is a device used to generate electrical energy through chemical reactions inside a small enclosed space (cell). When more energy is needed, two or more electrochemical cells are connected together to make a battery. The batteries you buy in a store have a set of electrochemical cells in them. However, to keep things simpler, they are just called a battery.

All batteries have two terminals. You have seen that one terminal is positive (+) and the other terminal is negative (–). Chemical reactions occur at each battery terminal. At the negative terminal, a reaction releases charged particles, but only if the circuit is completed and the particles can flow to the opposite terminal. When the chemicals that provide the charged particles have been used up, the battery is "dead."

Because the chemical reactions in a battery cannot begin until the terminals are connected by a circuit, batteries can store energy for a long time. Once the terminals are connected and the circuit is complete, the reactions start and produce an electric current. The battery is portable and inexpensive. However, its energy does not last long, and it can do only small amounts of work.

electrochemical cell: a device that generates electrical energy using chemical reactions inside a small enclosed space (cell).

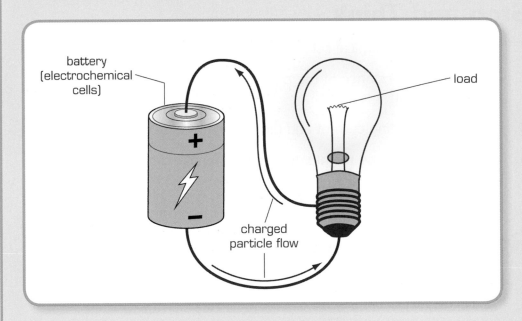

battery (electrochemical cells)

load

charged particle flow

ENERGY

direct current (DC): an electric current that flows in only one direction.

alternating current (AC): an electric current that reverses direction at a regular rate.

Direct and Alternating Current

Batteries work well for many purposes, but they are not the most efficient means of producing electric current. Batteries produce electrical current that moves in only one direction, from the negative (–) terminal to the positive (+) terminal. This is called **direct current (DC)**. Most portable electrical equipment operates on direct current. Generators can produce direct current or **alternating current (AC)**, depending on how they are designed. In an alternating current, the current constantly reverses direction. Describing how an alternating current is produced is fairly complicated. You will learn more about this in later science courses, or you may wish to read about it on your own. The type of current in the wall outlets of homes in the United States is AC.

Direct current is not different electrically from alternating current, other than it flows in the same direction all the time. Appliances can be designed to run on either direct or alternating current. The big advantage of alternating current is that it is easy to change the voltage. This makes it easier for power companies to transmit large amounts of electrical energy over long distances. You can read about how this is done in the *More to Learn, Bringing Power to the Neighborhood*.

Stop and Think

1. How do electrochemical cells function within a battery?

2. What is the importance of the positive terminal on a battery? What about the negative terminal?

3. How do alternating current and direct current differ?

4. Where in your house might you find alternating current? List three places.

5. Where in your house might you find direct current? List three places.

Reflect

1. Do you think electric energy is more like potential energy or kinetic energy? Why?

2. Do you think magnetic energy is more like potential energy or kinetic energy? Why?

3. Go back to your *Energy Types* page and record what you now know about the indicators for electric and magnetic energy, the factors that affect how much of each is available, examples, and your decision about whether each is a type of potential energy or a type of kinetic energy.

Update the *Project Board*

You now know a lot about how to generate and store electric energy, and what affects the amount of electrical energy that is available. You also know a lot about how magnetic energy is used to produce electric energy and how electric energy can produce magnetic energy. Add what you now know to the *What are we learning?* column of the *Project Board*. Do not forget to add evidence for each of your entries to the *What is our evidence?* column. If you have more questions for the *What do we need to investigate?* column, add them now. Make sure your personal *Project Board* matches the class *Project Board*.

What's the Point?

You observed two types of voltage sources—a battery and a generator. Each type of source has advantages and disadvantages. Large generators provide much more energy than batteries. The biggest disadvantage of a generator, however, is the cost of building one and the need for a reliable source of energy to spin the generator.

A battery produces direct current (DC), which flows in only one direction. Generators can produce either direct current or alternating current (AC). An alternating current reverses direction. This is the type of current available through the electrical outlets in most homes in North America.

It is important to remember that both a battery and a generator operate by transforming one type of energy into another. The electrical energy produced by a battery comes from chemical potential energy. When this chemical energy is transformed, charged particles can move through a circuit to do work. In a generator, the kinetic energy of spinning the magnets you observed is transformed into electrical energy. You will learn more about energy transformations in the next *Learning Set*. Energy transformations will be important in the Rube Goldberg machine you are designing.

More to Learn

Bringing Power to the Neighborhood

The generator you observed produced a voltage of about 1 V or less. This is enough voltage to move the needle on your galvanometer, but it is not enough to generate the electrical energy needed for your home. Household circuits usually use a voltage of 120 V. Electricity for your home and town comes from large power plants, usually many miles from where people live.

The generators in power plants are enormous, but they work on the same principle as the generator you saw in the demonstration. This generator was turned by hand. In a power plant, the generators are turned by **turbines**. A turbine rotates as a fluid flows by it. The fluid can be water, wind, or steam. The kinetic energy of the spinning turbines is then transformed into electrical energy. As the turbines rotate, they move coiled wire through a powerful magnetic field created by huge magnets. Just as an electric current was produced in the generator you observed, electric current is produced in the wire, but at much higher voltages—between 2300 V and 30,000 V.

turbine: a machine with a series of spinning blades in which the kinetic energy of a moving fluid (water, air, or steam) is transformed into kinetic energy of the turbine.

The kinetic energy of the large, spinning turbines in power plants transfers energy to generators which then transform that energy into electricity.

The electric current produced by generators leaves the power plant through power lines. As the current leaves the power plant, its voltage is increased by **transformers** to between 120,000 V and 500,000 V. A transformer can increase or decrease the voltage of an AC current.

The high voltages in power lines are dangerous, but necessary, so that electric current can be transmitted long distances with very little energy loss. If you see a sign that says, "High Voltage—Keep Away," do not attempt to go near it. The voltage really is very high and very dangerous. When the electric current reaches communities, the voltage is decreased by transformers. It is lowered even more, to 120 V, as it enters your home.

Electricity from power plants first travels through transformers on power poles before it enters your house. The wires in a circuit breaker box send electricity to different parts of your house.

transformer: an electric device by which alternating current of one voltage is changed to another voltage, either greater or smaller.

circuit breaker: a switch that opens a circuit when electric current reaches an unsafe level.

Electricity coming into your home goes through a meter that measures how much energy you use. From the meter, the wire leads into a **circuit breaker** box. Several separate circuits leave from this point, branching out to different areas of the building. One circuit may run to your kitchen. The wires making up this circuit go to wall outlets and light switches. These parallel circuits make it possible to leave an appliance off, or an outlet unused, without breaking the path of charged particles going to other outlets and appliances.

However, circuits can become overloaded. If the appliances on a circuit require more current than the circuit can handle, the wires will heat

power distribution grid (power grid): a system of high-tension cables by which electrical energy is distributed throughout a region.

blackout: a temporary cutoff of electrical energy in a region.

up. This can be a fire hazard, because heated wires can ignite building materials in the walls. This is what the circuit breaker is for. When the current in the wires is too high, the circuit breaker automatically opens the circuit so that charged particles cannot flow. Power to that circuit is discontinued until the circuit breaker is reset.

As you can imagine, delivering electrical energy to large populations can be complex. Power is delivered over large areas through **power distribution grids**. Sometimes these grids can become overloaded and shut down, resulting in a widespread **blackout**. This happens at times of peak energy usage, for example during a heat wave when many people have their air conditioners on all day.

Both direct current and alternating current can be used to operate electrical equipment. The equipment just needs to be designed to run on the current available. Alternating current was chosen in North America, because when large power companies were being established in the early twentieth century, AC systems were more reliable than DC systems. The problems in delivering direct current to widespread areas have been corrected. However, North American power companies continue to supply AC because the systems are already in place. In most of Europe, the current that is supplied to homes is DC.

Stop and Think

1. How do turbines in power plants work?

2. How do transformers and circuit breakers affect the electricity you use in your house?

3. What causes a blackout of power?

People take electricity for granted until there is a blackout. During the blackout of August, 2003, the lights went out across the Northeast. The picture on the left was taken by satellite 20 h before the blackout. The picture on the right was 7 h after the blackout.

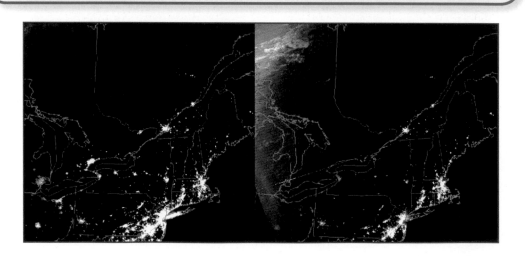

Project-Based Inquiry Science

Learning Set 5

Back to the Big Challenge

Design a Rube Goldberg Machine to Turn Off a Light

The *Big Challenge* you are working on for this Unit is *Design a Rube Goldberg machine to turn off a light*. You have designed many different sequences of steps to turn off a light. Most likely, none of your steps involved electricity or magnetism. You now know enough about electrical energy and magnetic energy to imagine how these might be transformed in your machine. However, before doing that, you will think once more about whether electrical energy and magnetic energy are kinetic energy or potential energy and how these types of energy can be transformed to do work.

Reflect

To help you think about electrical energy and magnetic energy, you will examine the energy-transformation cartoons again from the Unit *Introduction*. Identify the steps that involve electrical energy or magnetic energy in your group's cartoon. Then, for each, answer these questions. Be prepared to share your answers with the class.

The electromagnet used in a railway yard to lift heavy iron rails transforms both electrical and magnetic energy.

1. How do you know the step involves electrical energy or magnetic energy? What are the indicators? (You may have to search carefully to find indicators of magnetic energy.)

2. How does the step transform electrical energy or magnetic energy?

3. What are the effects of each step, and what kind of energy is produced by each step?

ENERGY

4. How could you change the effects of each step?

5. Is electrical energy more like kinetic energy or more like potential energy? Which answers to the other questions support your answer?

6. Is magnetic energy more like kinetic energy or more like potential energy? Which answers to the other questions support your answer?

Explain

Working with your group, develop two claims and explanations. One claim should answer the questions, "Is electrical energy kinetic energy or potential energy?" and "How can electrical energy be transformed to do work?" The other should answer the questions, "Is magnetic energy kinetic energy or potential energy?" and "How can magnetic energy be transformed to do work?" Use a different *Create Your Explanation* page for each claim.

After you have recorded your claims, work with your group to develop two explanations. Remember that an explanation has four parts: a claim, evidence, science knowledge, and an explanation statement. The evidence in each of your explanations will come from the data collected earlier in this *Learning Set* and your observations of the cartoons. The science knowledge in each will come from what you have been reading. Each explanation statement should tie together your claim, evidence, and science knowledge. The statement should help somebody reading it to understand why each type of energy is kinetic or potential. Make sure your statements include information about the role of electric forces or magnetic forces in doing work.

Create Your Explanation

3.BBC.2/4.2.1/4.5.3/ 4.6.1/4.BBC.2/5.BBC.1

Name:_____ Date:_____

Use this page to explain the lesson of your recent investigations.

Write a brief summary of the results from your investigation. You will use this summary to help you write your explanation.

Claim—a statement of what you understand or a conclusion that you have reached from an investigation or a set of investigations.

Evidence—data collected during investigations and trends in that data.

Science knowledge—knowledge about how things work. You may have learned this through reading, talking to an expert, discussion, or other experiences.

Write your explanation using your **Claim, Evidence** and **Science knowledge** from above.

© It's About Time

Plan Your Design

With your group, consider how you can transform electrical energy or magnetic energy in your design of a machine to turn off a light. You can revisit the energy-transformation cartoons if you have trouble coming up with ideas.

Design two sets of steps that transform electrical energy or magnetic energy in a machine that turns off a light. One should begin with a step that transforms electrical energy or magnetic energy; the other should begin with a step that produces electrical energy or magnetic energy. Both sets of steps should end with a step that turns off a light. Your machine needs to have at least three steps in it. You may also want to include a circuit connected to a source of electrical energy. It would be good if you can power two steps of your machine with the same source of electrical energy.

Sketch your steps, and label your sketch to show the type of energy being transformed in each step and the type of energy that it is transformed into. If you borrowed some of your ideas from other groups, record where you got your ideas. It is important to give credit when you borrow ideas from others.

You will need to carefully think through how the steps transfer energy to each other. Each step must be able to transfer energy smoothly to the next step, and the separate pieces of your machine need to work together to complete the task.

My Rube Goldberg Machine — 1.BBC.2/2.BBC.1/4.BBC.3/5.BBC.2/6.BBC.2/ABC.1

Name: _____ Date: _____

Sketch of machine. Label each step with a number.

Step	Description of step	Energy Type(s) In	Energy Type(s) Out	Work done
1				
2				
3				
4				
5				

Use this space to record ideas.

© It's About Time

Communicate

Plan Briefing

When it is time for you to present your designs to the class, show your sketches one at a time. For each, describe the steps, and tell the class how energy is transferred from one step to another. Try to be brief. If you are unsure about how to describe some energy transformations in your steps, ask the class for help.

Observe everyone's designs carefully, and listen to their descriptions of how energy will be transferred from step to step. If you think a group has not described an energy transformation well, raise your hand and ask for more information or offer a more complete description. Remember to be courteous and respectful. If a group asks for advice, offer your ideas.

Notice all of the different ideas your classmates have about transforming energy and about including electrical energy and magnetic energy in their machines. You might want to borrow some of those ideas later. Record which group came up with each idea so you can give them credit.

Record ideas you might want to remember on the bottom of your *My Rube Goldberg Machine* page. Remember to record which group presented each idea.

Reflect

Discuss answers to these questions with your group. Be prepared to share your answers with the class.

1. Which two ideas for transforming electrical energy or magnetic energy do you like the best? Why? Which type or types of energy does each transform? Which type or types of energy does each transform into?

2. List two things you know now about addressing the *Big Challenge* that you did not know before these presentations.

3. What else do you need to know about energy and energy transformations to address the *Big Challenge* successfully?

Add the ideas you like best to the class list of favorite steps. For each, record the type or types of energy it transforms, the type or types of energy it transforms into, and which group suggested the step.

Update the *Project Board*

The *What does it mean for the challenge or question?* column on the *Project Board* is where you should record how learning about electricity and magnetism can help you complete the *Big Challenge.* Share what you know about electrical energy and magnetic energy that you think are important to add to the *Project Board* and your evidence for each. As a class, decide what belongs in the *What are we learning?* column. Remember to include evidence in the *What is our evidence?* column. You must fit the pieces together of what was added to the class *Project Board* on your own *Project Board* page. Add any recommendations you have for addressing the *Big Challenge* to the *What does it mean for the challenge or question?* column.

Learning Set 6

How Is Energy Transformed?

Energy transformations are important in your daily life. For example, think about the energy transformations involved in blow-drying your hair. Electrical energy has been transported a long distance from a power plant to your home, and its voltage has been transformed several times along the way. The hair dryer transforms electrical energy to produce heat and the motion of air. The hair dryer has a fan that moves air. The fan's motor uses magnets to transform electrical energy into kinetic energy of the fan blades. The blades of the fan exert a force that does work to increase the kinetic energy of the air. The electrical energy to run the hair dryer travels from the outlet through wires into the dryer.

The electrical energy to operate your hair dryer was generated at a power plant, perhaps one that burns coal as fuel. In a coal-burning power plant, coal is burned to produce heat. The coal's chemical energy is potential energy. It takes some thermal energy to start coal burning. (You know this if you have ever started a charcoal fire for a barbecue.) Once the coal is burning, it releases thermal energy, which is used to heat water. As the water's thermal energy increases, its particles move faster, and the water turns to steam. The steam expands, which means it can do work to turn a turbine. The kinetic energy of the turbine is transferred to wire coils that spin in a magnetic field inside a generator. The generator transforms the kinetic energy of the turbine into electrical energy that is sent to your home.

The electrical energy you use in your house is generated in a power plant.

If you wanted to trace the energy back even farther, you would start with the Sun. Photons have been traveling through empty space from the Sun to Earth for billions of years. The photons struck the leaves of plants, and their energy was transformed in a chemical reaction to make sugars and starches, which store chemical energy. Over millions of years, the remains of plants were converted by heat and pressure into coal, which is a more concentrated form of chemical energy.

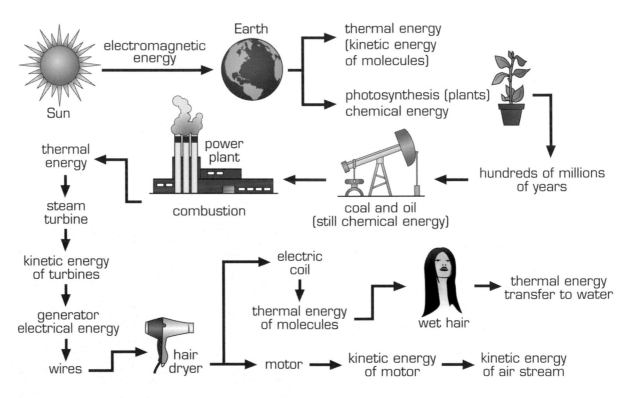

Many transformations of energy occur before it is used in your home.

Looking at this chain of events, you may once again recognize a complex process that is similar to a Rube Goldberg machine. One important difference, however, is that a Rube Goldberg machine is entertaining because it does not transform energy efficiently. Human goals are driven by the need to make energy transformations more efficient. In this *Learning Set,* you are going to explore how energy can be transformed efficiently from one type to another and what can happen to energy when it is transformed.

6.1 Understand the Question

Think About Energy Transformation

When you stretch a rubber band, it has elastic potential energy. You know this because of the indicators you can observe. The material is elastic and is deformed as it is stretched. As long as you hold the rubber band in this position, it has elastic potential energy. As soon as it is released, you see motion, an indicator of kinetic energy. The potential energy in the stretched rubber band is transformed into kinetic energy when you let go of one side of the band.

Energy transformations constantly happen all around you. They occur in your body every time you transform energy from food to take a breath or play sports. Sometimes one type of energy is transformed into more than one other type of energy. When you strike a match, for example, chemical energy is transformed into light energy, sound energy, and thermal energy.

To help you understand energy transformations better, you are going to take a closer look at some familiar examples of energy transformations. You will identify the type(s) of energy before the transformation and the types of energy after the transformation.

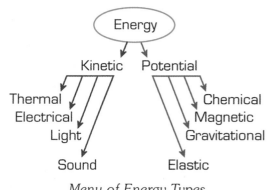

Menu of Energy Types.

When a match is lit, how many types of energy are transformed, and how many are they transformed into?

ENERGY

Get Started

You will begin by revisiting four devices that you analyzed earlier in the Unit. When you first looked at them, you were looking for indicators of the type of energy that was present. This time, you will be looking for ways in which one type of energy is transformed into other types as the device operates. You may observe more than one type of energy *before* and *after* each transformation.

Each group in the class will be assigned one of the following devices: a xylophone, a lemon battery, a toaster, or a flashlight.

A xylophone.

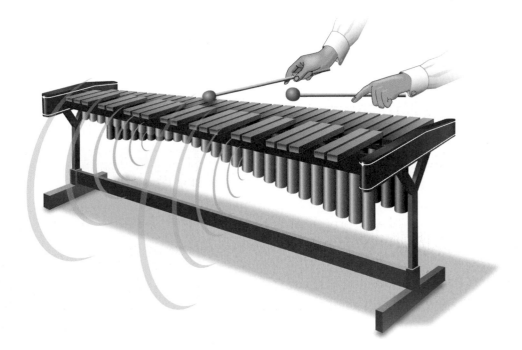

A lemon battery.

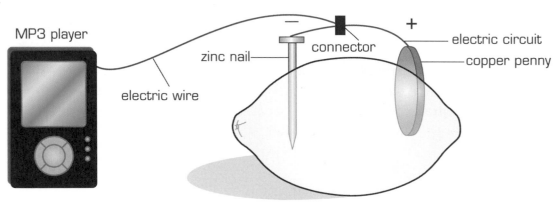

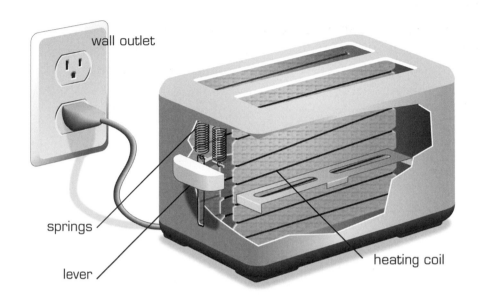

A toaster.

A flashlight.

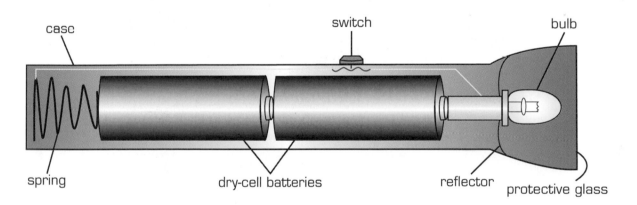

Work with your group members to identify the types of energy present in each part of the device before it operates. Then identify the types of energy in each part of the device after it operates. Make a table similar to the one below for recording your thoughts and observations as you examine the picture of your device. For each type of energy you identify, record its indicators.

Energy Transformations				
Picture	Energy before		Energy after	
	Energy type	Indicators	Energy type	Indicators

Analyze Your Data

1. Look at your table one row at a time. Which types of energy are listed in both the *Energy before* column and the *Energy after* column? Do you think the amount of this type of energy has changed? Why or why not?

2. Look at your table one row at a time. Which types of energy identified in the *Energy before* column are not in the *Energy after* column? What do you think happened to this energy? What makes you think that?

3. Look at your table one row at a time. Which types of energy identified in the *Energy after* column are not in the *Energy before* column? Where do you think this energy came from? Why do you think that?

Communicate

Share Your Ideas

Each group will get a turn to describe the energy transformations in the device they analyzed and point out their thoughts and observations. When it is your group's turn, describe to the class the parts of the device you analyzed, tell them the energy types you identified before operation and after operation, and then present your answers to the questions.

As you listen, review what each group found and see if you can come up with an explanation of what happens to energy during a transformation. To help the discussion along, you may think about a stretched rubber band and what happens to the elastic potential energy as it transforms to kinetic energy. Consider how each type of energy increases or decreases as the change occurs.

After all groups have presented, discuss the factors that influence how much of each type of energy is present *before* and *after*. What do you think are the factors that affect the amount of sound energy? Which factors do you think affect the amount of chemical energy? Thermal energy? Electrical energy?

Reflect

1. List three things you think you know about energy transformations.

2. List three questions you need answered to better understand the energy transformations that have just been presented.

Update the *Project Board*

Although you have observed energy transformations throughout the Unit, this is the first time you are focusing on what happens to energy before and after an energy transformation. Based on your experience, there may be some things you think you know about how energy transforms and what happens to energy after a transformation. These should be added to the *What do we think we know?* column of the *Project Board*.

In the *What do we need to investigate?* column, list the class's questions about energy transformation. If the class had disagreements during the presentations, record questions in this column that you could answer to resolve the disagreements.

What's the Point?

You have reviewed and observed several different types of energy transformations. A list of these, with indicators and factors, will be useful in achieving the *Big Challenge.* However, you do not know exactly what factors control energy transformations. You may have questions, such as, "How do I know if an energy transformation will occur?" or, "How much of the total energy will be transformed?" In the rest of this *Learning Set,* you will be investigating questions such as these.

6.2 Explore

What Happens to Mechanical Energy During Its Transformations?

Now you will focus your attention on what happens to mechanical energy during a transformation. You read earlier that mechanical energy is the sum of the kinetic energy, gravitational potential energy, and elastic potential energy in a system. You will collect data to determine what occurs during mechanical energy transformations. As you do that, you will see how it is possible to measure the decrease and increase in mechanical energy as energy transformations take place.

Your group will be assigned to one of four stations set up around the classroom. You might have to wait for a station. When you are finished at your station and are waiting for another station, use the time to read about the dancer-powered dance floor in the box, *Dancers Powering a Generator.* As you do, think about the energy transformations that are happening in that example.

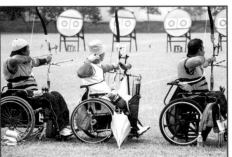

At one point, the bowling ball is motionless with potential energy. Then it is moving with kinetic energy down the bowling alley toward the bowling pins.

When the arrow is drawn back on the stretched bow, the arrow is motionless with potential energy. Then the arrow is moving fast with kinetic energy toward the target.

Stations 1 and 2—Energy Transformations in a Bouncing Ball

Procedure

1. Tape the sheet of poster paper to the wall. The paper should touch the floor.

2. One person should hold the ball 50 cm above the floor in front of the poster paper and drop it. Observe the ball as it bounces up and down. Identify the energy transformations that are happening as the ball bounces up and down.

3. Draw a diagram of the energy transformations you observed in the bouncing ball. Note where the ball has the most gravitational potential energy and where it has the most kinetic energy.

4. Repeat *Step 2,* but this time one group member should mark on the poster paper the peak height of the ball after each bounce. Continue recording peak heights until the peak height is less than 5 cm.

5. Measure the peak height of each bounce, using the meter stick. Record your measurements and plot them on a graph. The horizontal (x-axis) should be the bounce number from 0 to 10 (or more). The vertical (y-axis) should be the peak height in cm, beginning with 50 cm at 0 bounces.

Materials

- **marking pen**
- **large sheet of poster paper**
- **bouncy ball**
- **meter stick**

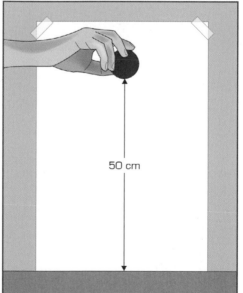

50 cm

One person drops the ball.

A second person marks the peak height of each bounce.

Stations 3 and 4—Energy Transformations in a Rolling Marble

Procedure

Materials
- **marking pen**
- **large sheet of poster paper**
- **marble, 2 cm in diameter**
- **track for marbles, 100 cm long**
- **meter stick**

1. Position the flexible track so the top of each end of the 100-cm length is 40 cm above the floor. The lowest point of the track should be on the floor. Tape the paper to the wall behind the track. The paper should touch the floor.

2. From the top of the track at one end, release the marble and observe the behavior of the marble as it rolls down one side of the track and up the other side. Identify the energy transformations as the marble rolls back and forth.

3. Draw a diagram of the energy transformations you observed in the rolling marble. Note where the marble has the most gravitational potential energy and where it has the most kinetic energy.

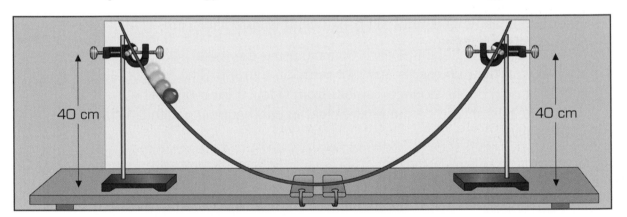

4. Repeat *Step 2,* but this time one group member should mark the height of the marble each time it reaches a peak, just before it reverses direction and rolls down the ramp again. Continue recording peak heights until the peak height is less than 5 cm.

5. Measure the peak heights using a meterstick. Record your measurements and plot a graph. The horizontal (x-axis) should be the successive rolls of the marble from 0 to 10 (or more). The vertical (y-axis) should be the peak height in cm, beginning with 40 cm at 0 rolls.

Analyze Your Data

1. How does the peak height of the ball or marble change as it continues bouncing or rolling?

2. Looking at the graph you made, what is the trend of the peak heights the ball or marble reached? How does the peak height compare to the original height?

3. If the ball or marble never gets back to the height at which it started, this means that some gravitational potential energy in the ball or marble is not transformed into kinetic energy. It may also mean that some kinetic energy is not transformed into gravitational potential energy. What evidence do you have that supports these statements?

4. What do you think might have happened to the "lost" energy? What evidence, if any, do you have that supports your answer?

5. How many bounces or rolls did you observe before the peak height was too small to measure?

Communicate

Share Your Results

When it is time for your group to present, begin by having one or two group members demonstrate what you did and how you took your measurements. Others in your group should then present your energy transformation diagram, your data, and your interpretation of the data. Make sure you address each of the *Analyze Your Data* questions as part of your presentation.

As you listen to other groups, notice the similarities and differences between their data and yours. Decide if you agree with their answers, but do not ask questions yet. Wait until everybody has presented before having a discussion.

After all the groups have made their presentations, look at the whole set of graphs. Discuss what you think happens to the original gravitational potential energy of the balls and marbles. See if you can come to agreement about what happened to the gravitational potential energy that caused the ball to stop bouncing or the marble to stop rolling. Support your ideas with evidence from the investigations.

ENERGY

Reflect

1. Which type of energy did you measure when you measured the peak height of the ball or marble?

2. What can you say about the kinetic energy at the peak height? (Hint: The speed is 0 at this point.)

3. What happens to the total mechanical energy of the ball or marble at the peak height? How do you know?

4. Where in the motion of the ball or marble do you think mechanical energy could be converted into other types of energy? What indicators tell you that other types of energy are produced?

5. Compare the number of bounces the ball made to the number of rolls the marble made. Which lost energy in the smaller number of bounces or rolls, the ball or the marble? Why do you think this was so?

Dancers Powering a Generator

Many people love to dance. When the music plays, the energy starts to flow and people want to move. Thinking back to the last time you moved to music, you probably noticed you were expending a lot of energy. Imagine the possibilities if you could harness that energy and convert it into electricity.

People like to dance to loud music and with light shows that use a lot of energy. Just one night of supplying energy to those sound systems and lights can use 50 times more energy than an average family of four uses in a year. Coming to the rescue is a nonprofit environmental organization based in the Netherlands. This group has investigated how to convert the kinetic energy of dancers into electricity.

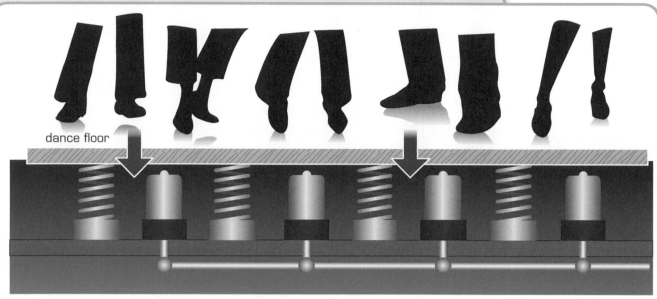

1. The dance floor is a "bouncing" floor made of springs and a series of power-generating blocks. Chemical energy in the dancers' muscles is transformed to kinetic energy in their feet. The kinetic energy of the feet is transferred to make kinetic energy in the floor

2. The blocks are made of crystals that produce a small electric current when squashed. Kinetic energy of the floor is transformed into electric energy.

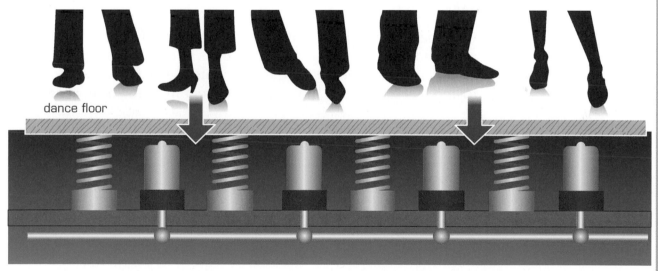

3. As dancers move up and down, the blocks are squeezed and the electric current is fed into nearby batteries. Electric energy from the blocks is transferred to batteries for storage.

4. The batteries are constantly recharged by the movement of the floor and used to power parts of the nightclub. Electric energy from the batteries is transformed into light energy when it passes through a light bulb, or sound energy when it passes through a speaker.

ENERGY

piezoelectric:
process in which
pressure applied to
crystals produces
an electric current.

The organization has made a dance floor that generates electricity. When a dancer pushes off the floor, the dancer's muscles use chemical energy to do work on his or her body. The dancer also does work on **piezoelectric** devices under the floor. These devices contain crystals that produce an electric current when the crystals are put under pressure. The work done by the muscles, propelling the dancer upward, also increases the dancer's kinetic energy. As the dancer rises to his or her peak height, kinetic energy is transformed to gravitational potential energy. On the way down, the gravitational potential energy is transformed back into kinetic energy. When the dancer strikes the floor, the kinetic energy is used to do work on the piezoelectric devices. Dancers are supplying the energy to make their own music happen!

Other forms of energy may be transformed by a dance floor in the future. Body heat from the dancers could be transformed to generate electricity. Heat from the floor lights could also be transformed. What other sources of energy do you think could be captured to reduce the energy cost?

Reflect

1. A dancer might dance for 3 minutes and reach the same height after each "bounce." Compare what happens to a dancer's mechanical energy to what happens to the mechanical energy of a bouncing ball or rolling marble. How is the dancer different from the ball or marble?

2. If you are good at it, you can keep a yo-yo going up and down for a long time. Describe the energy transformations in a yo-yo in terms of energy transformation and work. How is the yo-yo like a dancer who can keep dancing for a long time?

3. What else do you need to know about energy transformations to control all of the energy transformations in your Rube Goldberg machine?

Update the Project Board

Record what you think you know about energy transformations in the *What do we think we know?* column of the *Project Board.* You may have had disagreements with classmates about the investigation results. Put questions in the *What do we need to investigate?* column of the *Project Board* that will help you resolve those disagreements. Also add the questions you need to answer to control all of the energy transformations in the Rube Goldberg machine you are designing.

You can keep a yo-yo going up and down for a long time.

What's the Point?

The investigations with the ball and marble allowed you to measure what happens to mechanical energy during a series of transformations. The graphs of your data show a downward trend. This suggests that some of the energy the ball and marble started with was "lost." You might wonder what happened to that "lost" energy.

6.3 Explore

What Happens to the "Lost" Energy?

When you were carrying out the investigation with the bouncing ball and the rolling marble, you were focused on observing transformations between gravitational potential energy and kinetic energy. So it is not surprising that you may not have noticed other energy transformations that were happening. You will now have the opportunity to watch a demonstration that will give you clues about other energy transformations that were happening when you bounced your ball or rolled your marble. As you watch the demonstration, look for evidence of all the different types of energy that are present. After the demonstration, you may be able to figure out what happened to the energy that seemed to be "lost."

Chemical energy changes into light, sound, and thermal energy when fireworks explode. However, because the light and sound are so impressive, most people don't think about the thermal energy.

Demonstration

Observe

Your teacher will bounce a ball and then roll a marble down a ramp. Watch and listen carefully. As you observe each, try to find evidence of other energy types in addition to kinetic energy and gravitational potential energy. Record your observations. Besides kinetic energy and gravitational potential energy, what other energy types are you able to detect?

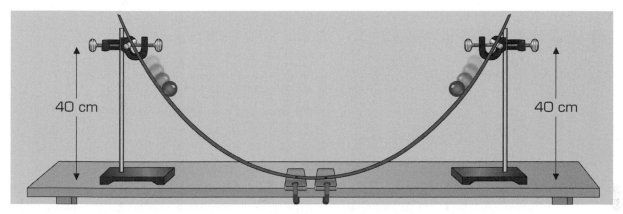

What kinds of energy transformations occur when two balls run down the track toward each other? What does this demonstration tell you about "lost" energy?

After observing the ball and the marble, you will observe a collision between two marbles as they roll down opposite sides of the track. Besides kinetic energy and gravitational potential energy, what other energy types are you able to detect? Record your observations.

Analyze Your Data

1. What do you think happened to the total amount of mechanical energy the ball had before the teacher dropped it? What do you think happened to the total amount of mechanical energy each of the marbles had at the top of the ramp? You may want to draw diagrams to help you identify all the energy changes you observed.

2. Examine the graphs you made in your investigation of the bouncing balls and rolling marbles. Describe any differences in the patterns found on the graphs. For example, one graph might show a steeper decline than the other graph. Use what you just experienced to explain why.

ENERGY

usable energy:
energy that can easily be transformed to other kinds of energy to serve a useful purpose.

Energy Transformation and Energy Losses

Energy transformations always involve a loss of **usable energy**. Usable energy is energy that continues to support the intended purpose of the energy.

In fact, in everyday experience, there are no energy transformations that end with exactly the same amount of usable energy they began with. Some energy is always transformed from a more usable to a less usable form. This is what happened with the balls and the marbles in your investigations.

When a marble was placed at the top of the ramp in your investigations, all of the marble's energy was gravitational potential energy. As it rolled down the ramp the first time, most of this potential energy was changed to kinetic energy. Kinetic energy is usable. It is the energy in the movement of the marble. However, not all of the marble's potential energy was changed to kinetic energy. As it rolled down the ramp, some of the marble's potential energy changed into sound energy. The sound energy was not usable for moving the marble. If you had a sensitive measuring device, you would also find that some of the kinetic energy was transformed into thermal energy. The thermal energy made the marble and the track warmer, but it was not usable for moving the marble. Then, when the marble rolled up the opposite ramp, its kinetic energy was changed back into gravitational potential energy. But not all of its kinetic energy was changed into potential energy. Some of its kinetic energy was converted to thermal energy and some was converted to sound energy before it reached the top of the ramp.

A roller coaster descending a hill is very much like a ball running down a track. What energy transformations can you identify?

On each successive roll up and down the ramp, the marble continued to lose usable energy. The "lost" energy was transferred into the track, into the ball, and into the air.

The same thing happened with the bouncing balls. With each successive bounce, some of the usable energy changed into sound energy and thermal energy. Neither of these is usable in keeping the ball moving.

Your body behaves in a similar way. It transforms the chemical energy in the food you eat into other forms of energy that your body needs to move, grow, and sustain itself. But a lot of the energy used by your body is lost as thermal energy. When you work out or play hard or dance, you notice how much heat your body gives off. As your body changes some of its chemical energy into kinetic energy, some of its chemical energy is also changed into thermal energy. The thermal energy makes you warm, but it does not contribute to your movement.

The amount of usable energy you get from a system is called its **energy efficiency**. If, after transformation, 90 percent of the energy is still usable, the transformation is said to be 90 percent efficient. Your body is a lot less than 90 percent efficient. But even an energy transformation that is not efficient does not lose energy. It just turns some of the energy into a form that is not usable for whatever work the system is doing.

energy efficiency: the degree to which a process produces a usable energy output for a given energy input.

Appliances are rated for their energy efficiency. You can find this information on a tag, which helps you make a better decision of which appliance to buy.

ENERGY

Reflect

Use what you just read to answer these questions. Be prepared to discuss your answers with the class.

1. What does it mean that some energy is not usable? What makes some forms of energy more usable than others?

2. Return to your data and drawings from your investigation with the ball or marble. Why did the ball stop bouncing? Why did the marble stop rolling?

3. Where is mechanical energy of the bouncing ball transformed into unusable energy? What changes could you make to reduce the amount of usable energy that is lost?

4. Where is mechanical energy of the rolling marble ball transformed into unusable energy? What changes could you make to reduce the amount of usable energy that is lost?

5. Look at your graphs from the investigations again. How can you compare the efficiency of the energy transformations in the bouncing ball with the efficiency of the energy transformations in the rolling marble? Which is more efficient? Why do you think this is so?

Conference

In your group, return to the energy-transformation cartoon you have been examining. There are many energy transformations illustrated in your cartoon. Choose five transformations you think are not very efficient. For each, record the types of energy before and the types after on an *Energy-transformation Cartoon* page. You have already recorded many of the usable types of energy transformations in your machine. This time, include types of energy that are not usable. Circle the types of energy that are not usable for each of the five transformations you have chosen.

Energy-transformation Cartoon   0.0.3/1.BBC.1/3.BBC.1/ 4.1.2/4.BBC.1/5.1.2/6.3.1

Name: _____   Date: _____

Fill in the letter of the step you are analyzing. Then fill in other information about that step.

Name of your machine:			Purpose of your machine:	
Step	Changes/Work done	Energy type in	Energy types out	Indicators of energy transformations

Record questions about anything on which your group does not agree and anything you do not understand.

© It's About Time

Then answer these questions. Be prepared to share your answers with the class.

1. What types of energy in your cartoon are not transformed in the next step? How could this unusable energy have been transformed if the step was different?

2. Based on what you have learned about energy efficiency, describe why you think the machine in the cartoon you have been examining is efficient or not efficient.

3. How could you increase the efficiency of one step in the machine?

4. Which step in the machine do you think is the most efficient? Why do you think this?

Communicate

Share Your Ideas

When it is your group's turn to present, remind the group which Rube Goldberg machine you were examining. Then present two of the inefficient energy transformations you identified. For each of the inefficient energy transformations, tell the class what type of energy was transformed into what other types, which types were unusable, and what happened to that unusable energy. Then tell the class how you think that step of the machine could be changed to be more efficient.

Also present the step you think is most efficient. Tell the class what makes the step you chose more efficient than other steps in the machine. End your presentation by telling the class whether you think the machine in the cartoon is efficient or not efficient and why.

As you are listening, pay attention to the energy transformations, and make sure you understand each one and agree with the presenters. If you do not understand or do not agree, raise your hand and ask a question. Remember to be respectful.

After everyone has presented, discuss how efficient you think each of the four energy-transformation cartoon machines is. Do you think one of them is a lot more efficient than the others? If so, why? Do you think one is a lot less efficient than the others? If so, why?

ENERGY

Update the *Project Board*

Record what you now know about energy transformations in the *What are we learning?* column of the *Project Board*. Record your evidence in the *What is our evidence?* column. If you still have questions about energy transformations, record those in the *What do we need to investigate?* column.

What's the Point?

The demonstrations with the ball and the marbles colliding provided you with some evidence that energy is not lost in energy transformations. In addition to the kinetic energy observed as the two marbles rolled down the ramps, you also observed evidence of sound energy. This sound energy flowed into the surrounding air. You might have also observed evidence of thermal energy, if you had a sensitive measuring device. The thermal energy warmed the marbles and the ramp. The potential and kinetic energy that changed into sound energy and thermal energy were no longer available to help the marbles move. While none of the potential energy of the marbles and balls disappeared, some of it was changed into forms that were not usable to do the work of moving the marbles or bouncing the ball. The more an energy transformation changes energy into a usable form, the more efficient the energy transformation is.

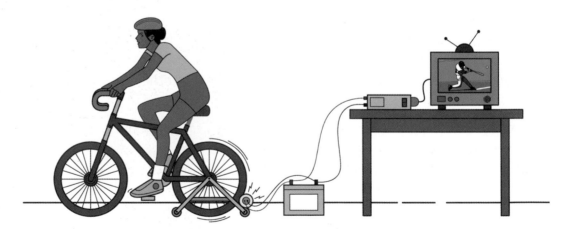

This bicycle provides electricity to a television. Some energy may appear to be lost in the energy transformations. What do you think happens to that "lost" energy?

6.4 Read

The Law of Conservation of Energy

The data gathered in your explorations show that mechanical energy decreased steadily in the bouncing ball and rolling marble. It appeared that the ball and the marble "lost" energy every time they traveled up or down. However, when you observed the demonstrations of the ball and the colliding marbles, you were able to hear the sound of the ball bouncing and moving through the air. You could also hear the sound of the marbles moving down the track. The energy that changed into sound energy was not useable for doing the work of moving the ball and the marbles. However, none of the energy disappeared.

The **law of conservation of energy** states that energy cannot be created or destroyed, but can only change form. The total amounts of energy before and after any energy transformation are equal. It is sometimes hard to know what happened to some of the energy. But energy is not destroyed. Instead, it is often transformed into some type of energy that may not be usable for the intended purpose.

law of conservation of energy: a law of physics that states that energy cannot be created or destroyed; it can only change form.

Energy of a system may decrease. If so, the system has lost energy, but that energy can be found in the environment around the system. Energy of a system also may increase. If so, the system has gained energy, so the energy of the surrounding environment must have decreased.

The story on the next page may help you better understand the idea of conservation of energy. This story comes from Richard Feynman, one of the greatest American physicists of the twentieth century.

Richard Feynman (1918–1988) was an American physicist and a member of the Manhattan Project team during WW II. In addition to winning a Nobel Prize for his work in quantum electrodynamics, he was a free spirit known for his pranks, painting, and bongo playing.

Where Did the Blocks Go?

A child plays with 28 blocks. Every day the child's mother counts the blocks and always finds the total to be 28. One day, she only finds 27 blocks, but after she looks around some more, she sees that one block is hidden in a box. On another day, she finds only 25 blocks, but she can see that the water in a nearby pail is higher than expected. Because she knows something about the original height of the water and the volume of a block, she guesses that the three blocks are below the surface of the water. She looks, and there they are.

But one day, the mother looks around the room and cannot find all of the blocks. Then she notices an open window. She peers outside the window and finds that the missing blocks are outside. The child must have thrown them out the window!

Another day she discovers an extra block. Where did it come from? Then she remembers that a neighbor had come over to play and had brought some of his blocks. He must have left one of the blocks at her house.

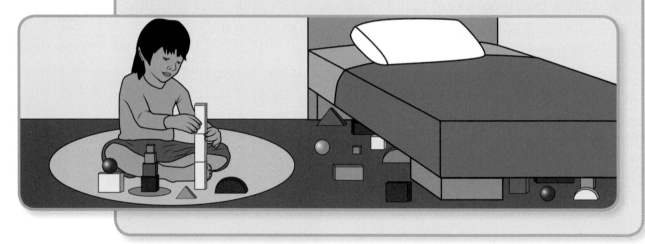

Reflect

1. How do you think this story relates to conservation of energy? How are the blocks like energy? How are they not like energy?

2. What is an example from the story that relates to energy being lost in a system?

3. What is an example from the story that relates to energy being added to a system?

4. Based on the story of the blocks, what do you think a *system* is? Describe what happens to energy in a system. Write a statement you think describes how energy could enter or leave a system.

Update the *Project Board*

Add what you have learned about the law of conservation of energy to the *What are we learning?* column. Do not forget to add evidence to the *What is our evidence?* column. In the *What do we need to investigate?* column, record any new questions you have about energy transformations and the law of conservation of energy.

What's the Point?

The law of conservation of energy states that energy cannot be created or destroyed but can only change form. Although it sometimes seems that energy is lost during an energy transformation, it is not lost, but rather, it is changed into a less easily observed type of energy, like sound energy or thermal energy.

It is not always easy to observe all the changes that are happening during an energy transformation. It is important to remember that sometimes things are not exactly as they appear. When you bounced the ball or rolled the marble back and forth on a ramp, it looked like energy was lost. However, that energy was not lost. It was changed into sound energy and thermal energy. Some of this energy may have left the system. If you had relied solely on the results of your investigation, it would have been easy to support a claim that energy was lost. However, when you investigated further, you found that if the energy of the system decreased, the energy of the surrounding environment must have increased.

6.5 Explore

The Energy Resources That Provide Electricity

The photograph below shows a satellite image of North America at night. The lights you see are powered by electricity. Lighting each of those lights requires energy transformations similar to the energy transformations needed to light one bulb. However, in the satellite image, you are seeing the light of billions of light bulbs. Thousands of electrical power plants around the world are generating the electrical energy needed to keep all of the world's bulbs lit.

Power plants that generate electricity transform some energy resource into electrical energy. Each power plant has huge generators that produce the electricity. These generators must turn constantly to provide a uniform source of power. Turning the generators is the job of giant turbines. Just like the spinning magnets in the generator you observed, the turbines need a source of energy to keep them in motion. Turbines can be powered by steam, water, wind, or other available sources of kinetic energy. Steam-powered power plants use some other energy resource to generate steam. Some power plants use the chemical energy in coal or oil. Some use nuclear energy. Some use the kinetic energy of moving water or wind, or the light energy of the Sun.

The lights you see in a satellite image of North America at night come from billions of light bulbs.

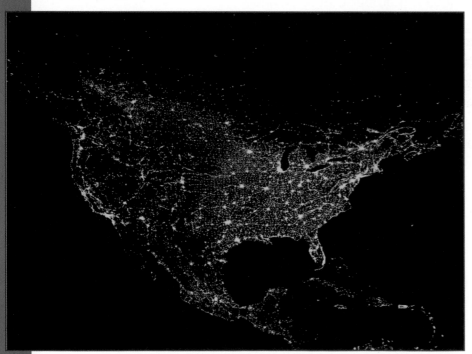

In this section, you will read about the different energy resources transformed into electrical energy. In the next section, you will have a chance to analyze the efficiency of these resources and the efficiency of the energy transformations that bring electrical energy to your home.

You will begin by reading about all the different energy resources that provide electricity for homes and other buildings—wind, hydroelectric power, the Sun, fossil fuels, trash, waves, and geothermal energy. Then each group in the class will be assigned a different energy resource. They will investigate the pros and cons of using that resource to generate electricity and report to the class. You may want to use some of what you learned in this section to design a Rube Goldberg machine that is energy-efficient or easy on the environment.

Read about all of the different energy resources. As you read, notice what makes each resource easy or difficult to use. Record the type of energy each resource provides, the way that resource is transformed into electricity, and the pros and cons on an *Energy Resources Pros and Cons* page. When you are finished reading, work with your group to answer the *Reflect* questions that follow.

Energy Resources Pros and Cons   6.5.1

Name: _____   Date: _____

Energy resource	Type of energy	How its energy is transformed into electricity	Pros	Cons
Wind energy				
Hydroelectric energy				
Solar energy				
Fossil fuels				
Trash and biomass				
Tidal energy				
Geothermal energy				

© It's About Time

Wind Energy

Wind energy captures the kinetic energy of wind. The force exerted by the wind turns a rotor shaft that is connected by gears to a turbine. The turbine's kinetic energy is transformed to electrical energy by a generator.

The kinetic energy of the wind moves the blades of the wind turbine and turns a rotor, which turns a generator/ turbine. Unusable energy is thermal energy and sound energy.

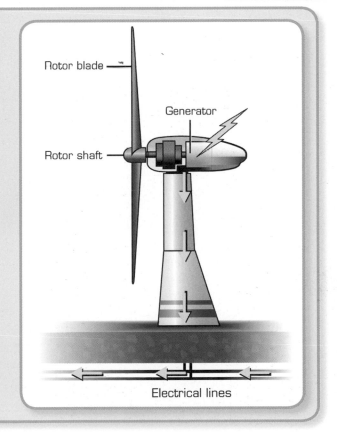

Rotor blade

Generator

Rotor shaft

Electrical lines

ENERGY

Hydroelectric Energy

Hydroelectric power comes from the potential energy of water. The energy extracted from the water depends on the volume of water and on the difference in height between the source of the water and the water's outflow. This height difference is called the *head*. The amount of potential energy in water is proportional to the head. That means that the larger the head, the more potential energy is available from the water. To obtain the most potential energy, a large dam is usually built that can hold the water up high. The water may then be run through a large pipe called a *penstock*. This enables turbines to transform the water's kinetic energy to electrical energy more efficiently than is possible if the water is simply falling. As the water rushes past the turbines, they spin, and the coils also spin in a magnetic field to convert kinetic energy to electrical energy.

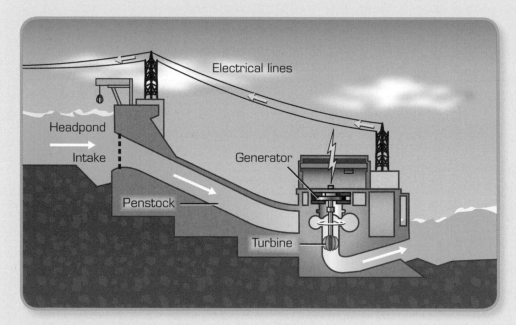

The potential energy in water is transformed into kinetic energy as it falls. The water spins the turbines, and the coils spin in a magnetic field to produce electrical energy. Unusable energy is thermal energy and sound energy.

Solar Energy

Solar energy captures light energy from the Sun. Solar cells are made of materials such as silicon. For solar cells, a thin silicon wafer is treated with chemicals to form two regions, positive on one side and negative on the other. When light energy strikes the solar cell, charged particles are knocked loose from the atoms in the silicon. If electrical conductors are attached to the positive and negative sides of the solar cell, forming an electrical circuit, the charged particles flow through the conductors to form an electric current—that is, electricity. This electricity can then be used for power.

A number of solar cells electrically connected to each other and mounted in a support structure is called a *photovoltaic module.* Modules are designed to supply electricity at a certain voltage. The amount of current produced depends on how much light strikes the module.

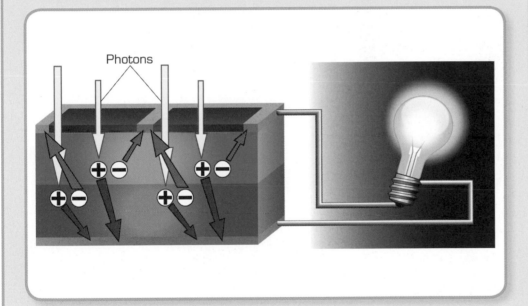

Solar cells use light energy from the Sun to transform silicon to positive silicon ions and charged particles. The positive and negative sides are connected to form an electric circuit, and the charged particles form an electric current. Unusable energy is thermal energy.

Fossil-fuel Energy

Most power plants burn fossil fuels to produce electricity. Fossil fuels are burned, and the resulting heat is used to boil water. The water changes into steam, and the steam builds up pressure. The high-pressure steam rushes past the turbines, causing them to spin. Coils attached to the turbines then spin in a magnetic field, which causes an electric current to flow. In this way, the chemical energy of the fossil fuels is converted into electrical energy.

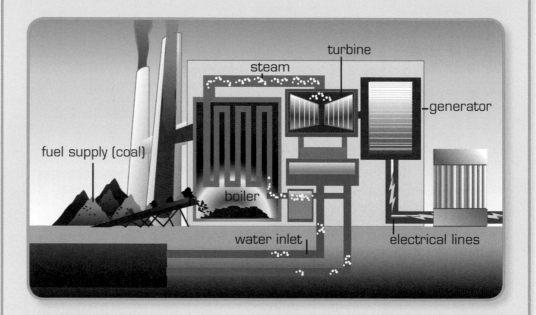

In a fossil-fuel power plant, the chemical energy in fuels, such as coal, is used to produce steam that spins a turbine in a magnetic field. This produces an electric current. Unusable energy is sound energy and thermal energy that leaves the plant as steam. Pollutants that go out the smokestack contain energy that is not transformed.

Trash and Biomass Energy

Some power plants use trash or biomass, such as cornstalks or sugarcane as a fuel. As with fossil fuels, trash and biomass are burned, and the resulting heat is used to boil water. The water changes into steam, and the steam builds up pressure. The high-pressure steam rushes past the turbines, causing them to spin. Coils attached to the turbines then spin in a magnetic field, which causes an electric current to flow. In this way, the chemical energy from the trash and biomass is converted into electrical energy.

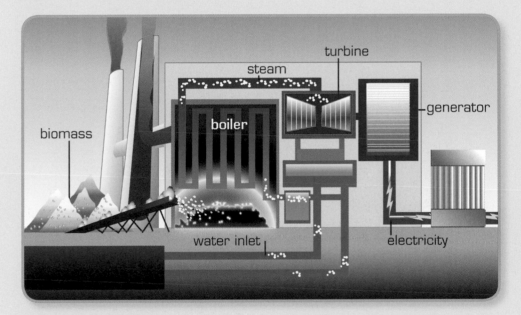

Trash- or biomass-burning power plants operate similarly to a fossil fuel-burning power plant. Instead of coal, oil, or natural gas, these power plants transform the chemical energy in plants or trash into electricity. Unusable energy is sound energy and thermal energy that leaves the plant as steam. Pollutants that go out the smokestack contain energy that is not transformed.

Wave Energy

Wave energy captures the energy of the ocean or of very large lakes. Wave-energy devices called *attenuators* are oriented parallel to the direction of the waves. One example is a series of long, cylindrical, floating devices connected to each other with hinges and anchored to the seabed. The cylindrical parts drive *hydraulic rams* in the connecting sections, and those in turn drive an electric generator. The devices send the electricity through cables (very thick wires) to the sea floor where it then travels through a cable to shore.

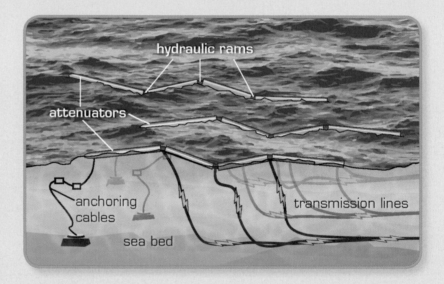

The kinetic energy in waves turns attenuators and sends the energy to an electric generator, which produces electricity. Unusable energy is sound energy and thermal energy.

Geothermal Energy

Geothermal energy uses the heat beneath the ground to produce steam. Steam under pressure emerges from the ground, or hot water emerges from the ground, and it heats a liquid that boils at a lower temperature to create a vapor. The pressure exerted by the vapor turns turbines that spin coils in a magnetic field to cause a current to flow. In this way, the thermal energy of the steam or hot water in the ground is converted to electrical energy.

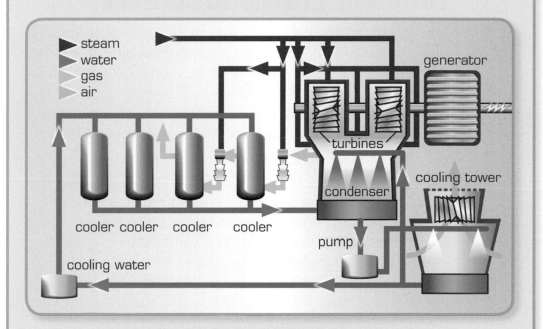

Steam from underground, or hot water boiled to produce steam, turns a turbine that spins coils in a magnetic field to produce electricity. Unusable energy is sound energy and thermal energy that leaves the plant as steam. Pollutants that go out the smokestack contain energy that is not transformed.

Reflect

1. If you had to choose a way to generate electricity for your community, what energy resource would you choose? Why? What energy resource or resources would you avoid? Why?

2. What else do you need to know about each energy resource to know better which is a good one for your community?

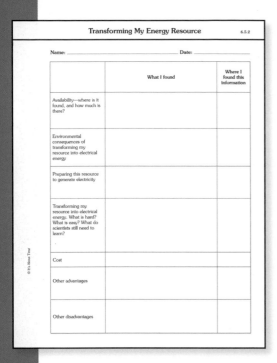

Transforming My Energy Resource

What Are the Pros and Cons of Different Energy Resources?

You do not yet know all of the advantages and disadvantages of each energy resource. Some are more available than others. Some are more costly. Some produce more pollutants than others. Each group will use library and Internet resources to investigate the advantages and disadvantages of one energy resource and report to the class. Afterwards, you will have a chance to compare the resources to each other.

Read about your resource. As you read, take notes about the availability of your resource, its impact on the environment, the processes and energy needed to prepare it for use, how much scientists know about using your resource to generate electricity, and the cost of using your resource. Be sure to note the source of each of your pieces of information in your notes. Record your information on a *Transforming My Energy Resource* page.

Communicate

Investigation Expo

After you have read about your resource, work with your group to prepare a presentation about the advantages and disadvantages of transforming your resource into electrical energy. Make sure your presentation answers these questions.

- How available is your resource? What makes it available or not available?

- How does your resource need to be prepared so that it can be used for generating electrical energy?

- What are the environmental consequences of transforming your energy resource into electrical energy?

- What do scientists know about transforming your resource into electrical energy? What is hard about transforming it? What is easy? What do scientists still need to find out?

- What is the cost of transforming your resource into electrical energy?

When it is your group's turn to present, make a presentation to the class about your energy resource. Make sure each member of your group has a chance to speak. As you are listening, notice the similarities and differences between your resource and other resources. Take notes on your *Energy Resources Pros and Cons* page.

Reflect

Work with your group to answer these questions. Be prepared to share your answers with the class.

1. Which resources have a large impact on the environment? What are the pros and cons of transforming these energy resources into electrical energy?

2. Which resources have less impact on the environment? What are the pros and cons of these "friendly" energy resources?

3. How does the cost of transforming your energy resource compare to the cost of transforming other resources?

4. If you had to choose a way to generate electricity for your community, what energy resources would you choose? Why? What energy resource or resources would you avoid? Why?

What's the Point?

There are many energy resources that can be transformed into electricity. These resources include fossil fuels, wind, sunlight, biomass, running water, and waves. Some of these resources took hundreds of millions of years to produce and are in such great demand that they cannot be replaced and are not renewable. Others seem to be in endless supply. Each of these resources has different environmental and economic impacts. This is why people must make wise choices about what resources they use.

PBIS

Another source of electrical energy is from nuclear energy power plants. Nuclear fuel is not renewable.

nuclear fusion: a change in which one or more low-mass elements produce a higher-mass element with a release of enormous amounts of energy.

nuclear reaction: a reaction in which the substance that is produced is a new element and has a smaller mass than the substances that combined to form it.

More to Learn

Nuclear Energy

Several times in this Unit, you read that most energy on Earth comes from the Sun. But what is the source of the Sun's energy? In the Sun's core, **fusion** releases enormous amounts of thermal energy as hydrogen is converted into helium. Fusion is a **nuclear reaction**, not a chemical reaction. In a chemical reaction, substances combine to produce new substances, but the elements remain the same with no change in mass. In a nuclear reaction, the substance that is produced is a new element and has a smaller mass than the substances that combined to form it.

$$4H + \text{heat and pressure} \rightarrow He + \text{energy}$$

Fusion is a nuclear reaction. A nuclear reaction is quite different from everyday chemical reactions. In a nuclear reaction like fusion, atoms interact in such a way that their nuclei are transformed. In this way, atoms of one or more new elements are formed, as occurs in stars when high temperature and pressure cause small nuclei, such as those of hydrogen atoms, to make larger nuclei, such as those of helium atoms. It is found that the mass of the helium atoms thus formed is less than that of the original hydrogen atoms.

This is quite different from everyday chemical reactions. In chemical reactions, the substances formed are measured to have the same mass as the substances that originally reacted. Now that you have been reading about "missing energy," you might be wondering about what happens to the missing mass.

You may have learned in chemistry about the *law of conservation of mass*. This law is very similar to the *law of conservation of energy*, but it applies to mass. It states that mass is not created or destroyed through ordinary chemical reactions. So what happens to the missing mass in a nuclear reaction? Albert Einstein, a German physicist, realized that mass could be converted into energy, and energy could be converted into mass. So when mass appears to be missing, it has really been transformed into energy. Einstein stated that mass is a form of energy. These ideas, called the law of conservation of mass and energy, explain the enormous energy released in fusion reactions. Einstein formulated his famous equation $E = mc^2$ (energy equals mass times the speed of light squared) to explain what happens to this "missing mass." The energy released in a nuclear reaction like fusion is called **nuclear energy**.

Fusion is the same process that releases energy in a hydrogen bomb. However, fusion reactions have never been used to generate electricity efficiently. In a power plant on Earth, it is very hard to recreate conditions of high temperature and pressure similar to those found inside the Sun. Thus far, on Earth, it has always taken more energy to make fusion happen than the energy produced by a fusion reaction. However, there is another nuclear energy process that has been used successfully to generate energy—**nuclear fission**. In nuclear fission, large atoms are split to make smaller atoms. Again, there is a tiny difference in mass, and this mass is converted into large amounts of energy.

Nuclear fission provides yet another way to make electricity by boiling water to make steam. In this process, the nuclei of uranium split into smaller atoms, releasing energy. This energy is used to heat water and create steam. The steam turns a turbine to produce electricity, just as in a coal-fired power plant.

Albert Einstein was one of the most famous scientists to study energy and energy transformations.

nuclear energy: energy released from a reaction in which atomic nuclei interact to form new nuclei that have a lower combined mass.

nuclear fission: a change in which one high-mass element produces two or more low-mass elements, with a release of enormous amounts of energy.

α-rays: radiation emitted during nuclear reactions; a helium nucleus with a positive charge.

β-rays: radiation emitted during nuclear reactions; an electron with a negative charge.

gamma rays: high energy electromagnetic radiation with no mass or charge.

condenser: a device that changes gases to liquid or solid form.

Because it emits none of the pollutants associated with coal, nuclear energy is considered by many people to be clean energy, but there are three problems. The first problem arises when the uranium ore is mined. There is pollution left from mining uranium that can damage the environment, and the miners who work in the mines can develop cancer from the radiation in the uranium. Radiation is the release of sub-atomic particles, **α-rays** and **β-rays**, or the release of energy in the form of **gamma rays**. All of these forms of radiation are dangerous and cause damage to tissues and genetic material.

The second problem is disposal of the nuclear fuel after it has been used. The term "spent fuel" refers to the nuclear fuel that has been used and can no longer be easily used in nuclear reactions. Spent fuel from a nuclear power plant is even more radioactive than the original uranium, and scientists are still seeking a way to store it for a hundred thousand years or more, far away from people. The third problem is the water that is used to keep the circulating water from the power plant's **condenser** cool. Usually, this water is taken from a lake or river and brought into the power plant to cool the condenser. Once it has been heated up, it is no longer useful for cooling and must be returned to the lake or river. Unless great care is taken, this heated water can damage the environment. This can also be a problem with electricity generated from steam in other ways.

The uranium that is used as a source of nuclear energy was formed in a star that exploded in the far, far, distant past. When our solar system formed from the remnants of an exploded star, the uranium was deposited on Earth, along with all of the other elements. That means that uranium is nonrenewable and therefore not a long-term solution to the problem of generating electricity on Earth. However, there is plenty of uranium available right now.

Reflect

1. How does a nuclear power plant generate electricity?

2. What are the advantages and disadvantages of a nuclear power plant?

3. Would you want a nuclear power plant near where you live? Why or why not?

6.6 Explore

Energy Transformations and Conservation of Resources

As you have read, most power plants are fueled by the chemical energy in fossil fuels. Turbines can also be powered by water, wind, solar, or nuclear energy. Other energy transformations happen as the electricity generated in the power plants is transported over power grids to the places where the power is needed.

Each of these energy transformations results in a loss of usable energy. In this section, you will explore what it takes to supply you, your neighborhood, and your nation with the power needed to turn on the lights and to run everything people use that is powered by electricity. You have read about many of the advantages and disadvantages of the different energy sources. However, you have not read yet about the efficiency of each of these resources as a source of electrical energy. You will use what you know about energy transformations and energy efficiency to figure out how efficient each of these sources of electrical energy is.

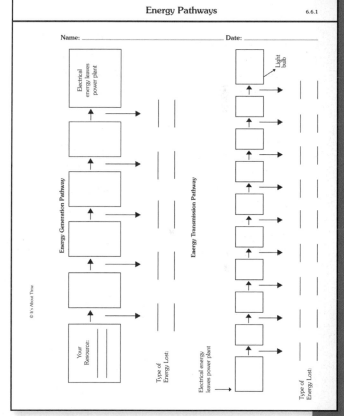

Where Does Energy Needed to Light a Bulb Come From?

You have read about how your energy resource is used to generate electricity. Now you will complete a chain of energy transformations connecting your resource to an electrical outlet in a home where electrical energy can light a bulb. You will complete your chain of energy transformations using the *Energy Resource* images and *Energy Transmission* images shown on the pages following the *Procedure*. Your chain of transformations might be very long. The instructions below will help you complete your chain.

Use an *Energy Pathways* page to organize your ideas about the ways energy is transformed from one of the energy sources to the light bulb.

Energy Resources: Procedure

1. Read again about how the energy resource you have been assigned is transformed into electrical energy. As you read, keep notes about all of the different actions and energy transformations that have to happen to generate electrical energy from your resource.

2. Share your list with your group and come to agreement about the sequence through which your energy resource is transformed into electrical energy.

3. Select *Energy Resource* images that show this sequence of energy transformations. List the images in the correct order so they show how your energy resource is transformed into electrical energy.

4. Write the numbers of the images and a description in the boxes of the *Energy Generation Pathway* diagram on an *Energy Pathways* page. In the first box, record the type of energy in your resource. In the other boxes, record the transformations that transform your resource's energy into electrical energy. Depending on the resource you were assigned, you might have blank boxes.

5. The boxes in your diagram show energy transformations that produce usable energy. Below the diagram, record the types of unusable energy that are produced in each step of the pathway.

6. Do your best to make an estimate of how efficient it is to use your energy resource to light a bulb. To do this, list other energy resources you think will be *more* efficient. Then list other energy resources you think will be *less* efficient.

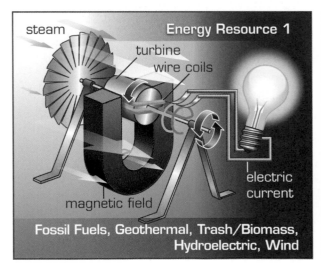

steam
Energy Resource 1
turbine
wire coils
electric current
magnetic field

Fossil Fuels, Geothermal, Trash/Biomass, Hydroelectric, Wind

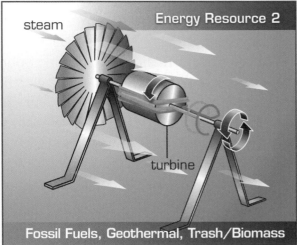

steam
Energy Resource 2
turbine

Fossil Fuels, Geothermal, Trash/Biomass

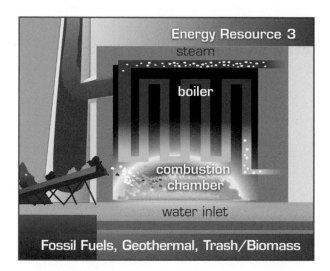

Energy Resource 3

steam

boiler

combustion chamber

water inlet

Fossil Fuels, Geothermal, Trash/Biomass

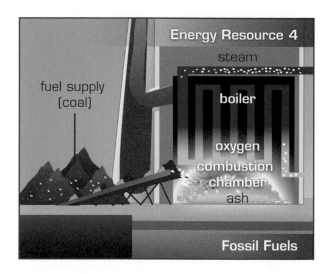

Energy Resource 4

steam

fuel supply (coal)

boiler

oxygen

combustion chamber

ash

Fossil Fuels

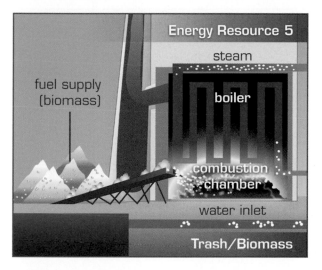

Energy Resource 5

steam

fuel supply (biomass)

boiler

combustion chamber

water inlet

Trash/Biomass

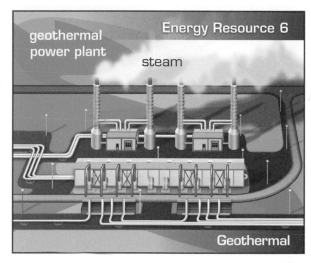

Energy Resource 6

geothermal power plant

steam

Geothermal

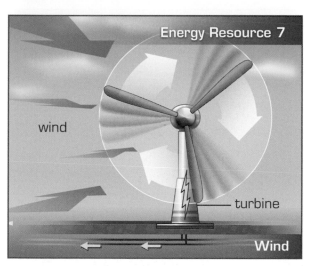

Energy Resource 7

wind

turbine

Wind

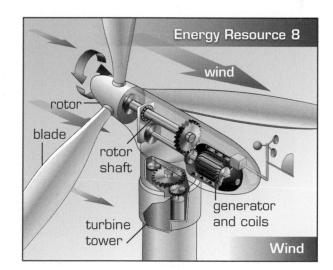

Energy Resource 8

wind

rotor

blade

rotor shaft

turbine tower

generator and coils

Wind

PBIS

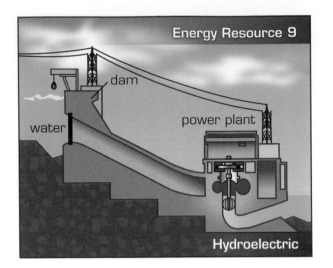

Energy Resource 9

dam

water

power plant

Hydroelectric

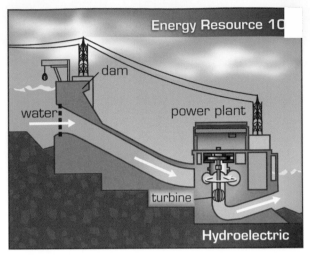

Energy Resource 10

dam

water

power plant

turbine

Hydroelectric

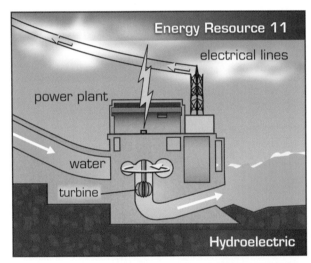

Energy Resource 11

electrical lines

power plant

water

turbine

Hydroelectric

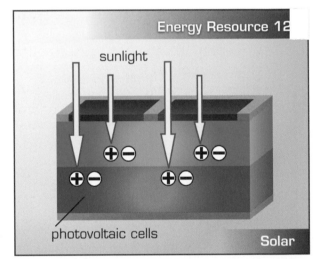

Energy Resource 12

sunlight

photovoltaic cells

Solar

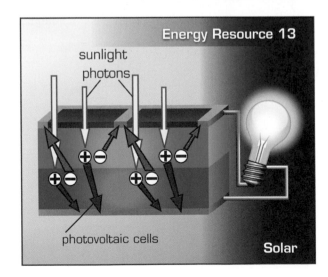

Energy Resource 13

sunlight

photons

photovoltaic cells

Solar

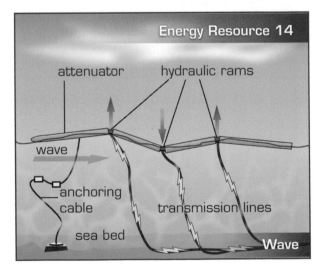

Energy Resource 14

attenuator   hydraulic rams

wave

anchoring cable

transmission lines

sea bed

Wave

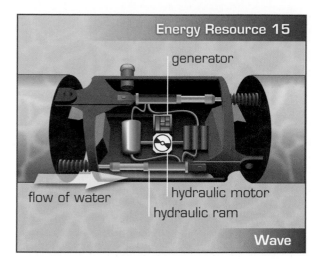

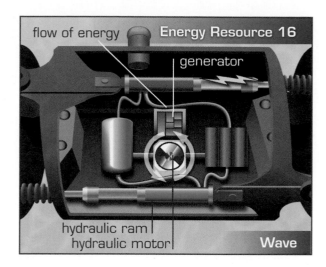

Energy Transmission: Procedure

1. Now identify the energy transformations needed to transmit the electrical energy to an outlet in a home and into a light bulb. To figure this out, you may want to reread *Energy From a Generator* in *Learning Set 5*. It describes how electrical energy generated in a power plant is transported to a home and through the wiring in a home to an outlet.

2. List the *Energy Transmission* images into a sequence of energy transformations that shows how electrical energy is brought to a light bulb in a home. Make sure your list is in the correct order.

3. When you think you have the correct sequence, fill in the empty boxes in the bottom *Energy Transformation Pathway* diagram on your *Energy Pathways* page.

4. The boxes in your diagram show energy transformations that produce usable energy. Below the diagram, record the types of unusable energy that are produced in each step of the pathway.

5. Make a list of the types of unusable energy generated along the whole pathway.

Energy Transmission A

Electrical energy is transmitted through low-power voltage lines such as those in neighborhoods.

Energy Transmission B

Electricity goes through a meter that measures how much electricity you use.

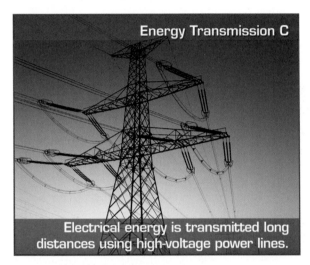

Energy Transmission C

Electrical energy is transmitted long distances using high-voltage power lines.

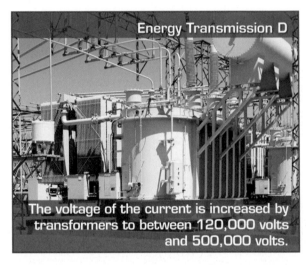

Energy Transmission D

The voltage of the current is increased by transformers to between 120,000 volts and 500,000 volts.

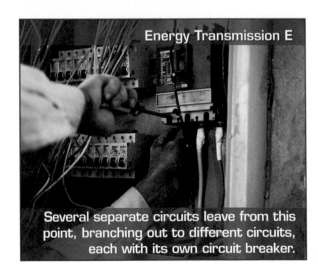

Energy Transmission E

Several separate circuits leave from this point, branching out to different circuits, each with its own circuit breaker.

Energy Transmission F

From the meter, the wire leads into a circuit breaker box.

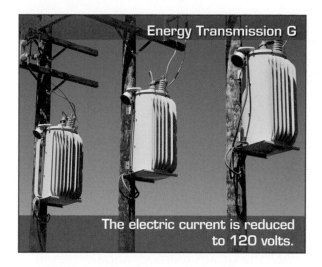

Energy Transmission G

The electric current is reduced to 120 volts.

Energy Transmission H

The voltage of the electric current is reduced at substations with transformers.

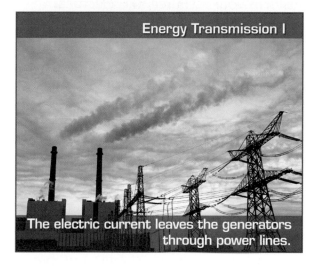

Energy Transmission I

The electric current leaves the generators through power lines.

Communicate

Investigation Expo

Each group in the class is expert on one energy resource. It is time now to report to the class about your resource so everyone will know about how to generate electricity from each resource, how each is transformed to light a bulb, and the efficiency of each of the energy resources. Spend time preparing your report. You might want to make a poster. Or you might want to make a computer presentation. Your report should include the following:

- The type(s) of energy in your energy resource.

- A description of the way your type of energy is transformed into electrical energy. Show the class the sequences on the *Energy Pathways* page. For each step in the sequence, describe the types of energy before the energy transformation, the actions or devices that transform energy from one type to another, and the types of energy after the energy transformation. Include both the usable energy and unusable energy that is generated.

- A description of the transformations needed to transport generated energy to the light bulb.

- A list of the "lost" energy for each step in these sequences.

When it is your group's turn to present, one group member should clearly present the transformations that transform your resource into electrical energy. Another group member should clearly present the transformations that transform electrical energy into light energy. The other group members should present what you know about the unusable energy that is generated and the efficiency of the energy transformations.

As you listen, notice similarities and differences in the energy transformation pathways being presented by the different groups. Notice which sources of energy are more efficient than others for generating electricity and turning on a light. As always, ask questions if you do not understand what a group is reporting or if you think they have not reported the processes accurately. However, save your comments about similarities and differences until all of the presentations are completed. Remember to be respectful.

When all of the presentations have been made, work as a class to put the resources into categories. Some are very much like one another. Some are a little like others. Some are different from all the others. Then discuss the answers to these questions as a class.

Reflect

1. For each category of resources, what is similar about the energy transformation pathways? For each, what is different?

2. Rank the sources of energy for their overall efficiency in lighting a bulb. Which is most efficient? Which is least efficient? What makes each more or less efficient?

3. Knowing what you know now about each of these sources of energy, which would you choose for your community? Why? Which would you want your community to avoid? Why?

Conference

Suppose a small community, located at the seashore far from any big city, is developing plans for an electric power plant. The citizens would like to consider all of the alternative types of energy sources before deciding what type they should use to run their plant. What resource do you think they should use to generate electricity? Consider these issues as you decide on your recommendation:

1. How readily available is the resource to the seashore?

2. How abundant is the resource?

3. How expensive is the resource?

4. What are the possible environmental concerns that may come from using this resource?

5. How appropriate is this resource for the location of the community?

6. Will this resource be available far into the future, or is there a probability that it may run out?

When you have decided on a recommendation, prepare a 3-part poster that describes the energy resource you have chosen. On one panel of the poster, list the advantages of the energy resource. On another panel, list the disadvantages. On the third panel, make a final recommendation about your energy resource for this community. State why you think it is the right resource.

Communicate

Share Your Ideas

When it is your group's turn to present, present your recommendation. Discuss the desirable and undesirable qualities of your energy resource, making sure you address each of the issues you discussed from the questions in your group conference.

After all of the groups have had a chance to present, decide as a class which energy resource would work best for this community, and give good reasons for your choice.

Update the *Project Board*

You have investigated the energy transformations that occur as energy resources are transformed to generate electricity for your home. You have also had an introduction to several different energy resources. Return to the *Project Board* and add your understanding of these ideas to the *What are we learning?* column. Make sure to include a description of the different stages in the chain of energy transformations that connect an energy resource with electricity in a home. Put your evidence, either from your energy transformation diagrams or your reading, in the *What is our evidence?* column.

What's the Point?

People who live near a power plant often do not like having it there because of how it lessens their enjoyment of their local environment. Fossil-fuel plants pollute the air with pollutants that can make it hard to breathe. Hydroelectric dams widen rivers and flood areas behind the dam, sometimes displacing people from their homes. They also affect fish that swim up and down the river past the dams. People who oppose wind and solar farms do not want new transmission lines built in the sparsely populated areas where wind and solar facilities are often placed, or they don't want to look at the wind farms. Wind farms also affect flying birds. But not everyone agrees, because there are always tradeoffs with any energy resource.

How do you think this small, seashore community gets their electricity?

Learning Set 6

Back to the Big Challenge

Design a Rube Goldberg Machine to Turn Off a Light

In *Learning Set 6,* you discovered an important concept. Whenever energy
of a particular type seems to disappear, it actually reappears as a different
type of energy. The total amount of energy you have at the beginning is the
same as the total amount you have at the end. However, some of the energy
may not be available to do what you want it to do. This is summarized in the
law of conservation of energy: Energy cannot be created or destroyed. It can
only change form. One of the criteria of the *Big Challenge* is that it should
be as energy efficient as possible. To help you think about how to keep your
machine energy efficient, you will first think about how you can identify energy
efficiency in a Rube Goldberg machine. Then you will analyze the machines
you have been designing to identify their efficiency.

Reflect

1. What would it mean for a Rube Goldberg machine to transform energy
   efficiently? Why?

2. How do you think you can determine how efficient a step in a Rube
   Goldberg machine is?

3. How do you think you can determine how efficient a whole Rube
   Goldberg machine is?

Analyze Your Ideas

You are getting close to achieving the criteria of the challenge and designing
a machine to turn off a light. You have identified many steps and sequences
of steps that can achieve parts of the challenge. Your challenge is to design a
machine with at least five steps and at least three energy transformations. In
addition, your machine should be as efficient as you can make it. To prepare
you for designing a machine that transforms energy efficiently, you will analyze
the sequences you have designed up to now and determine the efficiency of
each one.

ENERGY

Gather all of the sequences of steps you designed earlier in the Unit. You should have two sequences that involve thermal energy or chemical energy, two sequences that involve light energy or sound energy, and two sequences that involve electrical energy or magnetic energy. Of these, choose two sequences you think you are most likely to use as part of your final design.

1. Analyze each step of each sequence. Record your answers on an *Analysis of Steps* page.

   a) What type or types of energy go into the step? There may be some you have not yet listed.

   b) Where does the energy come from—the previous step of the sequence or somewhere else?

   c) How is energy transformed during the step?

   d) What types of energy are produced by the step? There may be some types you did not list previously. For example, a step that produces usable kinetic energy might also produce sound energy and thermal energy that are not usable to turn off a light. Record usable energy types in the *Usable energy out* column and unusable energy types in the *Unusable energy out* column of the *Analysis of Steps* page.

   e) How efficient is the step? In other words, how much of the energy produced by the step is usable? A lot of it? Some of it? Not much of it? How do you know?

2. For each sequence, find two ways to increase the efficiency of the sequence. How do you know you are increasing the efficiency?

3. If you had to choose one of these sequences as part of your final design, which one would you choose? Why? Your reason should include something about the number of energy types it involves and the efficiency of the sequence.

Analysis of Steps   6.BBC.1

Name: _____   Date: _____

Step number	Energy input	Energy from where?	How energy is transformed	Usable energy out	Unusable energy out	Efficiency

© It's About Time

Communicate

Plan Briefing

When it is your group's turn, present to the class the sequence you chose in *Question 3* of *Analyze Your Ideas.* Show the class your drawing of the sequence of steps. Then present the analysis you did of the steps. Say what type or types of energy go into each step, how they are transformed, what types of energy are produced by each step, and how efficient the step is. Then tell the class your two ways of making the sequence more efficient. Finally, show the class the sequence you did not choose in *Question 3,* and very briefly describe it and say why you chose the other sequence.

As you listen, notice whether you agree with the analyses presented by other groups. If you think they have not been clear enough about the energy transformations that are happening in each step, or if you think they forgot some type of energy, raise your hand and ask a question or offer your advice. Remember to be respectful, even when you are disagreeing.

Record ideas you might want to remember on the bottom of a *My Rube Goldberg Machine* page. Remember to record which group presented each idea. You will want to give credit if you use an idea presented by another group.

	My Rube Goldberg Machine		1.BBC.2/2.BBC.1/4.BBC.3/ 5.BBC.2/6.BBC.2/ABC.1

Name: _____   Date: _____

Sketch of machine. Label each step with a number.

Step	Description of step	Energy Type(s) In	Energy Type(s) Out	Work done
1				
2				
3				
4				
5				

Use this space to record ideas.

© It's About Time

Reflect

Answer these questions with your group. Be prepared to discuss the answers with the class.

1. Which two sequences do you think are the most energy efficient? Why?

2. List two things you know about addressing the *Big Challenge* that you did not know before these presentations.

3. Which two steps do you definitely want in your final design? Why?

4. Which steps do you want to avoid in your final design? Why?

Update the *Project Board*

Examine the questions about energy transformations and energy efficiency in the *What do we need to investigate?* column. If there are questions there that you now know the answer to, make sure the answers are in the *What are we learning?* column. Remember to include evidence for anything you add in the *What is our evidence?* column. The *What does it mean for the challenge or question?* column of the *Project Board* is where you record ideas about how to apply what you have learned to address the *Big Challenge.* Add any advice you want to remember to that column. You might also have new questions about energy or work. Add those to the *What do we need to investigate?* column. Remember to keep a record of what was added to the class *Project Board* on your own *Project Board* page.

Address the Big Challenge

Design a Rube Goldberg Machine to Turn Off a Light

You now know enough about energy and energy transformations to design your own Rube Goldberg machine. Like Rube Goldberg's machines, yours will involve a series of complicated steps to do something very simple. Your machine will pull a cord or flip a switch to turn off a light. You have already identified several possible last steps for your machine and the types of energy that might be transformed to power each of those last steps. You have also generated a lot of ideas about sequences of steps that can be used to turn off a light. However, you have not yet designed a sequence of steps that can fulfill all of the criteria and constraints of the challenge. It is now time to design the sequence of steps that can fulfill these criteria and constraints.

Remember that the challenge has several criteria and constraints. Because you will be working with sketches and not really building the machine, there is no limitation on the costs or types of materials you can select. However, each individual step in your machine must be logical, be capable of working, and must initiate the next step. Your machine must have at least five steps, and it must transform at least three different types of energy. You must also report on the efficiency of your machine. The less energy it needs to do its work, the better. There is one more thing. Your machine cannot be dangerous. For example, it can use fire in some steps, as long as the fire is contained. However, it cannot blow anything up. Your machine must be designed so that you would be willing to stand in the same room with it if it were built.

A solar calculator transforms several different types of energy to do the work of calculating math problems.

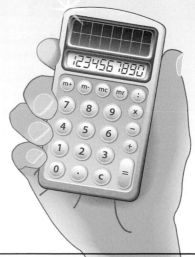

You will have a chance to work on two *iterations* of your design. An iteration is the repetition of a process in order to make something better over time. You will present the first iteration to the class. The class may give you ideas about how to make your design better. Then you will have time for a second iteration. Your design will have to fulfill the criteria and constraints, and you will also need to describe to the class how your machine transforms energy and how efficient it is.

Revise the Criteria and Constraints

Before you get started on your final design, restate the challenge in your own words. Then review the criteria and constraints you identified earlier in the Unit. If they need to be revised, do that now. Remember that criteria are conditions that must be satisfied to achieve the challenge, and that constraints are factors that limit how you can solve the problem. Below is a chart with some of the criteria and constraints filled in. Work together as a class to complete the chart.

Criteria	Constraints
Machine must have at least five steps.	Machine must not be dangerous.
Machine must use at least three types of energy.	
Machine must turn off a light.	

Plan Your Design

Throughout this Unit, you have been doing some planning for your design. Each time you learned about a new type of energy, you gave thought to how it might be transformed in your machine. Learning about energy transformations gave you the chance to think about how different energy types might be transformed, how much of each might be available before and after an energy transformation, and how this could work in the design of your machine.

You have many resources you can use for ideas. You have *Energy Types* pages and *Energy-transformation Cartoon* pages. You also have *My Rube Goldberg Machine* pages. All of these have ideas about energy transformations you might use in your design. Your class has also created a class list of possible steps and their energy transformations. And in the last *Learning Set,* you identified steps and sequences of steps you might want to use in your design. You also have notes from each of the *Plan Briefings*.

It is now time to pull together all that you have done in the earlier planning stages of your design. Work as a group to design a sequence of steps that achieves the criteria of the *Big Challenge* without violating the constraints. Use your *Energy Types* pages, *Energy-transformation Cartoon* pages, *My Rube Goldberg Machine* pages, and *Analysis of Steps* page from *Learning Set 6* to help you.

When you have a sequence of steps you like, sketch your proposed machine on a *My Rube Goldberg Machine* page, and mark each step with the following information.

- What work does the step do?

- What energy does the step transform? If there is any energy that does not come from the previous step, be sure to mark it in.

- How does the step transform its energy, and what types of energy does it produce?

- Show unusable energy from each step flowing out of the machine. Show usable energy from each step flowing into the next step.

- Where do you anticipate any problems occurring?

Now analyze your machine. See if there are steps where you can adjust something to make the step work more efficiently or more accurately. You may see a place where another energy transformation could be added. If so, now is the time to put it in. You will have one more opportunity to make revisions to your machine, and if something does not work logically, it can be changed. However, it will be much harder to add something later than to add it now.

Revise your sketch and the labels on each step if you change anything. Then analyze your machine again. Which steps do you have questions about? Which energy transformations do you have questions about? You will soon be presenting to the class, and when you do, you will have a chance to ask the class for advice. It would be a good idea, too, to make sure your sketch is neat and clear enough for others to be able to follow what you are proposing. Put your sketch on poster paper so it can be displayed to the class.

Communicate

Plan Briefing

When you are planning a design, the expertise of others can be helpful. The purpose of this *Plan Briefing* is to get advice from your classmates about how to make your machine even better. This means you must present it well enough so your classmates can understand your ideas. As a presenter, you will learn the most from this *Plan Briefing* if you can be specific about your design plans and about why you made your design decisions.

Groups will take turns making presentations. When it is your turn, show your sketch, and make sure to answer the following questions:

- What are the steps in your machine?

- Where does each step get its energy? What type or types of energy does the step transform? What energy transformations will occur in each step? What types of energy does each step produce?

- How do the different parts of the machine work together to achieve the criteria?

- What have you done to increase the efficiency of your machine, and what else do you think you might do to increase its efficiency?

- Are there any problems you think might occur with this design?

- What do you predict will happen when you use the machine to turn off a light?

- What, if anything, do you need help with?

As a listener, you will provide the best help if you ask probing questions about things you do not understand. Be polite when you point out errors and misconceptions in the reasoning of others. These kinds of conversations will allow other listeners to learn, as well. For each presentation, if you are not sure you understand the answers to the *Plan-Briefing* questions, make sure to question your classmates. When you ask them to clarify what they are telling you, you can learn more. They can learn, too, by trying to be more precise. Also, be generous with your advice. Do the best you can to help other groups design a smooth-working, energy-efficient machine.

Use another *My Rube Goldberg Machine* page to record any ideas you want to remember from the presentations.

Revise Your Design

Remember that an iteration is the repetition of a process in order to make something better over time. Designers use iterations to improve their designs. Each time they test a design, they usually find a way to make it better. Each change and the resulting new design are called an iteration.

You may still have ideas about how to make your design better, or your classmates may have asked you questions that tell you that you have more work to do.

Revise your design so you are satisfied that it could turn off a light if you built it. Use any ideas you received from the class in the *Plan Briefing* to improve on or to add more steps to your design.

Sketch your revised design on a new *My Rube Goldberg Machine* page. Do your best to make high-quality sketches that clearly show how your machine will work.

Label your sketch the way you labeled the previous version. Then develop a materials list to go with your finished design.

Communicate Your Design

Plan Showcase

You will present your final design to the class in a *Plan Showcase*. Because this is your final product, you will not be asking for help. Instead, you will be presenting a summary of your plan for turning off a light and telling the class how you arrived at this plan. You will also describe why you think this is a good design. Use the science you have learned to support why you designed your machine the way you did. This will help you better understand the science of energy.

To make an interesting and informative presentation, create a poster to showcase your plan. Your poster should include the following information.

- a clear sketch of your machine

- labels for each step of the machine that show:

  - the energy types and the energy transformations involved,

  - energy that is produced by each step, including which types are usable and which are not,

  - indicators for each type of energy you transform,

  - factors that affect each type of energy you transform, and

  - steps where energy is lost or seems to disappear, and where it goes.

- a chart that shows how you arrived at your final design. Include, for example, answers to these questions. What problems or questions did you have earlier? What did you do to address those questions? Why did you do those things? How did understanding the science of energy help you make your design better?

Use the following guidelines to help you in your presentation.

- Include the names of your group members.

- Briefly describe the challenge and how you chose the last step in your machine to turn off a light.

- Show your sketch, and walk the class through each step. Help the class understand the energy transformations in each step and how energy from each step flows into the next step. Tell them the factors that affect how much energy each step produces and how you controlled those factors.

- Consider the efficiency of your machine. Which step is the most efficient in transferring energy? Which step is the least efficient? Why? Discuss the overall efficiency of your machine.

- Report the science you used to make your machine more efficient or to control the energy in each step.

Listening to the presentations of others will provide you with chances to see different ways machines can use a series of energy transformations to perform a simple task. Make sure you understand how each machine works and the reasoning behind each design. How did other groups use energy transformations the same way your group did? How did other groups use energy transformations differently than your group did? Which energy transformations were most popular in the class? Why?

Reflect

1. Select one good idea from another group's machine design. What are the advantages of this design idea? What is the difference between how this group included energy transformations and how your group did?

2. Looking overall at the machines the class designed, are there any that are energy efficient? Do you think a Rube Goldberg machine can be energy efficient? Why or why not?

Update the *Project Board*

Over the past weeks, you have explored energy types and energy transformations in a lot of detail. It is time to update the *Project Board* one last time. Look at the first and second columns. Are there things you thought you knew that you can now state better and put into the *What are we learning?* column? Look for questions in the *What do we need to investigate?* column that have been answered. Put the answers in the *What are we learning?* column and the evidence to support them in the *What is our evidence?* column.

You now know several different ways of addressing the challenge. Update the *What does it mean for the challenge or question?* column with what you have learned about addressing the challenge. Each way of addressing the challenge involves different combinations of energy types and energy transformations. What you learned from others in the presentations can be used to update the *Project Board*.

Design a Rube Goldberg machine to turn off a light				
What do we think we know?	What do we need to investigate?	What are we learning?	What is our evidence?	What does it mean for the challenge or question?

English & Spanish Glossary

A

acceleration The rate at which speed changes.

aceleración El ritmo al cual la velocidad cambia.

alpha rays (α-rays) Radiation emitted during nuclear reactions; a helium nucleus with a positive charge.

rayos-α (rayos alfa) La radiación emitida durante reacciones nucleares; un núcleo de helio con una carga positiva.

alternating current (AC) An electric current that reverses direction at a regular rate.

corriente alterna (CA) Una corriente eléctrica que cambia su dirección a un ritmo regular.

amplitude The height of the crest in a transverse wave; a measure of how compressed the compressions are in a longitudinal wave.

amplitud La altitud de una cresta en una onda transversal; una medida de cuán comprimidas están las compresiones en una onda longitudinal.

anvil The second in a series of three small bones in the middle ear.

yunque El segundo de una serie de tres huesos pequeños en el oído medio.

attraction A pulling together.

atracción Agrupar.

auditory nerve A nerve that connects the inner ear with the brain and transmits sound, in the form of nerve impulses, to the brain.

nervio auditivo Un nervio que conecta el oído interno con el cerebro y transmite sonido, en la forma de impulsos nerviosos, al cerebro.

B

beta rays (β-rays) Radiation emitted during nuclear reactions; an electron with a negative charge.

rayos-β (rayos beta) La radiación emitida durante reacciones nucleares; un electrón con una carga negativa.

blackout A temporary cutoff of electrical energy in a region.

apagón Un cortocircuito temporero de electricidad en una región.

C

Calorie A unit of energy used to describe the amount of energy in food, also called a kilocalorie.

Caloría una unidad de energía usada para describir la cantidad de energía en los alimentos, también llamada una kilocaloría.

chemical change A change that produces one or more new substances.

cambio químico Un cambio que produce una o más substancias nuevas.

chemical energy Energy stored in chemical bonds.

energía química Energía almacenada en uniones químicas.

chemical reaction A process in which a new substance or substances are formed when atoms from the original substance or substances are rearranged.

reacción química Un proceso en el cual una sustancia nueva o sustancias se forman cuando los átomos de una sustancia original o sustancias se reordenan.

cilia Tiny hairs that line the cochlea and help turn vibrations into nerve impulses.

cilio Vellos pequeños que cubren la cóclea y ayudan a transformar las vibraciones en impulsos nerviosos.

circuit breaker A switch that opens a circuit when electric current reaches an unsafe level.

cortacircuitos Un interruptor que abre un circuito cuando la corriente eléctrica alcanza un nivel peligroso.

claim A statement that draws a conclusion about a set of facts or data.

reclamo Una declaración que llega a una conclusión sobre un conjunto de hechos o datos.

cochlea A spiral tube that makes up the part of the inner ear responsible for hearing.

cóclea Un tubo espiral que compone la parte del oído interno responsable de la audición.

combustion Any type of burning, usually a fuel with oxygen.

combustión Cualquier tipo de quema, generalmente un combustible con oxígeno.

compressed Squeezed or pressed together.

comprimido Apretado o compactado.

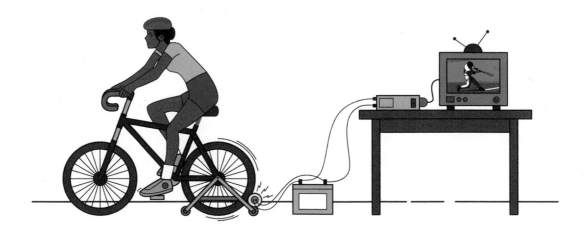

compression Region of a longitudinal wave where the particles of the medium have the highest density.

compresión Región de una onda longitudinal donde las partículas del medio tienen la densidad más alta.

conduct electricity Allow electricity to flow through a material.

conducir electricidad Permitir a la electricidad fluir a través de un material.

conduction The transfer of thermal energy by direct contact.

conducción La transferencia de energía térmica por contacto directo.

conductor A material that allows free charged particles to move easily from one atom to another.

conductor Un material que permite a las partículas libres de carga moverse fácilmente de un átomo a otro.

cones Cells that respond to bright light, responsible for color detection and sharpness of vision.

conos Células que responden a la luz brillante, responsables de la detección del color y la nitidez de la visión.

conservation of mechanical energy If there is no friction or air resistance, the mechanical energy of a system changes only if the system does not work on something else or energy is added from outside the system.

conservación de energía mecánica Si no hay fricción o resistencia al aire, la energía mecánica de un sistema cambia solamente si el sistema no funciona sobre alguna otra cosa o si la energía es añadida desde fuera del sistema.

constraints Factors that limit how you can solve a problem.

restricciones Factores que limitan cómo puedes resolver un problema.

control variables Conditions or procedures that are held constant.

variables controladas Condiciones o procedimientos que se mantienen constantes.

convection The transfer of thermal energy by the movement of a fluid, such as water or air.

convección La transferencia de energía térmica por el movimiento de un fluido, tal como agua o aire.

crest The highest point of a transverse wave.

cresta El punto más alto de una onda transversal.

criteria (singular criterion) Conditions that must be satisfied to successfully achieve a challenge.

criterios Condiciones que se deben satisfacer para lograr un reto exitosamente.

D

decibel A measurement used to compare intensity of different sounds. Each increase of 10 decibels is a sound intensity 10 times greater.

decibel Una medida utilizada para comparar la intensidad de diferentes sonidos. Cada incremento de 10 decibeles hay una intensidad de sonido 10 veces mayor.

deformed Changed in shape because of an applied force.

deforme El cambio en forma debido a una fuerza aplicada.

degrees Celsius (°C) A unit of measurement for temperature, abbreviated as °C. At sea level, water freezes at 0°C and boils at 100°C.

grados Centígrados (°C) Una unidad de medida para la temperatura, abreviada como °C. Al nivel del mar, el agua se congela a 0°C y hierve a 100°C.

degrees Fahrenheit (°F) A unit of measurement for temperature, abbreviated as °F. At sea level, water freezes at 32°F and boils at 212°F.

grados Fahrenheit (°F) Una unidad de medida para la temperatura, abreviada como °F. Al nivel del mar, el agua se congela a 32°F y hierve a 212°F.

dependent (resulting) variable A factor that is affected by changes in the independent (manipulated) variable.

variable dependiente (resultante) Un factor que es afectado por los cambios en la variable independiente (manipulada).

diffraction The ability of a wave to spread out or change direction as it passes through an opening or around an obstruction.

difracción La habilidad de una onda de dispersarse o cambiar de dirección cuando pasa a través de una abertura o alrededor de un obstáculo.

dispersion The spreading out of energy as it travels away from the source of the energy. The decrease in intensity as distance from an energy source increases.

dispersión La dispersión de energía mientras ésta viaja alejándose de la fuente de la energía. La disminución en intensidad mientras la distancia de una fuente de energía aumenta.

direct current (DC) An electric current that flows in one direction only.

corriente continua (CC) Una corriente eléctrica que fluye solamente en una dirección.

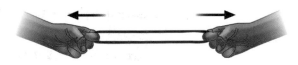

E

ear canal A tubelike structure connecting the external ear to the eardrum.

conducto auditivo Un estructura en forma de tubo que conecta el oído externo al tímpano.

eardrum The membrane separating the outer ear from the inner ear.

tímpano Una membrana que separa el oído externo del oído interno.

elastic energy The energy stored in an object when the shape of the object is changed.

energía elástica La energía almacenada en un objeto cuando se cambia la forma del objeto.

elastic limit Limit beyond which a deformed material does not return to its original shape.

Límite de elasticidad El límite más allá del cual un material distorsionado no regresa a su forma original.

elastic potential energy Stored energy released when an object's shape is changed (as in a stretched rubber band or a coiled spring.)

energía potencial elástica La energía almacenada liberada cuando se cambia la forma de un objeto (como una banda elástica o una bobina enrollada).

elasticity Ability of a material to return to its original shape after it is deformed.

elasticidad La habilidad de un material para regresar a su forma original después de haber sido deformado.

electric circuit A pathway where charged particles can move freely in a complete path.

circuito eléctrico Un sendero por dónde las partículas cargadas pueden moverse libremente en una senda completa.

electric current The flow of charged particles.

corriente eléctrica El flujo de partículas cargadas.

electric force The push or pull that moves charged particles.

fuerce eléctrica El empuje o halón que mueve partículas cargadas

electrical energy The energy of moving electric charges.

energía eléctrica La energía de cargas eléctricas en movimiento.

electrochemical cell A device that generates electrical energy using chemical reactions inside a small enclosed space (cell).

célula electrolítica Un aparato que genera energía eléctrica usando reacciones químicas dentro de un espacio pequeño cerrado (célula).

electromagnet A magnet that runs on electricity.

electroimán Un imán que funciona con electricidad.

ENERGY

electromagnetic radiation Radiant energy that can travel through a vacuum and through matter in the form of waves.

Radiación electromagnética Energía radiante que puede viajar a través de un vacío y a través de la materia en forma de onda.

electromagnetic spectrum A continuous range of wavelengths that includes all of the types of electromagnetic waves.

Espectro electromagnético Una gama continua de longitudes de onda que incluye todos los tipos de ondas electromagnéticas.

electromagnetism The relationship between magnetism and electricity.

electromagnetismo La relación entre magnetismo y electricidad.

endothermic Requires heat for a chemical change.

endotérmico El requerimiento de calor para un cambio químico.

energy efficiency The degree to which a process produces a usable energy output for a given energy input.

rendimiento energético El grado al cual un proceso produce un resultado de energía utilizable para un insumo dado de energía.

exothermic Giving off heat because of a chemical change.

exotérmico Emisión de calor debido a un cambio químico.

F

factor A characteristic that can be measured.

factor Una característica que puede ser medida.

force A push or pull that acts on an object.

fuerza Un empujón o halón que actúa sobre un objeto.

fossil fuel An energy source that comes from the remains of living things; for example, coal, oil, and natural gas.

combustible fósil Una fuente de energía que proviene de los residuos de organismos vivientes; por ejemplo, carbón, petróleo, y gas natural.

frequency The number of crests or compressions in a wave that pass a point per unit time, for sound waves, measured in hertz (Hz).

frecuencia La cantidad de crestas o compresiones en una onda que pasan por un punto por unidad de tiempo, medidas en hertzios (Hz), para las ondas sonoras.

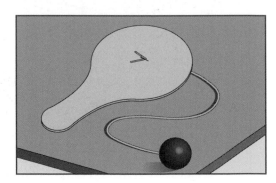

G

galvanometer A device for detecting or measuring small electric currents.

galvanómetro Un aparato para detectar o medir corrientes eléctricas pequeñas.

gamma rays High energy electromagnetic radiation with no mass or charge.

rayos gamma Radiación electromagnética de alta energía sin masa o carga.

generator A device that converts mechanical energy into electrical energy using the motion of a magnet inside a coil of wire.

generador Un aparato que convierte la energía mecánica en energía eléctrica usando el movimiento de un imán dentro de una bobina de alambre.

geothermal energy Energy that comes from the natural internal heat of Earth.

energía geotérmica La energía que surge del calor interno natural de la Tierra.

gravitational potential energy Stored energy of an object based on its position above the ground.

energía potencial gravitacional o gravitatoria Energía almacenada de un objeto basada en su posición sobre el terreno.

gravity The force of attraction between any two masses. Near Earth's surface, gravity is the force that attracts objects toward the center of Earth.

gravedad La fuerza de atracción entre cualesquiera dos masas. Cerca de la superficie de la Tierra, la gravedad es la fuerza que atrae los objetos hacia el centro de la Tierra.

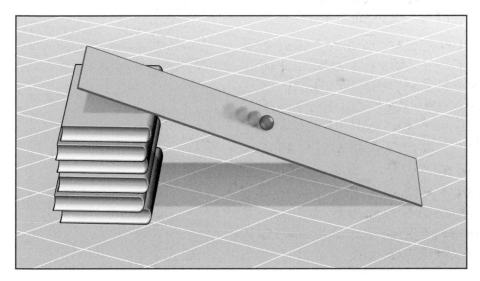

H

hammer The first in a series of three small bones in the middle ear.
martillo El primero de una serie de tres huesos pequeños en el oído medio.

heat Thermal energy that is transferred from one place to another.
calor La energía térmica que es transferida de un lugar a otro.

I

independent (manipulated) variable A factor that is changed to affect changes in the dependent (resulting) variable.
variable independiente (manipulada) Un factor que es cambiado para afectar los cambios en la variable dependiente (resultante).

indicate To show.
indicar Mostrar.

indicators Observations that can tell you about the presence of some state or condition.
indicadores Observaciones que pueden indicarte la presencia de algún estado o condición.

infer To interpret from observations.
inferir Interpretar a partir de observaciones.

inference A plausible conclusion or interpretation based on observations or evidence.
inferencia Una conclusión posible o interpretación basada en observaciones o evidencia.

insulator A material that limits the flow of charged particles.
aislador Un material que limita el flujo de partículas con carga.

intensity The amount of electricity, light, heat, or sound energy per unit area per unit time.
intensidad La cantidad de electricidad, luz, calor o energía sonora por área de unidad por unidad de tiempo.

interpret To find the meaning of something.
interpretar Encontrar el significado de algo.

iris A flat, colored, ring-shaped membrane, with an adjustable circular opening at the center.
iris Una membrana plana, de color y en forma de anillo, con una abertura circular ajustable en el centro.

J

joule A unit of measurement for energy, abbreviated as J; the amount of work required to lift a 100-g mass a distance of about 1 m.

julio Una unidad de medida para la energía, abreviada como J; la cantidad de trabajo requerido para levantar una masa de 100 gramos una distancia de alrededor de 1 m.

K

kelvin (K) A unit of measurement for temperature on the Kelvin scale.

kelvin (K) Una unidad de medida para la temperatura en la escala Kelvin.

Kelvin scale A temperature scale where absolute zero theoretically indicates that no thermal energy is present; 0 K = −273°C.

escala Kelvin Una escala de temperatura donde el cero absoluto indica en teoría que no hay energía térmica presente; 0 K = −273°C.

kinetic energy The energy an object has because of its motion.

energía cinética La energía que tiene un objeto debido a su movimiento.

ENERGY

L

law of conservation of energy A law of physics that states that energy cannot be created or destroyed; it can only change form.

Ley de conservación de energía Una ley de la física que declara que la energía no puede ser creada o destruida; puede solamente cambiar de forma.

lens A structure in the eye that changes shape to focus light and images onto the retina.

lente Una estructura en el ojo que cambia de forma para enfocar luz e imágenes en la retina.

light energy Visible energy that is given off by some objects in the form of radiation.

energía luminosa La energía visible emitida por algunos objetos en la forma de radiación.

longitudinal (compressional) wave A wave that causes a medium to vibrate in a direction parallel to the direction in which the wave travels.

onda longitudinal (de compresión) Una onda que causa que un medio vibre en una dirección paralela a la dirección en la cual viaja la onda.

M

magnetic field The strength and direction of the magnetic force a magnet exerts at each point in space; the magnetic field grows weaker as distance from the magnet increases.

campo magnético La fuerza y dirección de la fuerza magnética que un imán ejerce en cada punto en el espacio; el campo magnético se debilita mientras aumenta la distancia desde el imán.

magnetic force The force a magnet exerts on iron or another magnet.

fuerza magnética La fuerza que un imán ejerce sobre el hierro o cualquier otro imán.

mechanical energy The sum of the kinetic energy, gravitational potential energy, and elastic potential energy in a system.

energía mecánica La suma de la energía cinética, la energía potencial gravitacional, y la energía potencial elástica en un sistema.

mechanical wave A transfer of energy through a medium without a transfer of the medium.

onda mecánica Una transferencia de energía a través de un medio sin una transferencia del medio.

medium The material through which a mechanical wave travels.

medio El material a través del cual viaja una onda mecánica.

membrane A layer of tissue that serves as a covering, connection, or lining.

membrana Una capa de tejido que sirve como cobertura, conexión o forro.

N

nonrenewable resource A resource that exists in a limited supply; for example, coal and oil.

recurso no renovable Una fuente que existe en cantidades limitadas; por ejemplo, el carbón y el petróleo.

nuclear energy Energy released from a reaction in which atomic nuclei interact to form new nuclei that have a lower combined mass.

energía nuclear Energía liberada de una reacción en la cual el núcleo atómico interactúa para formar un núcleo nuevo que tiene una combinación de masa más baja.

nuclear fission A change in which one high-mass element produces two or more low-mass elements, with a release of enormous amounts of energy.

fisión nuclear Un cambio en el cual el elemento de masa mayor produce dos o más elementos de masa menor, con una liberación de enormes cantidades de energía.

nuclear fusion A change in which one or more low-mass elements produce a higher-mass element with a release of enormous amounts of energy.

fusión nuclear Un cambio en el cual uno o más elementos de masa menor produce un elemento de masa mayor con una liberación de grandes cantidades de energía.

nuclear reaction A reaction in which the substance that is produced is a new element and has a smaller mass than the substances that combined to form it.

reacción nuclear Una reacción en la cual la sustancia que es producida es un elemento nuevo y tiene una masa más pequeña que la sustancia que se combinó para formarla.

O

optic nerve Cells that transmit electrical signals from the retina to the brain.

nervio óptico Las células que transmiten señales eléctricas de la retina al cerebro.

oval window An opening between the middle ear and the inner ear.

ventana vestibular Una abertura entre el oído medio y el oído interno.

P

parallel circuit A closed circuit in which the current divides into two or more paths before recombining to complete the circuit.

circuito paralelo Un circuito cerrado en el cual la corriente se divide en dos o más senderos antes de volver a combinarse para completar el circuito.

period The time required to complete one cycle of a wave.

período El tiempo requerido para completar un ciclo de una onda.

photon A tiny particle or packet of light energy.

fotón Una partícula minúscula o paquete de energía de luz.

photosynthesis The process by which plants transform the energy from sunlight, water, and carbon dioxide to form sugars and oxygen.

fotosíntesis El proceso por el cual las plantas transforman la energía de la luz solar, el agua y el dióxido de carbono para formar azúcares y oxígeno.

piezoelectric A process in which pressure applied to crystals produces an electric current.

piezoeléctrico Un proceso en el cual la presión aplicada a los cristales produce una corriente eléctrica.

pitch How high or low a sound is.

tono Cuán alto o bajo es un sonido.

pollutant A harmful substance that is added to an environment.

contaminante Una sustancia peligrosa que se añade al medio ambiente.

potential energy Energy that is stored to be transformed at a later time.

energía potencial La energía que es almacenada para ser transformada más tarde.

power distribution grid (power grid) A system of high-tension cables by which electrical energy is distributed throughout a region.

red de distribución de energía eléctrica (red eléctrica) Un sistema de cables de alta tensión por los cuales la energía eléctrica es distribuida a través de una región.

pupil The circular opening in the center of the iris that controls the amount of light that enters the eye.

pupila La abertura circular en el centro del iris que controla la cantidad de luz que entra al ojo.

PBIS

R

radiate Give off energy.
   irradiar Emitir energía.

radiation Energy that moves in the form of rays, waves, or particles.
   radiación Energía que se mueve en forma de rayos, ondas o partículas.

reflect To turn back from a hard surface.
   reflejar Regresar de una superficie dura.

reflection When the medium and energy in a wave is turned back from a hard surface.
   reflexión Cuando el medio y la energía en una onda regresa de una superficie dura.

refraction The change in direction of a wave when it enters a new medium with a different wave speed.
   refracción El cambio en la dirección de una onda cuando entra a un medio nuevo con una velocidad de onda diferente.

renewable resource A resource that is continually resupplied; for example, light energy from the Sun.
   recurso renovable Un recurso que está continuamente rebasteciéndose; por ejemplo, la energía de luz del Sol.

repel To push apart.
   repeler Rechazar.

repulsion A pushing apart.
   repulsión Rechazo.

resistance Opposition to the flow of electric current.
   resistencia La oposición al flujo de la corriente eléctrica.

resistor An electric device that can control the current in a circuit.
   resistor Un aparato eléctrico que puede controlar la corriente en un circuito.

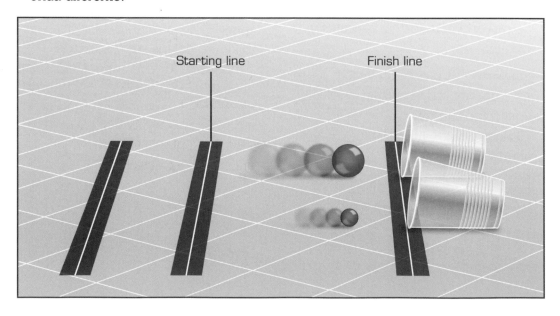

respiration The process by which stored energy is released from sugar by combining with oxygen to form carbon dioxide and water.

respiración El proceso por el cual la energía almacenada es liberada del azúcar combinándose con el oxígeno para formar dióxido de carbono y agua.

retina The layer at the back of the inside of the eye containing cells that respond to light and color.

retina La capa en la parte trasera del interior del ojo que contiene células que responden a la luz y al color.

rods Light-sensitive cells responsible for vision in dim light.

bastoncillos Células sensitivas a la luz responsables de la visión en una luz tenue.

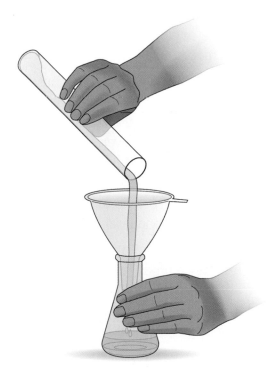

S

scatter To bounce off or deflect in different directions.

esparcimiento Rebotar o desviar en direcciones diferentes.

seismic Caused by an earthquake or vibrations inside Earth.

sísmico Causado por un terremoto o vibraciones dentro de la Tierra.

seismograph An instrument used to detect and record seismic waves.

sismógrafo Un instrumento usado para detectar y registrar ondas sísmicas.

series circuit A closed circuit in which all parts are connected end to end to provide a single path for the current.

circuito en serie Un circuito cerrado en el cual todas las partes están conectadas extremo a extremo para proveer un sendero individual para la corriente.

sound energy Vibrating air that travels as waves to your ears.

energía sonora Aire vibrando que viaja a tus oídos como ondas.

specific heat The heat required to raise the temperature of 1 gram of a substance 1°C.

calor específico El calor requerido para aumentar la temperatura de 1 gramo de una sustancia 1°C.

speed of a wave The distance a wave travels (crest, trough, crest) in a given period of time. Speed of a wave can be calculated by multiplying wavelength by frequency.

velocidad de una onda La distancia que recorre una onda (cresta, valle, cresta) en un período determinado de tiempo. La velocidad de una onda puede calcularse multiplicando la longitud de onda por la frecuencia.

speed of light The speed at which light travels in a vacuum, approximately 300,000 km/s.

velocidad de la luz La velocidad a la cual la luz viaja en un vacío, aproximadamente 300,000 Kms./s.

stirrup The third in a series of three small bones in the middle ear.

estribo El tercero de una serie de tres huesos pequeños en el oído medio.

system A collection of objects that interact.

sistema Una colección de objetos que interactúan.

T

temperature how hot or cold a substance or object is; a measure of the average kinetic energy of the particles in a substance.

temperatura Cuán caliente o fría es una sustancia u objeto; una medida de la energía cinética promedio de las partículas en una sustancia.

thermal energy Experienced as heat; the energy of motion of all the particles in an object.

energía térmica Experimentada como calor; la energía de movimiento de todas las partículas en un objeto.

thermometer An instrument for measuring temperature.

termómetro Un instrumento para medir temperatura.

transform To convert from one form into another form.

transformar Convertir de una forma a otra.

transformer An electric device by which alternating current of one voltage is changed to another voltage, either greater or smaller.

transformador Un aparato eléctrico por el cual la corriente alterna de un voltaje se cambia a otro voltaje, ya sea mayor o menor.

transverse wave A wave that causes a medium to vibrate in a direction perpendicular to the direction in which the wave travels.

onda transversal Una onda que causa que un medio vibre en una dirección perpendicular a la dirección en la cual la onda viaja.

trend A pattern or a tendency you can see over a broad range of data.

tendencia Un patrón o una tendencia que puedes ver sobre una amplia gama de datos.

trough The lowest point of a transverse wave.

depresión El punto más bajo en una onda transversal.

turbine A machine with a series of spinning blades in which the kinetic energy of a moving fluid (water, air, or steam) is transformed into kinetic energy of the turbine.

turbina Una máquina con una serie de aspas giratorias en las cuales la energía cinética de un fluido en movimiento (agua, aire o vapor) es transformada en la energía cinética de la turbina.

U

usable energy Energy that can easily be transformed to other kinds of energy to serve a useful purpose.

energía utilizable La energía que puede ser transformada fácilmente a otros tipos de energía para servir un propósito útil.

V

vacuum Space that contains no matter.

vacío Un espacio que no contiene materia.

vibrate To move back and forth.

vibrar Moverse de un lado a otro.

voltage A measure of the energy for an amount of charge.

voltaje Una medida de la energía para una cantidad de carga.

W

wave A disturbance that travels through a medium from one place to another.

onda Un disturbio que viaja a través de un medio de un lugar a otro.

wavelength The distance between successive crests or troughs in a transverse wave; the distance between two successive compressions in a longitudinal wave.

longitud de onda La distancia entre crestas sucesivas o depresiones en una onda transversal; la distancia entre dos compresiones sucesivas en una onda longitudinal.

wave-particle duality Light energy can at times show particle properties and at other times show wave properties.

dualidad onda-partícula La energía de luz puede, en ocasiones, mostrar propiedades de partículas y en otras ocasiones mostrar propiedades de ondas.

work A way to increase (or decrease) an object's energy by using a force to change the object's motion or position.

trabajo Una forma de aumentar (o disminuir) la energía de un objeto usando una fuerza para cambiar el movimiento o posición de los objetos.

Project-Based Inquiry Science

Index

C

Calorie, defined, EN 139

The Can Picker, EN 12, EN 14

cell respiration, *See* respiration

chemical change, and energy transformation, EN 128

    defined, EN 89, EN 122

    indicators of, EN 89 – EN 90, EN 127, EN 128

chemical energy, and chemical bonds, EN 133 – EN 134, EN 136

    and chemical reaction, EN 129 – EN 130, EN 136

    and dancers, EN 269

    and electrical energy, EN 25, EN 211

    and endothermic reaction, EN 128

    and exothermic reaction, EN 128

    and fossil fuels, *See* fossil fuels

    and human body, EN 139

    and light energy, EN 137, EN 202

    and photosynthesis, *See* photosynthesis

    and power plants, *See* power plants

    and respiration, *See* respiration

    and thermal energy, *See* thermal energy

    defined, EN 25

    indicators of, EN 122, EN 127

    stored, EN 211

chemical reaction, EN 127, EN 133

    and batteries, EN 251

    defined, EN 129

cilia, defined, EN 160

circuit(s), and electrical energy, *See* electrical energy

circuit breaker, defined, EN 251 – EN 252

cochlea, defined, EN 160

combustion, defined, EN 134 – EN 135

compressed, defined, EN 57

compression, defined, EN 167

compressional wave, *See* longitudinal waves

condenser, defined, EN 294

conduct electricity, defined, EN 211

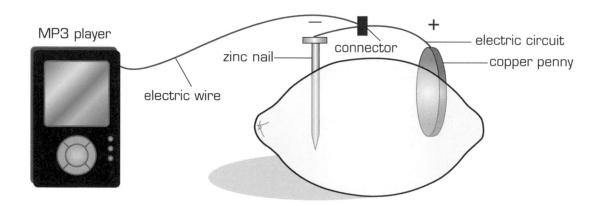

MP3 player

electric wire

zinc nail

connector

electric circuit

copper penny

E

ear canal, defined, EN 159

ears, EN 159 – EN 160

eardrum, defined, EN 159

echoes, *See* reflection of waves

Einstein, Albert, EN 293

elastic energy, and kinetic energy, *See* kinetic energy

   defined, EN 29

elastic limit, defined, EN 78

elastic potential energy, and kinetic energy, *See* kinetic energy

   and springs, *See* springs

   defined, EN 44, EN 62

   factors affecting, EN 57, EN 77 – EN 78, EN 80

   indicators of, EN 80, EN 194, EN 259

   transformation of, EN 74 – EN 77, EN 259

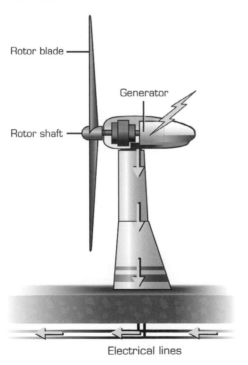

Rotor blade

Generator

Rotor shaft

Electrical lines

elasticity, defined, EN 77

   of metal, EN 77

electric circuit, and switches, EN 220, EN 223

   defined, EN 219 – EN 223

electric current, and electrical energy, *See* electrical energy

   and electromagnetism, EN 217, EN 219

   and magnetic field, EN 227

   defined, EN 219

   measuring, *See* galvanometer

electric force(s), and batteries, EN 220

   and magnetic force, *See* magnetic force

   defined, EN 220

electric potential energy, defined, EN 225

electrical energy, and batteries, *See* battery

   and chemical energy, *See* chemical energy

   and circuits, EN 223 – EN 226, EN 244

   and electrical current, EN 228

   and electromagnets, EN 211 – EN 212, EN 214

   and eyes, *See* eyes

   and generators; *See* generator

   and heat, *See* heat

   and kinetic energy, *See* kinetic energy

   and light energy, *See* light energy

   and magnetic energy, EN 193, EN 204, EN 214, EN 231- EN 233

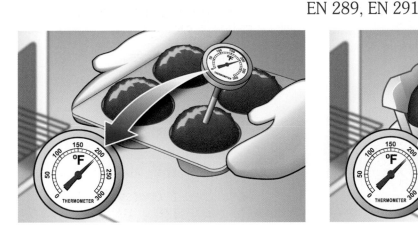

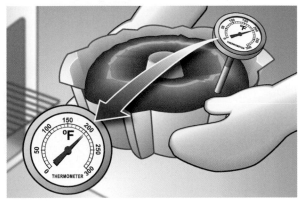

L

M

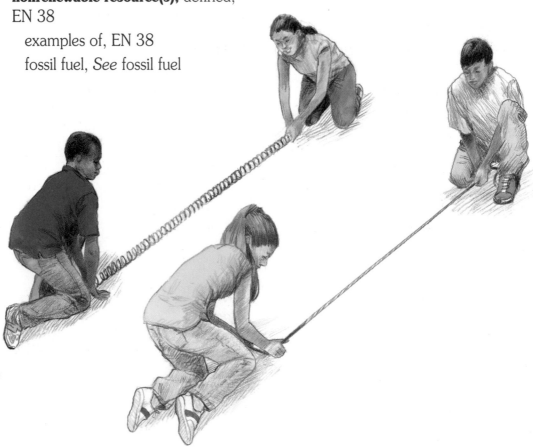

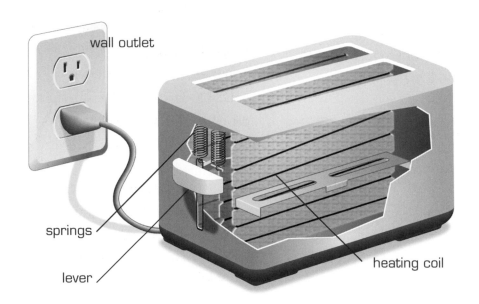

wall outlet

springs

lever

heating coil

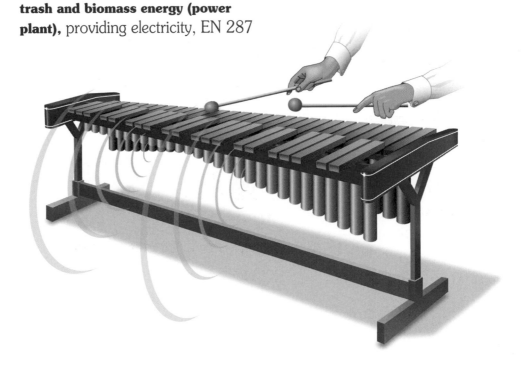

Project-Based Inquiry Science

Project-Based Inquiry Science

IT's ABOUT TIME ®
HERFF JONES EDUCATION DIVISION

84 Business Park Drive, Armonk, NY 10504
Phone (914) 273-2233 Fax (914) 273-2227
www.its-about-time.com

Publishing Team

President
Tom Laster

Director of Product Development

Barbara Zahm, Ph.D.

Managing Editor

Maureen Grassi

Project Development Editor

Ruta Demery

Project Manager

Sarah V. Gruber

Associate Editor, Student Edition

Gail Foreman

**Assistant Editor,
Teacher's Planning Guide**

Kelly Crowley

Safety and Content Reviewer

John Roeder

Equipment Kit Developers

Dana Turner

Henry J. Garcia

Creative Director

John Nordland

Production/Studio Manager

Robert Schwalb

Layout

Sean Campbell

Illustration

Dennis Falcon

**Technical Art/
Photo Research**

Sean Campbell

Jorge Cifuentes

Melissa Ericksen

Doreen Flaherty

Fredy Fleck

Michael Hortens

Marie Killoran

Louise Landry

Brittany Peters

Cora Roman

MaryBeth Schulze

Jason Skinner

Krystal Stephens

Pre-press

Rich Ciotti

Photography Credits